Primate Ecology and Social Structure

Volume 2: New World Monkeys, Revised First Edition

Robert W. Sussman
Department of Anthropology
Washington University

PEARSON
Custom
Publishing

Cover photograph by Robert W. Sussman.

Printed in the United States of America

10 9 8 7 6 5 4 3 2 1

ISBN 0-536-74364-9

BA 997664

LF/KG

Please visit our web site at *www.pearsoncustom.com*

PEARSON CUSTOM PUBLISHING
75 Arlington Street, Suite 300, Boston, MA 02116
A Pearson Education Company

THIS BOOK IS DEDICATED TO KATYA AND DIANA

Contents

Preface

This is the second of three volumes in which I review the literature on the ecology, social structure, and social behavior of free-ranging primates. In the first volume (PRIMATE ECOLOGY AND SOCIAL STRUCTURE, VOL. 1, LORISES, LEMURS AND TARSIERS, 1999), I focused on the prosimians. This volume also included two introductory chapters, one on general ecology and the other on the taxonomy, morphological characteristics, and origins of primates. In the current volume, I discuss the New World monkeys.

As in the first volume, each chapter covers a major taxonomic group. Thus, after an introductory chapter with an overview of New World monkeys and their evolution, the remaining chapters review the literature on each of the following taxa: Callitrichidae, including marmosets, tamarins, and the Goeldi's monkey (Chapter 2); Cebidae, including squirrel monkeys, capuchins, night monkeys, and titi monkeys (Chapter 3); and Atelidae, including spider monkeys, woolly monkeys, woolly spider monkeys, howler monkeys, sakis, bearded sakis, and uakaris (Chapter 4).

In this book, as in the other volumes, I review the literature on free-ranging populations of the taxa covered. Initially, I attempt to characterize these animals as they exist in their least disturbed state. When relevant, behavior in disturbed situations and captivity is compared to that in more undisturbed contexts. By doing this, I believe it is possible to gain a better understanding of the reasons primates behave as they do and the ways they fit into the communities in which they live. I realize this is an idealistic approach, since few if any localities inhabited by primates escape some level of human disturbance.

As in the first volume, to facilitate comparison, the general organization of each of these review chapters is similar. For each group, I review the literature on habitat and locomotion, diet, activity cycles, predation, social structure and organization, reproduction, and ranging behavior. In Chapter 5, I compare each of these topics among all of the taxa, examine patterns that emerge, and discuss the conservation status of New World monkeys and some of the problems faced in their future preservation. In Volume 3 of this series, I will review the literature on Old World monkeys and apes.

I have used earlier versions of this book for the past 20 years in teaching courses on primate ecology and social behavior. Besides being used as a course book for advanced undergraduate and graduate students, I hope that these volumes also will be useful as a reference for others interested in the behavior and ecology of free-ranging primates. I have benefited from input from colleagues and students in revising the manuscript. A few of my colleagues have read various versions of the book in its entirety and I especially appreciate their criticisms, comments, and suggestions. These include Thad Bartlett, John Buettner-Janusch, Ben Freed, Paul Garber, Terry Gleason, Lisa Gould, Charles Hildebolt, Robert Martin, Jane Phillips-Conroy, Alison Richard, Michelle Sauther, Ian Tattersall, Mildred Trotter, and Natalia Vasey. Besides the above, for each chapter, specialists on the taxa covered have generously agreed to read specific sections and offer their suggestions. These include Rogerio Castro and Paul Garber for Chapter 2, Linda Fedigan and Lisa Rose for Chapter 3, and Ken Glander, Terry Gleason, and Karen Strier for Chapter

4. My late friend, Warren Kinzey, reviewed earlier versions of all three of these chapters. I thank these people and eight anonymous reviews for the assistance, although I take responsibility for the final product. I also thank those who provided photographs and permissions to use various material in the book. Finally, I appreciate the assistance of Terry Gleason who served as my Research Assistant while putting together this final version, of Brett Nachman for his excellent job in copy editing, and of Wayne Spohr and Terry Brennan of Pearson Publishing Company for their encouragement and assistance throughout.

CHAPTER 1

Evolution of the Neotropical Primates

The earliest primates of modern aspect in the New World were the Eocene prosimian families: Adapidae and Omomyidae (see Volume 1, Chapter 2). These are found in North America, as well as Europe and (recently) Africa, but have not been uncovered in South America (Conroy 1990, Fleagle 1999). Prosimians decline in abundance toward the end of the Eocene.

The higher primates (suborder Anthropoidea), represented in the neotropics by the infraorder Platyrrhini, contain one superfamily, Ceboidea, or New World monkeys. Anthropoids differ from the prosimians in a number of characteristics, including a more conservative dentition in both dental formula and shape of the teeth and in a number of other anatomical features (Fleagle 1999; Fig. 1-1).

New World monkeys first appear in the latest Oligocene (about 25 million years ago) in Bolivia (genus *Branisella*) (Kay et al. 1999). The paleontological record of ceboid evolution is limited, consisting of a relatively small number of incomplete specimens (Simons 1972, Rose and Fleagle 1981, Conroy 1990, Fleagle et al. 1997, Fleagle 1999).

Generally, there is only a scattered array of isolated specimens from sediments as far south as Argentina to as far north as Jamaica. However, because of the overall similarity of many extinct species to modern lineages, it appears that many of the extant platyrrhines have been distinct since at least the Miocene (Fleagle et al. 1997, Fleagle 1999).

In this volume, I divide the superfamily Ceboidea into three families: Callitrichidae, Cebidae, and Atelidae. The Cebidae are further divided into two subfamilies, Cebinae and Aotinae. Atelidae is divided into Atelinae and Pitheciinae. Some distinctions between these taxa are illustrated in Figure 1-2.

Recently, Porter et al. (1997) have advocated dividing the platyrrhines into only two families, the Cebidae and Atelidae, with the former including Aotinae, Cebinae, and Callitrichinae. However, there are many unresolved questions concerning the systematics of the Neotropical monkeys, their relationships to fossil species, and

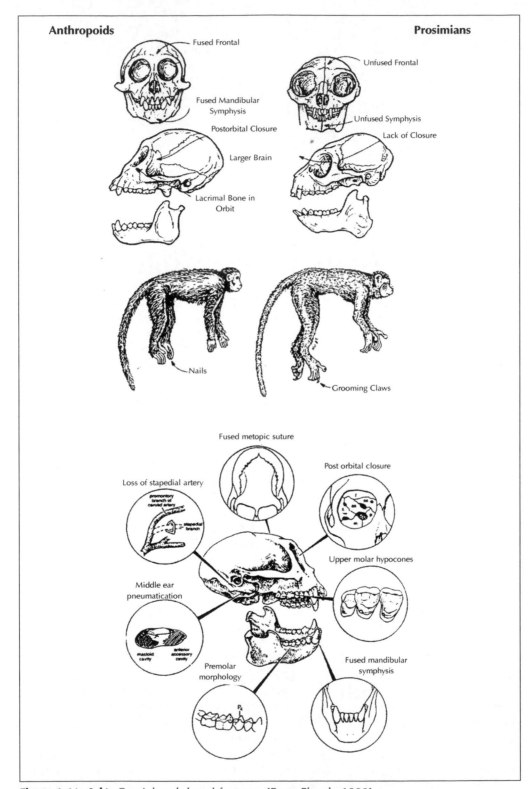

Figure 1-1(a & b) Cranial and dental features. [From Fleagle 1999]

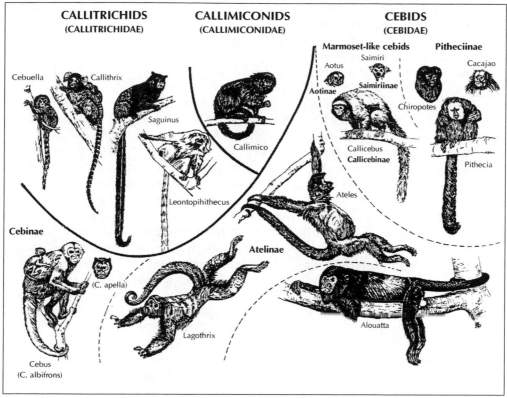

Figure 1-2 New World Monkeys. [From Hershovitz 1977]

the origins of the entire platyrrhine radiation. Furthermore, new fossil material is providing a number of challenges to previous views of platyrrhine evolution. With the continued improvement of the fossil record, many of the questions concerning New World monkey evolution and systematics may be refined and resolved (Fleagle et al. 1997). For the moment, however, the relationships between higher taxonomic groups are still being debated, and a number of alternate classifications exist. These will be discussed further in the following chapters.

There are two major questions which remain unanswered concerning the evolutionary history of the New World primates. The first involves the geographical origin of the Ceboidea, and the second concerns whether the callitrichids or the small cebids represent the ancestral ceboid morphology.

Until the appearance of *Branisella* in the Oligocene, there are no primates represented in the fossil record of South America. Throughout the early Tertiary, South America was an island continent, and the first primates most likely reached it, as a result of chance rafting, from either Africa (cf. Lavocat 1974, Hoffstetter 1972) or North America (cf. Simons 1976, Gingerich and Schoeninger 1977, Gingerich and Rose 1977). Both of these possibilities present some problems. An African origin of the fossil and extant ceboids would involve rafting over considerable expanses of ocean. A North American origin assumes rafting over an even greater distance and that prosimians in the Old and New Worlds developed common features. In the latter case, the similarities between Old and New World anthropoids would be parallelisms rather than characters indicative of a common primate ancestor. At the present time, both of these points of origin are still possibilities and the ultimate solution to this problem still remains unanswered (Rose and Fleagle 1981), though dispersal across the South Atlantic from Africa appears to be the most likely method (Conroy 1990, Fleagle 1999).

Concerning the second question, it has traditionally been assumed that many of the behavioral and morphological adaptations of the Callitrichidae represent ancestral or primitive retentions (Le Gros Clark 1959, Eisenberg 1977, Hershkovitz 1977). Some of these traits include claw-like nails, sternal and anogenital scent glands, the tendency to twin, small body size, highly insectivorous diet, and three cusped (tritubercular) upper molars. However, the dental formula, molar and digital morphology, and body size of the Oligocene and Miocene fossil platyrrhines approximate the cebid condition and not that of the callitrichids (Delson and Rosenberger 1980, Rose and Fleagle 1981). Based on immunological evidence, Sarich and Cronin (1980) also conclude that albumin and transferin proteins of the callitrichids are a specialized condition derived from a primitive cebid-like state. Furthermore, a number of investigators have provided convincing evidence that reduction of body size over time in this lineage (referred to as "phyletic dwarfing") has actually led to many of the specific morphological adaptations of the callitrichids and that these character states are therefore derived and not primitive among New World monkeys (Rosenberger 1979, Leutenegger 1979, Ciochon and Chiarelli 1980, Sussman and Kinzey 1984, Ford 1986). As we shall see in the next chapter, recent behavioral and ecological studies support this contention. However, some of the above features, such as a reduced third molar, once thought to be directly linked to reduction of body size, have been found in much larger, extinct species of Neotropical monkeys (Rosenberger et al. 1990, Kay 1994, Fleagle et al. 1997). Thus, some of the dental features found among the small callitrichids evolved before the size reduction of the extant members of that family.

Currently there are 16 genera of New World monkeys and approximately 57 species (though some list over 70 species) (Table 2-4). They are found in the tropical and subtropical wooded areas of the Americas. The Callitrichidae are distributed from about nine degrees north (Panama and southeastern Costa Rica) to about 24 degrees south latitude (Brazil and Bolivia) (Hershkovitz 1977). Although adequate distribution maps for most genera of Cebidae or Atelidae are not available, generally they are found as far north as 23 degrees north (coastal forests of Mexico) to approximately 30 degrees south latitude (Brazil). The distributions of specific genera and species are quite variable in extent. As will be seen in the following chapters, some are very localized while others have a wide distribution.

Unlike the prosimians and Old World monkeys of Africa and Asia, where congeneric species are often found living sympatrically, among New World monkeys most species within the same genus displace each other geographically. Only some species of *Cebus, Saguinus,* and *Callicebus* are congeneric sympatrics. This pattern of distribution suggests that there may be important differences in some of the factors that influenced the evolutionary history of primates of the New and Old Worlds (see Kinzey and Gentry 1979, Kinzey 1982, Fleagle et al. 1997).

Fleagle et al. (1997) point out that the New World monkeys differ from those of the Old World in that they are relatively small, there are fewer folivorous taxa, a number of them have prehensile tails, and there are no terrestrial forms. However, in general, the earliest Old World anthropoids were adaptively more similar to platyrrhines than to later Old World taxa in that they were smaller, there was a paucity of folivores, and there were no terrestrial forms.

It appears that in the New World many extant lineages have been present since the initial radiation of the group and have occupied the same niches as they do today. In contrast, the Old World anthropoids appear to have gone through a pattern of successive radiations with a great deal of adaptive diversity over the past 20 million years. Other differences may relate to the nature of the mammalian competitors of these forms (Fleagle et al. 1997). For example, caenolestid marsupials were present in the neotropics but prosimians were lacking over this evolutionary period.

BIBLIOGRAPHY

Ciochon, R., Chiarelli, A. 1980. Paleobiogeographic perspectives on the origin of the Platyrrhini. Pp. 459–493. In *Evolutionary Biology of the New World Monkeys and Continental Drift.* R. Ciochon, A. Chiarelli, Eds., New York, Plenum.

Conroy, G.C. 1990. *Primate Evolution.* New York, W.W. Norton.

Delson, E., Rosenberger, A. 1980. Phyletic perspectives on platyrrhine origins and anthropoid relationships. Pp. 445–458. In *Evolutionary Biology of the New World Monkeys and Continental Drift.* R. Ciochon, A. Chiarelli, Eds., New York, Plenum.

Eisenberg, J.F. 1077. Comparative ecology and reproduction of new world monkeys. Pp. 13–22. In *The Biology and Conservation of the Callitrichidae.* D.G. Kleiman, Ed., Washington, D.C., Smithsonian Institution Press.

Fleagle, J.G. 1999. *Primate Evolution and Adaptation.* New York, Plenum.

Fleagle, J.G., Kay, R.F., Anthony, M.R.L. 1997. Fossil New World monkeys. Pp. 473–495. In *Vertebrate Paleontology in the Neotropics: The Miocene Fauna of La Venta, Colombia.* R.F. Kay, R.H. Madden, R.L. Cifelli, J.J. Flynn, Eds., Washington, D.C., Smithsonian Institution Press.

Ford, S. 1986. Comments on the evolution of claw-like nails in callitrichids. *Am. J. Phys. Anthropol.* 70:25–26.

Gingerich, P., Schoeninger, M. 1977. The fossil record and primate phylogeny. *J. Hum. Evol.* 6:483–505.

Hershkovitz, P. 1977. *Living New World Monkeys (Platyrrhini) with an Introduction to the Primates.* Chicago, University of Chicago.

Hoffstetter, R. 1972. Relationships, origins, and history of the ceboid monkeys and caviomorph rodents: a modern reinterpretation. Pp. 323–347. In *Evolutionary Biology.* M.K. Hecht, W.C. Steere, Eds., New York, Appeleton-Century-Crofts.

Kay, R.F., Madden, R.H., Mazzoni, M., Vecetich, M.G., Re, G., Heizler, M., Sandeman, H. 1999. The oldest Argentine primates: first age determination for the Colhushuapian South American land mammal "Age". *Am. J. Phys. Anthropol.* Suppl. 28:166.

Kay, R.F. 1994. "Giant" tamarin from the Miocene of Columbia. *Am. J. Phys. Anthropol.* 96:34–48.

Kinzey, W.G. 1982. Distribution of primates and forest refuges. Pp. 455–482. In *Biological Diversification in the Tropics.* G.T. Prance, Ed., New York, Columbia University Press.

Kinzey, W.G., Gentry, A.H. 1979. Habitat utilization in two species of *Callicebus*. Pp. 89–100. In *Primate Ecology: Problem Oriented Field Studies*. R.W. Sussman, Ed., New York, Wiley.

Lavocat, R. 1974. The interrelationships between the African and South American rodents and their bearing on the problem of the origins of South American monkeys. *J. Hum. Evol.* 3:323–326.

Le Gros Clark, W.E. 1959. *The Antecedents of Man*. New York, Harper and Row.

Leutenegger, W. 1980. Monogamy in callitrichids: a consequence of phyletic dwarfism? *Int. J. Primatol.* 1:95–98.

Porter, C.A., Czelusniak, J., Schneider, H., Schneider, M.P.C., Sampaio, I., Goodman, M. 1997. Sequences of primate e-globin gene: implications for systematics of the marmosets and other New World primates. *Gene* 205:59–71.

Rose, K., Fleagle, J. 1981. The fossil history of non-human primates in the Americas. Pp. 111–167. In *Ecology and Behavior of Neotropical Primates*. A. Coimbra-Filho, R. Mittermeier, Eds., Rio de Janeiro, Academia Brasiliera de Ciencias.

Rosenberger, A. 1979. Cranial anatomy and implications of *Dolichocebus*, a late Oligocene ceboid primate. *Nature* 279:416–418.

Rosenberger, A.L., Setoguchi, T., Shigehara, N. 1990. The fossil record of callitrichine primates. *J. Hum. Evol.* 19:209–236.

Sarich, V.M., Cronin, J.E. 1980. South American mammal molecular systematics, evolutionary clocks, and continental drift. Pp. 399–421. In *Evolutionary Biology of the New World Monkeys and Continental Drift*. R. Ciochon, A. Chiarelli, Eds., New York, Plenum.

Simons, E.L. 1972. *Primate Evolution: An Introduction to Man's Place in Nature*. New York, Macmillan.

Simons, E.L. 1976. The fossil record of primate phylogeny. Pp. 35–62. In *Molecular Anthropology*. M. Goodman, E. Tashian, J. Tashian, Eds., New York, Plenum.

Sussman, R.W., Kinzey, W.G. 1984. The ecological role of the Callitrichidae: a review. *Am. J. Phys. Anthropol.* 64:419–449.

CHAPTER 2

Callitrichidae

INTRODUCTION

Marmosets, tamarins, and Goeldi's monkey form a monophyletic group of New World primates that fills a unique ecological role in the forests of Central and South America. Traditionally, these primates have either been regarded as a single family, the Callitrichidae, or as two distinct families, the Callitrichidae (which includes the genera *Saguinus, Callithrix, Cebuella,* and *Leontopithecus*) and the Callimiconidae (which includes the single genus and species *Callimico goeldii*) (Hershkovitz 1977). In this latter classification, *Callimico* is distinguished from tamarins and marmosets because it gives birth to a single infant and retains its third upper and lower molars. However, these two traits represent the primitive platyrrhine condition, and therefore, their presence in *Callimico* cannot be used to exclude a close evolutionary relationship with tamarins and marmosets. Moreover, based on morphological and biochemical evidence (Ford 1992, Rosenberger 1979, 1981, Sarich and Cronin 1980, Schneider and Rosenberger 1996, Davis 1996, Garber et al. 1996) there is no justification in separating these taxa into two distinct families.

In this book, I place all five genera into a single family, the Callitrichidae.[1] Grouping all tamarins, marmosets, and Goeldi's monkey into a single taxonomic group serves to highlight their adaptive unity. For example, in supporting Rosenberger's classification, Szalay and Delson state:

> *Callitrichines may be viewed as representing a radiation taking its origin in an ancestral species that evolved clawlike tegulae from the*

---

[1] Recent revisions of the Neotropical primates (Rosenberger 1979, 1981, Rosenberger et al. 1990, Garber et al. 1996b) advocate placing all five genera in the subfamily Callitrichinae. Such an approach is extremely useful because, rather than isolating major adaptive radiations, it fosters a system of classification in which subfamilies can be linked into families based on their common evolutionary history. Recent molecular evidence, for example, appears to support a close phylogenetic relationship between callitrichids, *Cebus,* and *Saimiri* (Schneider et al. 1993, Schneider and Rosenberger 1996).

> nail-like ones found in other platyrrhines, possibly in order to pursue
> a gum-resin and/or insect diet on broad branches and tree trunks
> (1979:288–289).

The presence of claw-like nails is, in fact, one of the primary adaptations which has allowed callitrichids to exploit their unique ecological niche.

Until the early 1980's, there were several common misconceptions regarding marmosets and tamarins. They were regarded as the ecological equivalent of squirrels (Eisenberg 1977, Szalay and Delson 1979), strictly monogamous and territorial (Leutenegger 1980, Redican and Taub 1981), and morphologically primitive (Kinzey 1973, Hershkovitz, 1977). However, in a review of their ecology and social behavior, Sussman and Kinzey (1984) stressed that field studies did not support these earlier contentions.

The Callitrichidae are small, long-tailed New World monkeys that exhibit a number of morphological characteristics that are rare among extant anthropoid primates (Fig. 2-1). These include very small body size, tendency to twin (except for *Callimico*), the appearance of claw-like nails on all digits except the hallux, and a three-cusped (tritubercular) upper molar morphology (except *Callimico*). They also lack a third molar in both maxilla and mandible (except *Callimico*), thus having a dental formula of 2.1.3.2 rather than 2.1.3.3 as in all other New World monkeys. Callitrichids are all diurnal.

The Callitrichidae have been divided into two functional groups based on the morphology of lower incisors and canine teeth. The first group includes the marmosets, *Callithrix* and *Cebuella*, in which the lower incisors are narrow, elongate and reach the occlusal level of the canines (Fig. 2-2). In fact, recent biochemical evidence suggests that *Callithrix* and *Cebuella* should be placed in the same genus (Barroso et al. 1997, Porter et al. 1997). The second group includes the tamarins, lion tamarins, and *Callimico* (*Saguinus, Leontopithecus,* and *Callimico*) with a more typically anthropoid canine-incisor relationship in which the incisors are spatulate and shorter than the canine teeth (Fig. 2-3). These are descriptive, not taxonomic, terms. They are useful in distinguishing two broadly different adaptive groups, but not necessarily two phylogenetic clades (see for example Rosenberger and Coimbra-Filho 1984). It must be noted, however, that there exists considerable variability in diet, dentition, gut morphology, and gum-feeding behavior among marmoset species (Hershkovitz 1977, Garber 1992, Rylands 1993) and that lion tamarins, tamarins, and *Callimico* also differ in ecology, behavior, and morphological characteristics. Therefore, any distinction based solely on incisor/canine proportions may mask important ecological and behavioral differences.

Figure 2-1 The common marmoset (*Callithrix jacchus*) illustrating typical characteristics of the callitrichids. [From Sleeper 1997]

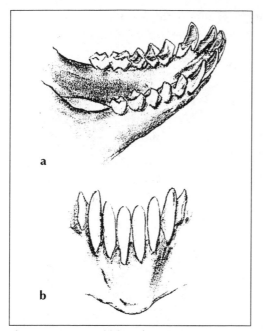

Figure 2-2 Mandible of *Callithrix jacchus*. [From Sussman and Kinzey 1984]

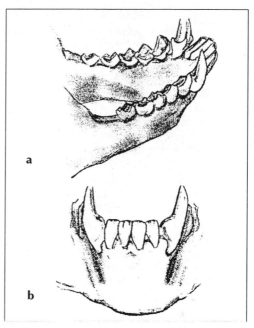

Figure 2-3 Mandible of *Saguinus midas*. [From Sussman and Kinzey 1984]

Traditionally, there are two genera of marmosets, *Callithrix* and *Cebuella*. Here, we follow the classification of Rylands et al. (1993). According to this classification, there are ten species of *Callithrix* (Fig. 2-4, Table 2-1). The genus is widely distributed in South America east of the Madeira River (Fig. 2-5). Three species (*C. humeralifer, C. emilae* and *C. nigricaps*) are found mainly in the Amazon region; a fourth species (*C. argentata*) is located in Amazonia, central-western Brazil, eastern Bolivia and northern Paraguay (Stallings and Mittermeier 1983); and the other six species (considered subspecies of *C. jacchus* by Hershkovitz [1975, 1977]) are located in eastern Brazil. *Callithrix* species range in adult body weight from around 300–500 g (Ferrari 1993, Smith and Jungers 1997, Table 2-1). Only one species of *Cebuella* is recognized, *Cebuella pygmaea* (Fig. 2-6). It is commonly referred to as the "pygmy marmoset" because it is appreciably smaller than any *Callithrix*. In fact, *Cebuella* is

Figure 2-4 *Leontopithecus, Callimico,* and some marmoset species. [From Emmons 1990]

Table 2-1 Classification of the Family Callitrichidae.
Average weights of Wild-Caught Males Are Given for Some Species.*

Species and common name	Avg. Weight (gm)	N
Callimico (Goeldi's monkey)		
C. goeldii	360	8**
Saguinus (tamarins)		
S. nigricollis (Black-mantle tamarin)	468	8
S. fuscicollis (saddle-back tamarin)	343	69
S. tripartitus (golden-mantle saddle-back tamarin)		
S. mystax (moustached tamarin)	510	191
S. labiatus (red-chested tamarin)	490	136
S. imperator (emperor tamarin)	474	4
S. inustus (mottled-face tamarin)	585	2
S. midas (golden-handed tamarin)	515	34
S. bicolor (bare-face tamarin)	428	4
S. leucopus (silvery brown bare-face tamarin)	494	2
S. oedipus (cotton-top tamarin)	418	37
S. geoffroyi (Geoffroyi's tamarin)	482	55
Leontopithecus (lion tamarins)		
L. rosalia (golden lion tamarin)	620	50+
L. chrysomelas (golden-headed lion tamarin)	620	2
L. chrysopygus (golden-rumped lion tamarin)	575	4
L. caissara (black-faced lion tamarin)		
Callithrix (marmosets)		
C. argentata (bare-ear marmoset)	330	8
C. emiliae (Snethlage's marmoset)	313	12
C. nigriceps (black-headed marmoset)	370	3
C. humeralifer (tassle-ear marmoset)	475	15
C. jacchus (common marmoset)	362	3
C. penicillata (black tufted-ear marmoset)	344	8
C. kuhli (Wied's marmoset)		
C. geoffroyi (Geoffroyi's tufted-ear marmoset)	482	55
C. aurita (buffy tufted-ear marmoset)	429	3
C. flaviceps (buffy-headed marmoset)		
Cebuella (pygmy marmosets)		
C. pygmaea	110	36

*Reference for weights is Smith and Jungers (1997). Here, I only include weights for males because female weights change significantly during various reproductive stages. **Weights for *Callimico* are from Encarnación and Heyman (1997) from individuals captured in the wild.

the smallest anthropoid, with non-pregnant adults weighing about 120 g (range 85–140 g, N-63; Soini 1993). It is found in tropical forests of the upper Amazon region (Fig. 2-5).

Until recently, *Callithrix* had been poorly studied in the wild. However, now a number of field studies have been conducted, including relatively long studies of seven species (Table 2-2) (Kinzey 1997). These long-term field observations have provided new insights into marmoset feeding ecology, social organization, mating, group stability, ranging patterns, and behavioral variability (Ferrari 1988, 1991, Rylands 1984a, Digby 1994, Ferrari et al. 1996).

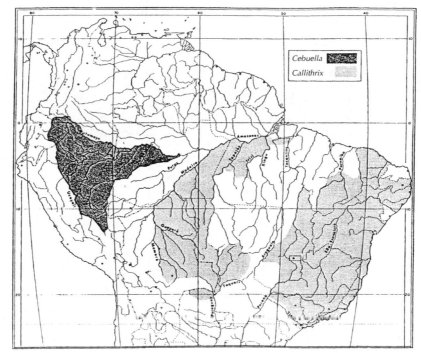

Figure 2-5 Map of distribution of *Callithrix* (light shading) and *Cebuella* (heavy shading) adapted from Hershkovitz (1977, 1979) and Kinzey (1982). Major rivers are labeled.

Figure 2-6 Pygmy marmoset. [From Rowe 1996]

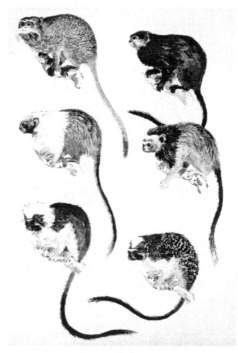

Figure 2-7 Some tamarin species. [From Emmons 1990]

Table 2-2a Field Studies of *Callithrix*

Species	Reference	Duration	Location
C. humeralifer	Rylands (1982, 1984, 1986b)	12 mo	Mato Grosso, Brazil
C. kuhli	Rylands (1982, 1984, 1989b)	6 mo	Bahia, Brazil
C. argentata melanura	Stallings and Mittermeier 1983) Stallings (1985) Stallings et al. (1989)		N.E. Paraguay
C. flaviceps	Ferrari 1989b)	12 mo	Minas Gerais, Brazil
C. aurita	Torres de Assumpção (1983b)	13 mo	São Paolo, Brazil
C. aurita	Muskin (1984a,b)	5 mo	Minas Gerais, Brazil
C. aurita	Stallings (1988) Stallings and Robinson (1991)	12 mo	Minas Gerais, Brazil
C. jacchus	Maier et al. (1982) Alonso and Langguth (1989)	14 mo	Paraiba, Brazil
C. jacchus	Stevenson and Rylands (1988) Hubrecht (1984, 1985) Scanlon et al. (1988, 1989)	6 mo 7 mo 18 mo	Pernambuco, Brazil
C. penicillata	Lacher et al. (1984) Fonseca and Lacher (1984)	4 mo	Distrito Federal, Brazil
C. penicillata	Faria (1984a,b 1986, 1989)	12 mo	Distrito Federal, Brazil

[From Rylands and de Faria 1993]

Rylands et al. (1993) recognize twelve species of *Saguinus*, which differ in size and especially in pelage characteristics (Fig. 2-7). They are widely distributed in Central and South America north of the Amazon, and west of the Madeira River south of the Amazon (Fig. 2-8). Mean adult body weights of *Saguinus* species range from around 300-600 g (Table 2-1)(Garber 1993a, Smith and Jungers 1997). Four species of lion tamarins are currently recognized (Fig. 2-9). Body weights of wild adult female golden lion tamarins (*Leontopithecus rosalia*) range from 575–622 g (Dietz et al. 1994, Smith and Jungers 1997). Lion tamarins are found in three restricted regions of eastern Brazil (Fig. 2-8). Traditionally, the genera *Saguinus* and *Leontopithecus* have been referred to as 'tamarins'. However, the taxonomic position of *Leontopithecus* is unclear, and in various reviews, it has been aligned with *Saguinus*, with *Callithrix*, and with *Callimico* (Rosenberger and Coimbra-Filho 1984, Sussman and Kinzey 1984, Garber 1994).

Callimico is represented by a single species, *C. goeldii* (Fig. 2-10). It weighs approximately 360 g (Encarnación and Heymann 1997). This was the last genus of New World monkey described and is distributed throughout the upper Amazon region of Colombia, Ecuador, Peru, Bolivia, and Brazil (Hershkovitz 1977). However, within this range, its distribution is patchy, and population densities are low (Heltne et al. 1981). To date, there are no long term field studies on *Callimico*.

Although tamarins were utilized extensively in laboratory and medical research, field studies of these primates in their natural environment were either very short-term or completely lacking until the mid-1970's and early 1980's. Reports based on surveys, short observations (one to several weeks), or broad synecological studies are available for a number of species. Seven of the twelve species have been the subjects of detailed systematic investigations lasting five or more months (Table 2-2)(Kinzey 1997). Thus, there is now a broad and comparative data base from which to examine feeding ecology and social organization in several species. However, little is known for the remaining species.

Table 2-2b Long-Term Field Studies of *Saguinus*

Species	Duration	Location	Reference
S. geoffroyi	19 mo	Panama	Dawson (1976, 1978, 1979)
S. geoffroyi	8 mo	Panama	Garber (1980a,b, 1984a,b)
S. oedipus	24 mo	Colombia	Neyman (1978)
S. imperator°	24+ mo	Peru	Terborgh (1983, 1985, 1986)
S. labiatus° labiatus	6 mo	Bolivia	Izawa and Yoneda (1981) Yoneda (1981, 1984a)
S. labiatus° labiatus	5 mo	Bolivia	Pook and Pook (1982)
S. labiatus° labiatus	5 mo	Bolivia	Buchanan-Smith (1990)
S. mystax° mystax	12 mo	Peru	Garber (1986) Garber (1988a,b) Garber and Teaford (1986)
S. mystax mystax	5 mo	Peru	Pruetz and Garber (1991)
S. mystax° mystax	10 mo	Peru	Norconk (1986)
S. mystax° mystax	15 mo	Peru	Ramirez (1989)
S. nigricollis	7 mo	Colombia	Izawa (1978)
S. fuscicollis illigeri	15 mo	Peru	Soini (1987i)
S. fuscicollis weddelli	15 mo	Peru	Crandlemire-Sacco (1986)
S. fuscicollis° weddelli	5 mo	Bolivia	Pook and Pook (1982, 1982)
S. fuscicollis° weddelli	6 mo	Bolivia	Izawa and Yoneda (1981) Yoneda (1981, 1984a,b)
S. fuscicollis° weddelli	24+ mo	Peru	Terborgh (1983, 1985, 1986)
S. fuscicollis° weddelli	24+ mo	Peru	Goldizen (19837a,b, 1990)
S. fuscicollis° nigrifrons	10 mo	Peru	Norconk (1986)

° Formed a mixed species troop with another tamarin species.
[From Garber 1993a]

HABITAT SELECTION

Callitrichids are quite diverse in their selection of habitats. Some forms such as *Saguinus fuscicollis, Callimico goeldii, Cebuella pygmaea,* and several *Callithrix* species are reported to exploit low levels in the canopy and are frequently found in secondary forests and edge habitats. The importance of a mix of habitat types and access to gum-producing trees within the home range of tamarin, and especially marmoset groups, has been noticed by a number of authors (e.g., Thorington 1968, Dawson 1979, Rylands 1979, 1981, 1993, 1996, Garber 1980a, 1993a, Terborgh 1983a, Yoneda 1984a,b, Terborgh and Stern 1989, Snowden and Soini 1988).

In Panama, *Saguinus geoffroyi* is found mainly in low, dense primary forests and also in abandoned, overgrown slash-and-burn agricultural fields. In fact, Moyni-

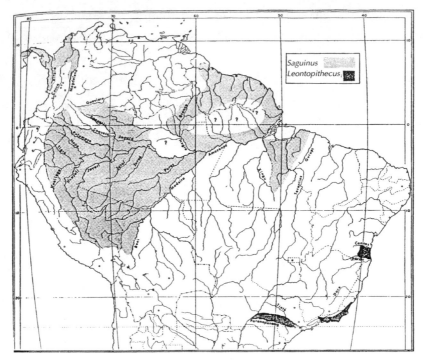

Figure 2-8 Map of distribution of *Saguinus* (light shading) and *Leontopithecus* (heavy shading) adapted from Hershkovitz (1977) and Kinzey (1982). Major rivers are labeled.

han (1976a) believes this species to be a commensal of humans in Panama. Using radio-tracking techniques, Dawson (1979) analyzed the use of space, ranging patterns, and habitat preference of groups of *S. geoffroyi* in a dry tropical forest site on the Pacific Coast of Panama. He found low bush and forest edge used to a greater extent than would be expected by chance. Gallery forest of *Anacardium excelsum* (cashew trees) and forest edge with emergent royal palms (*Scheelea rostrata*) were also important habitats. Although habitats with open canopies or a scarcity of vines were avoided by tamarins, Garber (1980a) observed groups crossing grassy, open areas on the ground from one forest patch to another once or twice a day.

S. fuscicollis, S. labiatus, S. midas, S. mystax, and *S. nigricollis* also are found both in primary and secondary forests (Coimbra-Filho and Mittermeier 1973, Castro and Soini 1977, Izawa 1978, Mittermeier and van Roosmalen 1981, Yoneda 1984a,b, Norconk 1986, Garber 1988a, Peres 1996, Tovar 1994). In extensive surveys of Surinam forests, Mittermeier and van Roosmalen (1981) found *S. midas* living in all forest types inhabited by monkeys. They were most frequently seen in high rain forest, but of the eight species studied, *S. midas* was the only one to prefer edge habitats to non-edge habitats within the forest. In a recent survey in Guyana, *S. midas* also was found in a variety of habitats but was more common in secondary forest near human habitation (Sussman and Phillips-Conroy 1995). In a recent survey of the western Amazon, Peres (1996) reported that callitrichids were not found in large extensions of flooded forests where they were largely replaced by squirrel monkeys.

Terborgh (1983a,b) found *S. fuscicollis* and *S. imperator* in Peru to be quite generally distributed, but their home ranges always contained a number of habi-

Figure 2-9 Lion tamarin. [Photo by R.W. Sussman]

Figure 2-10 *Callimico.* [From Rowe 1996]

tat types, including abundant edge. Furthermore, the two species did not occupy the large tracts of mature forest. This led Terborgh and Stern (1989) to conclude that habitat diversity is an essential requisite of tamarin home ranges.

S. fuscicollis (Fig. 2-11) has a wider geographical distribution than other tamarin species and forms stable long-lasting associations with other callitrichids, such as *S. imperator, S. labiatus, S. mystax,* and *S. nigricollis,* as well as *Callithrix emiliae* (Soini 1987a, Garber 1993b, Rylands 1993, Lopes and Ferrari 1994). In tamarin mixed-species groups, individuals of each species feed, forage, travel, rest, and cooperatively defend a single home range, although associations in some species are more cohesive than in others. *S. fuscicollis* appears to be able to exploit a wider range of habitats and is more adaptable and successful than other tamarin species partly because of its propensity to form mixed-species groups (Ferrari 1993).

Leontopithecus utilizes large home ranges and feeds opportunistically on plant gums, as does *Saguinus,* but it may rely more on vertebrate prey than do other callitrichids. Lion tamarins exploit highly seasonal tropical and subtropical mature rainforests (Coimbra-Filho 1976, Rylands 1993, 1996, but see Dietz et al. 1997). They sleep in tree-holes and must have sufficient tree-hole shelters, which are usually found in large trees. Furthermore, they must have adequate densities of animal prey, and *L. chrysomelas* and *L. rosalia* require epiphytic bromeliads as foraging habitats. The forests occupied by all species, except *L. chrysopygus,* are abundant in these bromeliads. *L. chrysopygus* lives in forests that lack epiphytic bromeliads and are more seasonal than those of other lion tamarins. This species also has larger home ranges, smaller groups, and feeds on exudates more than the other species (Passos and Carvalho 1991, Rylands 1993, 1996).

The widespread geographical distribution of marmosets implies the ability of the genus to occupy a wide range of habitats. Throughout Amazonia, *Callithrix* is found in both old and relatively young secondary growth, semi-deciduous forest patches within savannah and white sand regions, gallery forests, subhumid and seasonal forests, near plantations, and in primary forests with dense undergrowth, and swamp forests (Moynihan 1976a, Hershkovitz 1977, Rylands 1981, Rylands and Faria 1993). The genus, however, is generally absent from seasonally or permanently flooded forest (Ryland and Faria 1993). *C. jacchus* and *C. penicillata* live in forest patches and riverine forest in the dry thorn scrub forests (*cerrado* and *caatinga* habitats) of the Atlantic coast of Brazil. Four other species, *C. aurita, C. flaviceps, C. geofroyi,* and *C. kuhli,* occupy both the aseasonal evergreen forests and the more inland, seasonal semi-deciduous forests of the Atlantic coast of Brazil. Unifying features of all marmoset species are their use of edge or secondary growth habitats (Rylands 1987, Faria 1986, Stallings 1988, Ferrari and Mendes 1991, Rylands and Faria 1993, Ferrari et al. 1996) and their ability to gouge holes and exploit plant gums when fruits and other resources are unavailable.

Figure 2-11 Saddle-backed tamarin. [From Rowe 1996]

The natural habitat of *Cebuella* consists principally of riparian and floodplain forests (Moynihan 1976a, Ramirez et al. 1977, Izawa 1979, Soini 1982). In fact, Soini (1993) considers this species to be a habitat specialist, using mainly the edges and interior of seasonally inundated mature floodplain forests. When *Cebuella* has been reported in mature nonflooded forest (Hernandez-Camacho and Cooper 1976), it is probably the result of humans having altered the original habitat (Soini 1982, 1993). *Cebuella* often occupies edge habitat, however, whether in seasonally inundated or in mature forests (Moynihan 1976b, Castro and Soini 1977, Freese et al. 1982, Izawa 1976, 1979, Soini 1982, Terborgh 1983b).

With some exceptions, many tamarin and marmoset species spend a great deal of time foraging in the dense undergrowth below the canopy and in the middle and lower levels of the tree crown. Tree trunks also serve as an important foraging substrate (Garber 1992) when exploiting insects, small vertebrates, and plant gums. Several species are reported to climb high in the canopy and into emergents while foraging for fruits, floral nectar, and insects or come to the ground while searching for specific foods (Garber 1993b, Ferrari 1993). This propensity to exploit various habitat zones and substrates, including edge habitats, is the hallmark of callitrichid ecology. Many morphological characteristics of this group can best be understood in light of this adaptability.

Although *Callimico* has been sighted in mature forest, it appears to specialize in scrub forest or forest with ample areas of dense undergrowth (Moynihan 1976a, Izawa 1979, Pook and Pook 1981). It is often reported to be associated with patches of bamboo. In fact, 31 of 37 *Callimico* sites surveyed by Izawa (1979) were bamboo forest, however, Christen and Geissmann (1994) never observed them in bamboo. *Callimico* usually stays in the understory of the forest. Pook and Pook (1981) reported that 88% of their sightings of *Callimico* were at 5 m or lower. This monkey also comes to the ground to forage for insects and escapes on the ground when frightened.

POSITIONAL BEHAVIOR

It was once thought that the Callitrichidae filled a niche similar to that occupied by squirrels. For example, Eisenberg (1977:13) stated:

> *In many respects, the New World callitrichids appear to occupy ecological niches which are exploited in the Paleotropics by rodents of the family Sciuridae.*

Szalay and Delson (1979:288), in an extensive review of primate evolution, concluded that, "The marmosets lead a squirrel-like life." It is the locomotor behavior especially that had been described as squirrel-like (see for example Bates 1864, Enders 1935, Cruz Lima 1945, Napier and Napier 1967, Thorington 1968, Hladik 1970, Hershkovitz 1972, Cartmill 1974, Dawson 1976).

The idea that callitrichids filled niches generally occupied by tree squirrels in Africa and Asia seemed reasonable on first inspection, since tree squirrels did not reach the tropical forests of Central and South America until approximately 3–5 million years ago (Patterson and Pascual 1972, Webb 1978). Despite a very limited platyrrhine fossil record and controversy over which, if any, fossil specimens belong to the tamarin and marmoset clade, a recent origin for callitrichids is unlikely.

Kay (1994) has argued that a fossil platyrrhine, *Lagonimico,* from Miocene (13.5 mya) deposits in Colombia is a tamarin and marmoset ancestor. Similarly, Rosenberger (1992) has linked *Mohanimico* (dated 12–16 mya) as a putative ancestor to *Callimico.* Moreover, a recent discovery of 25 million year old primate fossils from La Salla, Bolivia contains forms that some argue are callitrichid-like in morphology (Takai and Anaya 1996, but see Kay et al. 1997). In addition, genetic evidence suggests that tamarins and marmosets diverged from cebid ancestors around 11 mya (Barroso et al. 1997). Taken together, these data suggest that the initial callitrichid radiation is not recent and dates to at least the middle Miocene. Thus, for the majority of their evolutionary history, New World monkeys have occupied forests devoid of arboreal squirrels. In their absence, it has been suggested that tamarins and marmosets have opportunistically radiated into a tree squirrel niche (Hershkovitz 1972, 1977, Eisenberg 1977). Callitrichids are not squirrel-like in movement or habitat selection. The most detailed study of callitrichid positional behavior and ecology was done by Garber (1980a, 1980b, 1984a, 1991, 1998, Garber and Sussman 1984). He first collected quantitative data on *Saguinus geoffroyi* and *Sciurus granatensis* (the

17

red-tailed squirrel) in Panama. Later, Garber (1991) studied *Saguinus mystax* and *S. fuscicollis* in Peru and compared the locomotor behavior of these three species of tamarin.

Garber found that Panamanian red-tailed squirrels and tamarins used arboreal supports in a very different manner. Whereas the squirrels avoided thin flexible supports, approximately half of travel and movement, 66% of fruit feeding, and 85% of insect predation of the Panamanian tamarins took place on supports less than 3 cm in diameter. Unlike squirrels, tamarins did not transport plant foods obtained in the canopy from thin supports to larger horizontal boughs to feed; rather, they consumed fruits where they were acquired (Garber and Sussman 1984). The Panamanian tamarins ranged through the canopy via a series of long acrobatic leaps that began and ended on thin, fragile, terminal branches (Fig. 2-12). Their claw-like nails did not seem to limit movement on small supports. During travel and movement, only around 7% of their locomotor behavior involved large vertical supports (Table 2-3). In contrast, during travel, *Sciurus granatensis* traveled up and down these supports commonly and with equal frequency. *Saguinus geoffroyi,* however, avoided descending large vertical supports (Table 2-3) and selectively ascended rather than descended large oblique supports.

The different preferences in substrate utilization between the Panamanian tamarin and the red-tailed squirrel are related especially to morphological differences in the hind limbs and the claws. Vertical descent poses a specific set of problems with balance and weight bearing that necessitates the ability to rotate the feet laterally and to hyperextend the claws. Head first descent "depends on an ability to supinate or laterally rotate the extended hind limb so that the plantar surface of the volarflexed foot can be applied to the surface with digits pointing caudad" (Cartmill 1974:61). Cartmill found that approximately 170° of supination is necessary for controlled headfirst descent. In species incapable of this degree of supination, descent of large vertical supports is awkward and usually avoided. The squirrel

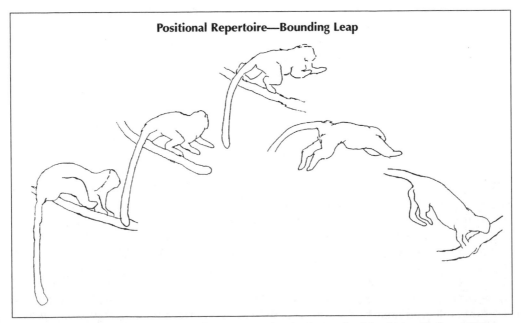

Figure 2-12 Leaping tamarin. Note the extensive in-air phase of stride. [From Garber 1980a]

Table 2-3 Use of Vertical Supports by Sympatric *Saguinus geoffroyi* and *Sciurius granatensis* During Travel and Movement in Panama*

| | Branch diameter (cm) | | | | | | Total |
	0–1.5	1.5–3	3–8	8–16	16 +	Total	travel
Tamarin							
N	43	52	82	53	73	299	3134
%	1.4	1.6	2.6	1.7	2.3	9.5%	
				6.6%			
Squirrel							
N	19	35	105	67	126	352	1038
%	1.8	3.4	10.1	6.4	12.1	33.9%	
				28.7%			
Tamarin[a]							
UP	22	31	31	27	36	147	
DOWN	9	10	12	10	13	54	
	31	41	43	37	49	201	
				$x^2 = 21.57$, df = 4 $p<0.001$			
Squirrel[a]							
UP	8	14	43	24	43	132	
DOWN	5	11	44	31	51	142	
	13	25	87	55	94	274	
				$x^2 = 1.30$, df = 4 $p<0.05$			

*Numbers refer to instantaneous positional events recorded every 2½ minutes; adapted from Garber (1980a)

[a]Data include only locomotion occurring on a single support.

is able to accomplish such movements of the ankle, hindfeet and claws (Fig. 2-13), but behavioral observations indicate that the tamarin is less able to perform such behaviors (Garber 1980a, b). Furthermore, the structure of the tamarin claw-like nail suggests that it plays a minor role in weight bearing during locomotion (Garber 1980b, Hamrick 1998) (Fig. 2-14). On the other hand, animals (like squirrels) lacking opposable digits on their feet and hands are generally less agile on small, non-horizontal supports.

It is not the case that squirrels are incapable of locomoting on terminal supports nor that callitrichids never move on large branches or trunks. Rather, the locomotor adaptations of these two taxa lead to basically and statistically different habitat preferences and allow them to perform different ecological roles (see also Lemelin and Grafton 1998). During most of their locomotor activity, callitrichids behave like other primates with grasping extremities and not like squirrels.

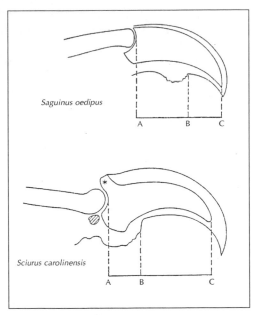

Figure 2-14 Sagittal section throught the middle and terminal phalanges of *Saguinus* (above) and *Sciurus* (below). Note the well developed extensor process (marked with an asterisk) and the presence of a sesamoid bone (shaded area) in the distal interphalangeal joint in *Sciurus*. [From Garber 1980a]

Figure 2-13 Squirrel descending a substrate. [From Cartmill 1974]

In comparing *S. geoffroyi* with *S. mystax* and *S. fuscicollis,* Garber (1991) found that all three species exhibited a similar pattern of positional behavior, with quadrupedal walking, running, bounding, and leaping accounting for approximately 50–90% of travel (Table 2-4). Prehensile activities (grasping and climbing) accounted for 7–12% of travel, and clinging with claws and scansorial movements for 4–8%. Most travel at Garber's site took place in the lower to middle layer of the forest.

Even though *S. mystax* was the largest of the three species and *S. fuscicollis* the smallest, these two species had a similar pattern of substrate preference, using larger (> 10 cm in diameter) and smaller (< 5 cm) supports frequently rather than supports of moderate size. *S. geoffroyi* displayed a clear preference for traveling on the smallest branches. On large vertical or sharply inclined branches, these primates do not use their grasping and prehensile abilities, but rather embed their clawlike nails into the bark for support. Large vertical or sharply inclinded branches are used mainly when foraging and feeding on trunk resources, such as bark refuging insects, prey in crevices and knotholes, and plant exudates.

Other descriptions of the locomotor behavior of marmosets and tamarins are similar to those reported by Garber (1991). In a study of seven sympatric species of monkeys in Surinam, Fleagle and Mittermeier (1980) found approximately 80% of the locomotor behavior of *Saguinus midas* during travel to be quadrupedal walking, running, or bounding on branches less than 3 cm in diameter. Casual descrip-

Table 2-4 Positional Behavior During Travel in Three Species of Tamarins

Species	Positional Category				
	Quad	Climb/Grasp	Leap	Cling/Scans	Total
S. fuscicollis	1510	395	1033	201	3170
(%)	47.6	12.4	32.5	6.3	
S. geoffroyi	1139	194	1090	204	2627
(%)	43.3	7.4	41.5	7.7	
S. mystax	1792	418	1072	151	3468
(%)	51.6	12.0	30.9	4.3	

Quad = quadrupedal progression such as walking, running, and bounding.

Climb/Grasp = includes a variety of prehensile climbing activities and grasping postures.

Lead = includes acrobatic leaps, bounding leaps, and leaping to and/or from vertical trunks.

Cling/Scans = includes claw-clinging and scansorial travel on large vertical or sharply inclined supports.

Adapted from Garber (1991)

tions of the locomotor behavior of *S. geoffroyi* (Moynihan 1970, 1976a), *S. oedipus* (Neyman 1977), *S. midas* (Thorington 1968), *S. mystax* (Castro and Soini 1977), and *S. imperator* (Terborgh 1983b) all characterize these species as quadrupedal, running, and leaping along medium to small branches and jumping between trees among the fine terminal branches and leaves. Preliminary descriptions of the travel paths of the golden lion tamarins indicate that they have a similar pattern of locomotion (Coimbra-Filho and Mittermeier 1973, Kleiman et al. 1988). However, there is some indication that this species may use quadrupedal walking and bounding more, and leaping less frequently than *Saguinus* and *Callimico* (Rosenberger and Stafford 1994). Although little is known regarding positional behavior in wild Goeldi's monkeys, they have been observed frequently to leap from trunk-to-trunk in the forest understory (Garber and Rehg 1998).

A pattern of running and leaping locomotor behavior is typical of many arboreal, quadrupedal primates. However, there are thirteen species of *Saguinus,* some of which are sympatric, varying in body size by a factor of two, and we should expect variation in behavior and ecology among these forms. In fact, Garber (1991) found that, although trunk-to-trunk leaping is observed in many tamarin species, among those taxa studied it is a common and dominant mode of locomotion only in *S. fuscicollis* (and possibly in *S. bicolor*). Terborgh (1983b) studied sympatric groups of *S. imperator* and *S. fuscicollis* in southern Peru, and he also found their locomotor behavior to differ. *S. imperator* moved in the quadrupedal style described above; the smaller *S. fuscicollis,* on the other hand, frequently locomoted in a vertical clinging and leaping mode of progression. This method of progression by *S. fuscicollis* has been observed by a number of authors (Moynihan 1976a, Crandelmire-Sacco 1986, Norconk 1986, Soini 1987a). This and some foraging and feeding differences (described below) may enable sympatric species of *Saguinus* to avoid competition.

Other sympatric callitrichids, such as *L. chrysomelas* and *C. kuhli,* may show similarly contrasting patterns of behavior (Rylands 1993).

There is little quantitative data on positional behavior in marmosets. Given their greater reliance on plant gums, marmosets are more likely to adopt vertical clinging postures and exploit trunks than tamarins. *Cebuella* has been described as a vertical clinger and leaper. Kinzey et al. (1975) found that 85% of all leaps of the pygmy marmoset were to and/or from vertical supports and that animals spent 57% of their non-travel time clinging to vertical branches or trunks. Like *Saguinus geoffroyi, Cebuella* utilized its claws primarily for clinging to large vertical supports while feeding rather than for locomotor activity (Kinzey et al. 1975, Kinzey 1997b). In fact, among marmosets, vertical clinging is most developed in the smallest species, *Cebuella* and *C. jacchus,* both of which are most dependent on tree exudates. Less clinging is observed in *C. humeralifer,* which depends more on fruits (Garber 1992).

It is important to point out that, in many callitrichids, vertical clinging is best thought of as a feeding/foraging posture, which is separate from activities associated with leaping. Callitrichids commonly cling to large supports to consume resources or as a perch from which to scan for insect prey (Fig. 2-11). Leaping in most callitrichids occurs in the canopy and on small, flexible supports and not from one vertical trunk to another. The known exceptions are *Saguinus fuscicollis, Callimico goeldii,* and possibly *Saguinus bicolor,* although leaping may occur more commonly in species that have yet to be studied. *Callimico* travels almost exclusively by vertical clinging and leaping and often rests in a vertical position (Heltne et al. 1981, Garber and Rehg 1998).

In summary, tamarins are able to exhibit a remarkable range of locomotor plasticity, using both very large and very small arboreal supports (Garber 1991). Furthermore, squirrels use their claws mainly as *locomotor* adaptations, aiding the animals as they move up and down large oblique and vertical supports within the forest. As will be described in more detail below, callitrichids generally use their claws mainly for *postural* activities related to specific feeding behaviors.

DIET

Marmosets and tamarins both feed on four primary types of food items: insects, ripe fruits, floral nectar, and plant exudates; however, they utilize these items at different frequencies. Because of their nutritional content, seasonal availability, and distribution, each of these foods requires different foraging strategies and techniques of exploitation. The ranging patterns and positional behaviors required for obtaining each food type also differ. The callitrichids represent an adaptive array of trunk foragers. Trunks represent an important microhabitat for several groups of insect feeders and sap feeders such as woodpeckers, woodcreepers, certain phalangerid marsupials, and several primates. Given that the taxa most derived in body size, dental morphology, and digestive morphology are specialized gum feeders (species of *Callithrix jacchus* group and *Cebuella*), tree-gouging and gum feeding are unlikely to represent the ancestral condition. Rather, the initial callitrichid radiation may best be represented in terms of opportunistic gum feeding and insect/small vertebrate predation on trunks (Sussman and Kinzey 1984, Garber 1992). In *Callithrix* and *Cebuella* a progressive dependence on exudates and tree gouging undoubtedly led to the evolution of derived morphological specializations to exploit this resource.

Insect Prey

The proportion of insects or leaves in the diet of primates is generally related to body size (Charles-Dominique 1971, Kay 1975). Most small primates are able to obtain their protein and lipid needs directly from insects, whereas larger forms utilize folivorous items to fulfill some or all of their protein requirements. Marmosets and tamarins are among the smallest anthropoids and among the smallest of all primates, and as we would expect, a large proportion of their diet consists of insect prey (though this is less so in the smaller, gum-feeding marmosets). Approximately 30–80% of the feeding and foraging time is accounted for by arthropods (Hladik and Hladik 1969, Dawson 1976, 1979, Ramirez et al. 1977, Garber 1980a,b, 1984b, 1993a, Terborgh 1983a, Stevenson and Rylands 1988, Snowdon and Soini 1988, Rylands and Faria 1993).

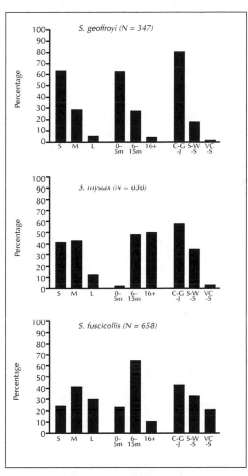

In many tropical forests the structurally diverse vegetation of the understory includes the greatest diversity and abundance of insects (Janzen 1973a,b). Many marmosets and tamarins forage for insects in the dense tangle of branches and vines in the shrub layers of the forest. Their small size enables them to move about relatively quietly in the dense underbrush. Garber (1993a), however, has noted three patterns of foraging among callitrichines (Fig. 2-15): (1) active hunting on small supports, (2) visual scanning of exposed prey using a stealthy type of locomotion on medium sized branches, and (3) specific site, sedentary foraging on large supports using visual or tactile scanning.

S. geoffroyi, using the first foraging pattern, hunts and captures insects by moving cautiously but rapidly on thin flexible supports in the dense vegetation some 1–5 m above the ground. Climbing, grasping, and jumping account for 81% of the positional behaviors during for-

Figure 2-15 Support preference during insectivory: S, small (supports of approximately ≤5 cm in diameter, which tamarins can grasp with their hands and feet); M, medium (supports of approximately 5–10 cm in diameter, which tamarins can grasp with their arms and legs); L, large (supports in excess of 10 cm in diameter, too large to be grasped by tamarins). Positional behaviour: C-G-J, climbing, grasping, and jumping; S-W-S, standing, walking, and sitting; VC-S, vertical clinging and scansorial locomotion. [From Garber, 1993a]

aging. Success is related to the ability of the monkey to move cryptically and with minimal disturbance in the understory. Prey are captured from leaf surfaces by striking rapidly with the forelimbs while maintaining a firm grip with the hindlimbs.

The second mode of foraging is seen in *S. mystax, S. labiatus, S. imperator, S. midas* (Terborgh 1983a, 1985, Garber 1988a, 1993b), and in several species of *Callithrix* (Rylands and Faria 1993). In these callitrichids, visual scanning plays a primary role in detecting exposed and mobile prey. They search for insects in living and dead leaves, in holes, in branches, and on trunks while moving slowly and close to the substrate. This involves a stealthy stalk and pounce, foliage-gleaning method in the understory and middle levels of the forest. A large percentage of foraging time is spent in more sedentary postures such as walking, standing and sitting, and on moderate sized supports.

The third insect foraging technique is noted in the saddle-backed tamarin (*S. fuscicollis*) and also may be used by *S. nigricollis, S. bicolor, Callimico goeldii*, and, in a modified way, by *Leontopithecus* ssp. As well as searching regularly for insects in the dense underbrush using the second technique described above, in all areas where the saddle-backed tamarin has been studied, it also finds large orthopterans on trunks or uses trunks to scan the ground and nearby trunks for prey. As indicated by Terborgh (1983a: 100, 110–112):

> *Instead of foraging continuously for long periods as do other species,* fuscicollis *concentrates its searching in brief, intense bouts, usually on giant vine-draped trees . . . In keeping with its propensity for cling-and-leap locomotion and its great agility on trunks,* fuscicollis *is a bark and cavity specialist. The animals do nearly all of their foraging on vertical surfaces.*

The saddle-backed tamarin is able to embed its elongated and laterally compressed claw-like nails into the bark, and manually explore knotholes, crevices, and other regions of the trunk. This is accomplished by its elongated forelimb, fingers, and narrow hands (analogous in certain ways to the hand morphology in *Leontopithecus*). Thus, this species procures insects in all levels of the forest canopy and on a wide array of substrates. However, most of its insects are captured on small supports in the undercanopy, or on moderate to large-sized trunks. Trunks also provide a scanning platform for locating terrestrial prey.

The use of trunks to prey on insects is probably one of the ways in which *S. fuscicollis* is able to coexist with many other species of tamarin and minimize competition for insect resources. In fact, the saddle-backed tamarin appears to feed on a different spectrum of insect prey from sympatric congenitors. For example, in Peru, of 35 prey species eaten by both *S. fuscicollis* and *S. mystax,* 25 were captured only by the former and seven only by the latter. Only three species were shared by both (Nickle and Heymann 1996).

Although there are few data available, *Callimico* may use a similar bark surface insect foraging pattern to that of the saddle-backed tamarin. It appears to search for insects on vertical trunks at the lowest level of the vegetation or on the ground while clinging and leaping in the undercanopy (Moynihan 1976a, Izawa 1979, Pook and Pook 1981).

The lion tamarins, *L. rosalia* and *L. chrysomelas,* also use tree trunks and vertical clinging postures to procure insects. However, these species are manipulative foragers that exploit their prey under bark and especially inside epiphytic bromeliads in the undercanopy using touch rather than sight (Peres 1986a, Rylands 1986a,

1993, Garber 1992, Dietz et al. 1997). They use long and slender arms and elongated and webbed fingers to probe and extract largely non-mobile prey. They also probe for prey in leaf litter, under bark, and in crevices and holes in trees. Because lion tamarins remain immobile while probing for insects in specific microhabitats, they have been categorized as specific-site foragers. A third species, *L. chrysopygus*, forages in a very similar manner in leaf litter and on the ground, but bromiliads are not found in the areas where it has been studied (Rylands 1993).

Some species of *Callithrix* (*C. humeralifer, C. flaviceps, C. geoffroyi,* and *C. kuhli*) take advantage of insects disturbed by swarm raids of army ants and are reported to spend up to three hours at a time within two meters of the ground stealing insects from the ants or picking off those disturbed by the swarm (Stevenson and Rylands 1988, Rylands and Faria 1993). Prey located near the ground are underutilized by many New World primates (Heltne et al. 1981), but as mentioned above, some marmosets and tamarins will come to the ground to catch insects. Goeldi's monkey frequently captures prey by jumping on the ground and then returning to a low vertical perch to eat, very much like *Tarsius* (Pook and Pook 1981).

Orthoptera, especially large grasshoppers, are the most common prey item of callitrichids (Fig. 2-16). Orthopterans constituted 70% of the volume of prey material in stomach contents of *S. geoffroyi* collected by Dawson (1976) and represented about 60% of the insect feeding bouts of *S. imperator* and *S. fuscicollis* observed by Terborgh (1983a) in Peru. Izawa (1978) considered large grasshoppers to be the most important single food item of *S. nigricollis* in Colombia. The most frequently observed insect prey for *Cebuella* (Soini, 1982), *Callithrix humeralifer intermedius, C. flaviceps* and *C. kuhlii* were grasshoppers including both Acrididae and Tettigoniidae (Stevenson and Rylands 1988, Ferrari, 1993), and *Callimico* also has been observed eating large grasshoppers. Maier et al. (1982) described the hunting behav-

ior of *C. jacchus* in searching for large animal prey such as locusts, grasshoppers, beetles, and lizards. Other prey items of callitrichids include Lepidoptera (larval and adult moths and butterflies), Coleoptera (beetles), ants, spiders, snails, and small vertebrates (lizards, nestling birds, and bird eggs).

Tamarins and marmosets feed on larger insect prey than do larger omnivorous South American monkeys. It may be that their ability to sneak up on large prey without being noticed enables the emperor tamarin (*S. imperator*) to prey successfully on large grasshoppers (Terborgh 1983a). Terborgh believes that larger monkeys are not as adept at catching large prey as are the smaller callitrichids. The latter move slowly and cautiously until the final leap, they live in small groups, and individuals often forage a few meters separately from one another. In contrast, groups of larger monkeys, such as capuchins, squirrel

Figure 2-16 Tamarin feeding on a large grasshopper. [From Izawa 1978]

monkeys, and even *Callicebus torquatus,* which lives in groups of 2–5 individuals, often flush out large prey as they move through an area.

However, it is unlikely that body size and group size alone provide the entire explanation. For example, when tamarins forage in mixed-species associations, troop size can exceed 20 individuals, and orthopterans continue to be the most common prey consumed. Moreover, Peres (1991) has suggested that one of the advantages to tamarins in forming a mixed-species troop is that flushing or dis-turbing prey increases capture rates. Squirrel monkeys are also small and there is no evidence that individuals in smaller groups exploit larger or more mobile insects than individuals in larger groups. Knowledge of the relationships between insect behavior and microhabitat preferences and the positional behavior, capture tech-niques, manual dexterity, and nutritional and energetic requirements of the forager are needed before species differences in predatory behavior among primates are better understood.

In some tamarin species, the timing and location of foraging activities may be strongly influenced by the activity pattern of its prey. Dawson (1979) suggests that the activity cycle of *Saguinus geoffroyi* coincides with the period of greatest vul-nerability of large orthopterans. Because of their low surface to volume ratio, larger insects warm at a slower rate than do smaller ones. The tamarins he studied in Panama awoke late, in most cases approximately three quarters of an hour after full light. This was the time of the day when large insects began to emerge from their nocturnal resting places but were not fully mobile. Although data were not collected on temporal differences in hunting success, it is possible that factors such as temperature, humidity, and time of day affect insect capture success.

Seasonality may also influence the choice of large insects as prey (Pack et al. 1999). The abundance and diversity of insects, as well as fruits and leaves, can fluc-tuate significantly throughout the year, especially in response to temporal changes in climate. Janzen and Schoener (1968, Janzen 1973a,b) found from sweep sam-ples that large bodied insects were better able to withstand the rigors of the dry season than were smaller forms. Large orthopterans, coleopterans, and hemopter-ans were the three insect families that remained relatively abundant during the dry season. Dawson (1976) found that orthopterans (78%) and coleopterans (9%), along with lizards (10%), made up 97% of the animal prey captured by *S. geoffroyi* dur-ing the dry season.

In seasonal forests, the ability of these large bodied insects to survive during the dry season provides tamarins with a stable source of animal protein during times of the year when other foods are less available. The propensity for many callitrichids to forage in the understory or near the forest floor also may be related to their taste for large orthopterans, since these insects account for a substantial amount of the biomass at this strata (Penny and Arias 1982).

Fruits, Flowers, and Nectar

Fruits, flowers, and nectar contain a high proportion of nonstructural carbohy-drates and sugar. Although these resources may differ in seasonal availability and renewal rates, they are treated together in this discussion because they are exploited using similar foraging strategies. Both marmosets and tamarins eat ripe fruits, but most tamarins appear to include more fruit in their diet than do many marmosets.

Estimates of the proportion of fruit and floral nectar in the diet of *Saguinus* vary from about 20–70% (Hladik and Hladik 1969, Dawson 1976, Garber 1980a,b,

1993a, Mittermeier and van Roosmalen 1981). In *Leontopithecus rosalia* (Peres 1986a, Dietz et al. 1997) and *L. chrysomelas* (Rylands 1993), ripe fruits, floral nectar, and flowers account for 70–90% of feeding observations. The fruits and flowers utilized, as with the insects exploited, are generally dispersed and of low density. Most of the fruits are found scattered on vines, bushes, or patchily distributed in periphery of subcanopy tree crowns (Fleagle and Mittermeier 1980, Yoneda 1981, Terborgh 1983a, Crandlemire-Sacco 1986, Garber 1993a, Dietz et al. 1997).

In contrast to insect hunting, patterns of fruit and flower feeding are quite similar between various callitrichid species (Garber 1993a). Terborgh (1983a), however, found important differences between plant resources used by tamarins and those utilized by larger sympatric primate species. Compared with other species, which frequently fed on fruit in tall large-crowned trees, *Saguinus imperator* and *S. fuscicollis* at Manu National Park in southern Peru were the most consistent in maintaining their feeding height, usually at 20–25 m. For the most part, preferred trees had a canopy diameter of less than 15 m and were little used by other primates.

Additionally, the fruits of these small trees and vines ripened in a piecemeal fashion. Thus, only a small quantity of ripe and ready to harvest fruit is available on the tree at any one time. Tree and liana species exploited by these tamarins were characterized by intraspecific synchrony, with most or all trees of the same species bearing fruit at the same time. This adds an element of predictability to the tamarin resource base. In addition, although fruit production per tree, per day was limited, trees often fruited over a period of several weeks. During the dry season, fruit feeding continued but was supplemented with either gums or floral nectar. Terborgh (1983a) suggests that fruit production in tree species commonly utilized by tamarins was quite low and not normally sufficient to satisfy large groups of capuchins or squirrel monkeys. One indication of limited fruit production is the fact that a mixed-species tamarin troop will visit an average of 12–14 trees each day in order to obtain a sufficient quantity of fruit (Garber 1993b).

In both Panama and Peru, species of *Saguinus* were observed to feed on many species of plants throughout the year, but they also showed a propensity to concentrate on one or a small set of favored species at a time, depending on availability, and only to snack on others. According to Terborgh (1983a), in southern Peru, *Saguinus imperator* and *S. fuscicollis* harvested identical plant resources while moving in mixed-species groups, even though the two species searched independently for insects in different locations (see also Peres 1996). During the course of a year, *S. fuscicollis* and *S. imperator* relied on only five to seven plant species as major resources to supply the bulk of their carbohydrate and caloric needs.

On average, seeds swallowed and voided by *Saguinus* are larger in size than seeds swallowed by baboons, forest guenons, macaques, and even chimpanzees. Garber (1994) and Garber and Kitron (1997) have argued that seed swallowing in tamarins serves an important curative function in mechanically expelling spiny headed worms (Acanthocephala) from their digestive tract. These parasites can attach to the gut lining and cause inflamation, lesions, and death. Exposure and re-exposure to these parasites may result from consuming orthopteran prey. It is likely that orthopteran insects serve as intermediate hosts. Daily swallowing and voiding of seeds may serve to dislodge intestinal parasites prior to or during the initial stages of attachment (Garber and Kitron 1997).

In southern Peru, during the dry season when fruits were scarce, over 70% of the tamarin's diet was floral nectar. Thus, when fruit was in limited supply, nectar provided an alternative resource for *Saguinus* as well as for other non-flying animals. Similar observations have been made of flower feeding by *Leontopithecus ros-alia* during the dry season in Brazil (Dietz et al. 1997). The flowering plants fed upon may become keystone species for these primates during the dry season (Terborgh 1986, Terborgh and Stern 1989). Janson et al. (1981) provide evidence that *Saguinus* and a number of non-flying mammals visit several flowering trees in the same day and may serve as pollinating agents for these plants. This is similar to the co-adapted pollination systems involving non-flying mammals found in Madagascar (lemurs), South Africa (rodents), and Australia (marsupials) (see Volume I, Chapter 2).

The amount of fruit eaten by different species of marmoset is inversely related to the proportion of gums in their diet. Initial studies show *C. humeralifer* and *C. kuhli* as highly frugivorous and *C. penicilata, C. jacchus,* and *C. flaviceps* as highly exudativorous with little fruit in their diet (Tables 2-5 and 2-6). Rylands (1993) points out two factors that may affect the proportion of fruit in the diet of various marmoset species and populations. First, in all long-term studies, it appears that fruit-eating is seasonal and suitable fruit is eaten where and when it is available. Second, although these primates have specialized lower incisors that enable them to gouge holes in tree bark in order to elicit the flow of gums, this may be an energetically costly activity relative to feeding on fruits. Moreover, given the renewal rates of many plant gums, gouging holes in the morning requires that individuals return to the same site later in the afternoon to feed.

Table 2-5 Percentage of Daily Activity Spent in Exudate Feeding in *Cebuella* and *Callithrix*

Species	Percentage	Range[a]	Duration of Study	Reference
Cebuella pygmaea	32.0	–	5 months	Ramirez et al. (1978)
C. jacchus	>29.0	–	3 weeks	Maier et al. (1982)
C. jacchus	15.0	–	12 months	Alonso and Langguth (1989)
C. kuhli	7.0	6.6–7.1	3 months	Rylands (1982, 1989b)
C. humeralifer	3.0	0.8–9.8	12 months	Rylands (1982)
C. flaviceps	8.8	6.8–10.1	12 months	Ferrari (1988b)

[a] Range of monthly estimates during the study.

Table 2-6 Percentage Composition of the Plant Part of the Diet in *Cebuella* and *Callithrix*

Species	Exudate (per cent)	Fruit, nectar, flowers, seeds (per cent)	Reference
Cebuella pygmaea	67.0	not est.	Ramirez et al. (1978)
C. humeralifer	17.2	82.5	Rylands (1982)
C. flaviceps	72.5	15.9	Ferrari (1988b)
C. kuhli	32.6	67.4	Rylands (1982, 1989b)
C. penicillata	est. >70	not est.	Fonseca and Lacher (1984)

[From Rylands and de Faria 1993]

When feeding on gums, patterns of ranging are restricted, and this might impact on opportunities to search new areas for insect prey. In addition, marmoset species differ in incisor and possibly digestive morphology. Species like *Callithrix jacchus* and *Cebuella pygmaea* have longer and more procumbent lower incisors and an enlarged caecum. The incisors provide an advantage in bark scraping and gouging (Natori 1986a), and the large caecum may be required to breakdown structural carbohydrates of some plant gums (Ferrari 1993). Marmosets with longer, more derived lower incisors (used for gouging) rely more on exudates than those with shorter ones (Table 2-7).

The pygmy marmoset is an extreme specialist in exudate-feeding, and fruit and other plant parts form only a minor portion of its diet. In a 16-month study of *Cebuella*, Ramirez et al. (1977) found that from July to September, *Cebuella* spent a very small amount of time eating fruit. As in *Saguinus* and *Leontopithecus*, floral nectar is consumed by *Cebuella* (Terborgh 1983a,b) and by *C. humeralifer, C. kuhli,* and *C. flaviceps* during the dry season (Stevenson and Rylands 1988, Ferrari and Strier 1992). At the beginning of the dry season, 25% of feeding observations on *C. humeralifer* were on flowers of the vine, *Mendoncia aspera.* The floral nectar of *Symphonia* was an important food source for *C. kuhli* (as it is for several *Saguinus* and *Leontopithecus* species) and nectar of *Mabea fistulifera* was a valuable but not essential resource for *C. flaviceps* during a period of relative fruit scarcity. *M. fistulifera* is a small tree, and Ferrari and Strier (1992) point out that it has a wide range of flying and non-flying vertebrate pollinators, including other primates.

Callimico feeds on the fruits and buds of low bushes and epiphytes located at heights 3–4 m above the ground. Fruits of taller trees are eaten as they become available, with groups using from one to three particular species for periods of 4–10 days (Pook and Pook 1981).

Exudates

Plant exudate is a general term that includes sap, gum, and resin (see Bearder and Martin 1980 for definitions) and is a resource fed upon by a number of primates

---

Table 2-7 Ecological Groupings for the Genus *Callithrix*

1. *C. jacchus, C. penicillata*
   Northeast and central Brazil, very seasonal habitat, highly exudativorous, small home ranges.

2. *C. kuhli, C. geoffroyi*
   Atlantic coastal, lowland, forest of southeast Brazil, less exudativorous than Group 1 but better adapted for tree-gouging than Groups 3 and 4, home ranges larger than Group 1 but smaller than Group 4.

3. *C. aurita, C. flaviceps*
   Southernmost forms in seasonal, high altitude Atlantic coastal forest in southeast Brazil, relatively poor adaptation for tree-gouging, proportion of exudates in the diet dependent on availablility, home ranges larger than Group 1 but smaller than Group 4. (*C. argentata melanura* in highly seasonal extra-Amazonian habitats (e.g. *chaco* of Paraguay).

4. *C. humeralifer, C. argentata*
   Amazonia, highly frugivorous (seasonally exudativorous), relatively poor adaptiation for tree-gouging, large home ranges.

[From Rylands and de Faria 1993]

(Nash 1986). Virtually all species of callitrichids studied, except *Callimico,* feed on exudates (Fig. 2-17). In fact, the callitrichids appear to represent an adaptive array filling an exudate-feeding guild among New World primates. As pointed out by Garber (1992), the amount of exudate in the diet, and adaptations for extracting this resource, reflect an evolutionary progression of a number of derived traits within this subfamily (Fig. 2-18).

Most species of *Saguinus* have been observed feeding on plant exudates in the wild (Garber 1992). Unlike marmosets, however, tamarins do not possess specializations of the lower incisors for chewing wood, nor do they gouge holes to stimulate the flow of exudates. Rather, they feed entirely on exudates that result from natural injuries to bark and from the parasitic activities of wood-boring insects. Exudate feeding in this genus is highly seasonal and can account for over 50% of the plant-feeding diet over a 2–3 month period (Garber 1980b, Norconk 1986, Soini 1987b, Ramirez 1989). During these periods, exudates become a major dietary staple.

Garber (1980b, 1984b) has proposed that plant exudates are extremely important for the nutrition of tamarins. During his study of the Panamanian tamarin, he found that exudates accounted for 14% of feeding time. The tamarins fed primarily on the exudates of two tree species, *Anacardium excelsum* and *Spondias mombin,* both members of the Anacardeaceae, an important family of tropical gum producing trees (Howes, 1949). Exudates of *A. excelsum* alone accounted for over 23% of the non-insect portion of the tamarin diet (98% of the time spent feeding on exudates).

A nutritional analysis of *A. excelsum* exudate indicates the presence of several minerals, and Garber ascribes its importance to its high calcium/low phosphorus ratio. The calcium/phosphorus content of *A. excelsum* exudate ranged from 31:1 to 142:1. A high calcium/phosphorus ration appears to characterize other plant exudates as well (Bearder and Martin 1980). On the other hand, many insects have a low calcium and high phosphorus content except in the chitinous exoskeleton, which is usually undigestible (Uvarov 1966, Martin et al. 1976). At present we know of only one primate, the potto, that has the appropriate enzyme, chitinase, for breaking down insect chitin (Goffart 1978).

A number of investigators have documented a relationship between calcium/phosphorus imbalance and certain metabolic bone diseases. In most mammalian species, including humans, optimal calcium/phosphorus ratios range from 1:1 to 2:1 (Robinson 1980). Thus, in order to avoid inadequate mineral balance, it may be necessary for some insectivorous mammals to include a

Figure 2-17 Marmoset feeding on gum. [From Ferrari 1992b]

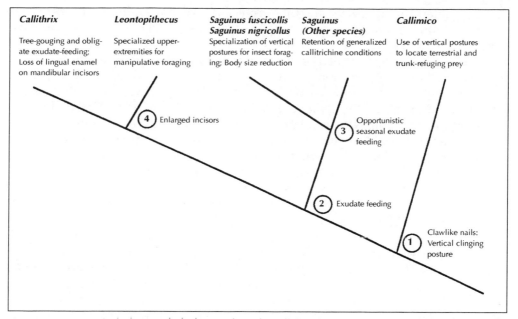

Callithrix	*Leontopithecus*	*Saguinus fuscicollis* *Saguinus nigricollus*	*Saguinus* *(Other species)*	*Callimico*
Tree-gouging and oblig- ate exudate-feeding; Loss of lingual enamel on mandibular incisors	Specialized upper- extremities for manipulative foraging	Specialization of vertical postures for insect forag- ing; Body size reduction	Retention of generalized callitrichine conditions	Use of vertical postures to locate terrestrial and trunk-refuging prey

(4) Enlarged incisors

(3) Opportunistic
seasonal exudate
feeding

(2) Exudate feeding

(1) Clawlike nails:
Vertical clinging
posture

Figure 2-18 Morphobehavioral cladogram based on dietary features in Callitrichinae. [From Garber 1992]

resource in their diets which is high in
calcium and low in phosphorus. Plant
exudates may serve such a function, at
least for some species of tamarin, and
possibly for other callitrichids as well.
This has been suggested for gum-feeding in galagos also (Bearder and Martin
1980). In addition, some exudates may
contain high levels of protein, water,
and structural carbohydrates (Garber
1993a).

As stated earlier, Panamanian
tamarins forage and feed primarily on
thin supports. Branch size *during feeding,*
however, has a bimodal distribution (Fig.
2-19). Over 20% of all feeding bouts occur
on supports greater than 32 cm diameter, and approximately 95% of these
bouts involve the postural act of clinging
to a vertical trunk while feeding on exudates. *Saguinus geoffroyi* does not regularly use large vertical supports during
any other activity! When clinging to large
vertical trunks these primates are probably quite vulnerable to predators and
behave more nervously than when feeding in dense vegetation. Garber (1980a,b)

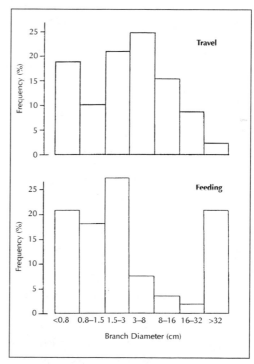

Figure 2-19 Diameter of supports preferred by
the Panamanian tamarin, *S. geoffroyi,* during
travel and feeding, based on 1,200 hours of data
by P. Garber. Adapted from Garber (1980a,b)
with permission.

has suggested that cryptic coloration protects *S. geoffroyi* and possibly other callitrichids from predators as they cling to trunks and feed on plant exudates and insects (see below).

The three species of *Leontopithecus* studied to date (there are no published studies of *L. caissara*) are opportunistic exudate-feeders and, like *Saguinus,* eat exudates mainly during the dry season when fruit availability is low (Peres 1986a, 1989a, Passos and Carvalho 1991, Rylands 1993). However, *L. rosalia* has been observed chewing bark to stimulate exudate flow (Peres 1989a). Furthermore, enlarged mandibular and maxillary incisors in *L. chrysomelas* may reflect some incisor harvesting, especially for wood-boring insects (Rosenberger and Coimbra-Filho 1984), but gouging behavior to elicit exudate flow has not been observed in either *L. chrysomelas* or *L. chrysopygus* (Rylands 1989, 1993, Carvalho and Carvalho 1989). As do some tamarins, *Leontopithecus chrysomelas* consumes the liquid-like exudate found in pods of the genus *Parkia* (Rylands 1993).

In contrast to the opportunistic exudativory of tamarins, marmosets can be considered specialized exudativores having a modified dental anatomy to procure exudates. The dental morphology of marmosets includes an interrelated complex of features specifically adapted for obtaining plant exudates (see Rosenberger 1979). The enamel is very thick on the labial side of the lower incisors and totally lacking on the lingual side, thus maintaining a chisel-like edge for gouging (Rosenberger 1978). Marmosets also have long, relatively pointed lower incisors that are approximately equal in length to the lower canines (Figs. 2-2, 2-3).

For marmosets, plant exudates are not simply a dietary supplement but represent a major source of food. Species differences in the degree of exudate-feeding appears to be related to the degree of development of the dental gouge (lower incisors)(Maier et al. 1982, Natori 1986a, 1990, Natori and Shigehara 1992, Kinzey 1997b). Marmosets utilize their unusual lower dentition to gouge holes and thus induce the flow of gums in trees and vines. The trees utilized for gum feeding are normally riddled with characteristic holes, which are usually round or transversely elongated (Fig. 2-20). Species like *C. jacchus, C. penicillata,* and *Cebuella pygmaea* have the most derived condition and are highly exudativorous, whereas *C. humeralifer* and *C. argentata* are the least specialized and are relatively poorly adapted for tree-gouging among the marmosets. Other species are intermediate (Rylands and de Faria 1993, Table 2-7). *C. jacchus* also has a large complex caecum and internal ribbonlike structures (taeniae), which may facilitate more complete digestion of the complex carbohydrates contained in some plant exudates (Coimbra-Filho et al. 1980, Garber 1992, Ferrari 1992).

Figure 2-20 Trunk of tree illustrating holes gouged by marmosets. [From Coimbra-Filho and Mittermeier, 1977]

Cebuella is the most specialized exudate feeder among the callitrichids (Garber 1992, Kinzey 1997b). More than two-thirds of its feeding time is devoted to exudates, and it generally eats very little fruit or other plant material (Ramirez et al. 1977, Soini 1982, 1993). Though, as stated earlier, in some forests, *Cebuella* relies on nectar during the dry season (Terborgh 1983a). *Cebuella* has an Amazonian distribution, unlike the other highly specialized marmoset gum feeders, and is frequently found in forests with one or two *Saguinus* species. *Saguinus fuscicollis* has been observed to occasionally parasitize gum holes excavated by *Cebuella*. In general, however, these genera exploit different species of plant exudates and are characterized by important differences in feeding ecology and patterns of habitat utilization.

In *Cebuella,* the proportion of time spent feeding on insects and exudates shifts throughout the day. For example, gum holes may be excavated just before nightfall, possibly to maximize exudate flow during the night. The gum is then harvested immediately in the morning (Ramirez et al. 1977).

Ramirez et al. (1977) provide measurements of holes gouged by *Cebuella:* one tree had approximately 1300 holes per square meter on a portion of its trunk. Soini (1982) provides a list of 29 species of trees, vines, and hemiepiphytes used as exudate sources by *Cebuella.* Like tamarins, marmosets use their claw-like nails to cling to vertical supports (Fig. 2-17) while feeding on exudates (Kinzey et al. 1975).

In sum, the marmosets and tamarins studied to date are omnivorous with a significant percentage of their diet consisting of insects. The diet of tamarins is predominately insects plus ripe fruits. The insects utilized most frequently are large-bodied, especially grasshoppers, and are generally larger than those hunted by larger primates. These large insects are found throughout the canopy, are dispersed and of low density, and are able to withstand the dry season better than smaller insects; thus, they are available throughout the year. Three methods of foraging for insects have been described. Where two species of tamarins are sympatric, one species uses a different insect-foraging technique.

Fruit and floral nectars comprise up to 70% of the callitrichid diet but appear to be less important for some marmosets than for tamarins. Like insects preyed upon, fruit and flowers are scattered and patchily distributed. Callitrichids usually concentrate on the fruit or flowers of a small set of plant species at a time, depending upon availability, and these plants may offer a reliable though scanty supply over many weeks. The plants used are often small crowned trees, legumes pods, and liana fruits. All species of *Saguinus* studied to date swallow large seeds (1–2 cm in length) that pass through their digestive tract unharmed (Terborgh 1983a, Garber 1986, 1994, Garber and Kitron 1997). These seeds are typically voided singly and scattered 150–300 meters from the parent tree. In terms of their ecological impact on the forest, tamarins may act as important seed dispersers for a number of plant species. Marmosets tend to swallow small seeds but unlike tamarins drop large seeds during fruit feeding. Given their nectar feeding activities, both tamarins and marmosets may act as pollinating agents for some trees.

Besides insects, plant exudates are an important component of the diet of tamarins, and especially of marmosets. The importance of exudates in the diet of different taxa is reflected in the relative distribution of certain derived morphological traits (e.g., gouging dentition and expanded caecum). Goeldi's monkeys have not been reported to consume plant exudates. Whether this is the result of an important dietary distinction between these and other callitrichids or a consequence of the extremely limited observations of these primates in the wild remains unknown.

Tamarins feed on exudate but do not chew bark to obtain it, whereas marmosets gouge tree bark to stimulate exudate flow. The pygmy marmoset is the most specialized exudate feeder. In exploiting this resource, callitrichids cling to large vertical trunks, and the claw-like nails are adaptations for this feeding posture. In contrast, while feeding on fruits and flowers as when foraging for insects, most callitrichids use their grasping extremities in the same manner as do other primates. The claw-like nails obviously do not prohibit this kind of movement on thin flexible branches.

DAILY ACTIVITY PATTERN

A callitrichid activity pattern can be described only in the most general terms, since there is so much variation among species, seasons, and study sites (see for example Tovar 1994). Marmosets and tamarins generally leave their sleeping positions shortly after dawn and return to sleeping sites as early as 1–2 hours before sunset (Moynihan 1970, Neyman 1977, Dawson 1979, Garber 1980a, 1993b, Soini 1982, Maier et al. 1982, Snowden and Soini 1988, Stevenson and Rylands 1988). The first two hours after leaving the sleeping site involve intensive foraging and/or feeding. This is generally followed by a shift in activity early in the morning, and the remainder of the day is spent intermittently foraging and resting. Often there is an extended period of inactivity (resting and grooming) from 10:00 a.m. until noon. During midday, there is a period of reduced activity. Following are some of the variations noted in the literature.

The best data on activity cycles of tamarins are those of *S. fuscicollis, S. imperator, Saguinus mystax, S. geoffroyi,* and *S. nigricollis* (Terborgh 1983a, Soini 1982, Garber 1993b, Tovar 1994). Several authors have noted that tamarins arise late in the morning compared with most other primates (Moynihan 1970, Neyman 1977, Dawson 1979, Snowdon and Soini 1988), usually not moving until about three fourths of an hour after full light. Late rising and early retiring is rare among diurnal birds and mammals generally, although it has been reported for the lesser tree shrew (D'Souza 1974). Dawson (1979) has suggested that the adaptive significance of late arousal (and early retiring) may be related to the optimal availability of large-bodied insects discussed above or may allow *Saguinus* to escape competition from sympatric crepuscular (and nocturnal) mammals such as the night monkey (*Aotus trivirgatus*) or the woolly opossum (*Caluromys derbianus*). Most likely, a reduced period of daily activity serves to minimize exposure to predators and reduce energy expenditure in this small primate. This pattern of a short activity period was not observed in *S. nigricollis* living in a very seasonal habitat (Tovar 1994).

Dawson (1979) observed that the first two hours after leaving the sleeping tree involved a great deal of movement and intensive foraging and/or feeding. During the first half-hour to hour, foraging for insects appeared to be the primary activity (though other researchers have observed fruit feeding to precede insect foraging in both *Saguinus* and *Callithrix* [Snowden and Soini 1988, Stevenson and Rylands 1988, Garber 1993b]). While insect foraging, the group was generally scattered over a 40–70 m area. Contact calls ("long whistles" of Moynihan 1970) were exchanged between group members. Then the emphasis shifted to eating fruits, at which time the group often fed together in a single tree or in concentrated food patches and contact calls became less frequent.

By about 10:00 a.m., the animals began to move out of low bush areas and into areas of shade, often centered around stands of tall canopy trees such as *Anacardium excelsum*. During rest periods both autogrooming and allogrooming frequently occurred. Between 10:00 and 15:00 h, activity did not cease altogether, but animals moved significantly less than at other times of the day. At 15:00 h, the tempo of activity again began to increase in Dawson's study groups. Travel at this time was directional and rapid. Although insects were eaten, most activity was oriented toward fruit sources. The animals usually traveled 100 m or more in five or fewer minutes and then spent 15–30 minutes in a fruit tree.

Sleeping trees used by Panamanian tamarins were generally higher than surrounding vegetation and/or lacked extensive vine connections with other trees. *Saguinus* ssp. rarely return to the same sleeping tree on consecutive nights (Snowden and Soini 1988, Garber pers. obsrv.). The members of a group normally huddle together while sleeping. This may be a means by which these small animals thermoregulate, reducing heat loss during chilly nights (Snowden and Soini 1988). *Saguinus* has not been observed sleeping in holes in trees. *Leontopithecus*, on the other hand, does use holes for sleeping sites (Coimbra-Filho 1977, Rylands 1982, Peres 1986a, Carvalho and Carvahlo 1989), and because of this, lion tamarins are limited to forests where tree holes are available (Rylands 1993). The roosting habits of tamarins and marmosets seem to be predator-proof in a number of ways to be discussed in the next section.

Terborgh (1983a) found that the activity pattern of both *S. fuscicollis* and *S. imperator* varied radically in different seasons. The wet season corresponded with both a superabundance of food and the birth of infants. Soon after birth, the infants were carried, mainly by males, adding 20% or more to the weight of the carrier. During this time, the group traveled little, rested a great deal (60% of the time), and remained in a small portion of its home range. Other seasonal variations could be related to different handling times for certain resources. For example, when nectar from flowers was the principle source of carbohydrates (e.g., in July), the animals were required to visit hundreds of flowers to satisfy themselves and the proportion of time spent foraging was great. When soft fruits were available, these could be harvested at a much higher rate, and thus foraging and feeding time was reduced. Garber (1993b) and Tovar (1994) also observed differences in activity patterns and especially foraging and feeding between seasons in *Saguinus* ssp. Overall, however, groups of moustached tamarins and saddle-back tamarins were active approximately 10 hours and 20 minutes per day, but this included a variety of low-energy behaviors such as resting and grooming (Garber 1993b). Between 30–40% of each day's activity pattern included grooming and resting. Thus, despite traveling 1–2 km per day and visiting 12–14 feeding trees, these tamarins were characterized by an activity pattern that limited energy costs.

Callithrix and *Cebuella*, like tamarins, generally arise shortly after dawn (Stevenson and Rylands 1988, Soini 1988). Activity cycles vary between species and populations; however, resting can take up a significant portion of the day in some populations. For example, in *C. jacchus* resting accounted for 53% of daily activity (Stevenson and Rylands 1988). Terborgh also noted that resting accounted for 44% of the daily budget in *S. fuscicollis* (Terborgh 1983a), more than any of the other five sympatric, insect-eating primates that Terborgh studied. Other *Callithrix* populations have been observed to spend less time resting, approximately 30% or less of the day, and seasonal differences in activity patterns have been reported in a number of studies of *Callithrix* (see Passamani 1998).

Callithrix spends most of its midday resting time in areas of low dense growth where observation is difficult. *C. humeralifer* rested during midday at sleeping sites (Stevenson and Rylands 1988). Both *Cebuella* and *Callithrix* have short periods of inactivity throughout the day with a more prolonged period of rest at midday (Ramirez et al. 1977, Rylands 1981, Soini 1982). Resting and daily range path were found to increase and decrease, respectively, when *C. jacchus* individuals were carrying infants (Digby and Barreto 1996).

The activities of individuals in a *Cebuella* group often were not coordinated (Ramirez et al. 1977, Soini 1988). "While some individuals were eating exudate, others would hunt insects and others would rest in the crown of a tree, so that at any one time the troop members were dispersed, often over a large portion of their (very small) range" (Ramirez et al. 1977:99). Given that pygmy marmosets have home ranges that are often less than 0.1 hectares, dispersed individuals can maintain visual and/or vocal contact.

Like the tamarins, *Callithrix* and *Cebuella* both enter sleeping trees for the night while it is still light. Sleeping sites are dense, vine covered vegetation. Both *Callithrix* and *Cebuella* sleep in dense foliage (Maier et al. 1982, Rylands 1981, Stevenson and Rylands 1988, Soini 1988) or, more rarely, in tree holes (Moynihan 1976a, Izawa 1979, Rylands 1982). *C. jacchus* and *Cebuella* groups have been observed using the same sleeping sites continuously or repeatedly (Stevenson and Rylands 1988, Soini 1988), whereas *C. humeralifer* and *C. kuhli* did not sleep in the same site on consecutive nights (Rylands 1982).

Callimico moved little during the dry season in Bolivia (Pook and Pook 1981). It was active in the morning and evening and rested in the undergrowth during the warmest portions of the day. As the wet season progressed, the animals were more active and moved much more. There were brief rest periods throughout the day, with two longer rest periods in late afternoon and early evening. However, during this season, the group only spent 16% of the day resting. They traveled further in the afternoon. Morning travel was often quick and the animals moved from one fruit tree to another, whereas during the afternoon, the group moved more slowly while foraging for insects and other food items.

PREDATION

Because of their small size, callitrichids are potentially vulnerable to a large number of predators. Terrestrial predators that can prey on callitrichids are the tayra (*Eira barbara,* a mustelid) and smaller felids such as the ocelot (*Felis pardalis*), the jaguarundi (*F. yagouaroundi*), and the margay (*F. wiedii*) (Soini 1988). The tayra has been observed carrying a dead tamarin (Moynihan 1970), and a number of predation attempts by tayra have been reported (Galef et al. 1976, Izawa 1978, Snowdon and Soini 1988). Emmons (1987) identified remains of saddle-backed tamarin in ocelot scats, and Dietz (in Kinzey 1997b) observed an ocelot kill a reintroduced lion tamarin. Dietz also witnessed lion tamarins being chased by capuchin monkeys. These monkeys are aggressive towards marmosets in some areas (Fonseca et al. 1980), whereas in other areas capuchins and marmosets interact without aggression or fear (Rylands 1982, Muskin 1984).

Callitrichids mob terrestrial carnivores and give calls similar to the vocalizations they use toward dogs and unfamiliar humans (Neyman 1977, Izawa 1978,

Rylands 1981, Stevenson and Rylands 1988, Passamani 1995). At least some species have different alarm calls for terrestrial and aerial predators (Epple 1975a, Neyman 1977), and some may react differently towards fecal scents of predatory and non-predatory mammals (Caine and Weldon 1989).

Large arboreal snakes are also predators of callitrichids. Both Heymann (1987) and Dietz (in Kinzey 1997b) have observed snakes approach, capture, kill, and eat adult tamarins. In the first case, an anaconda preyed upon a moustached tamarin, and in the second, a boa constrictor captured a lion tamarin. Bartecki and Hermann (1987) witnessed a group of saddle-backed tamarins mob a snake.

Birds of prey are undoubtedly the most important predators of callitrichids (Moynihan 1970, Ferrari and Lopes Ferrari 1990, Caine 1993, Ferrari 1993), and many observations of attempted or successful attacks have been reported (Dawson 1976, Neyman 1977, Izawa 1978, Terborgh 1983a, Goldizen 1987, Soini 1988, Heymann 1990a,b, Caine 1993). Goldizen (1987) saw an average of one raptor attack per week for each mixed *S. imperator-S. fuscicollis* study group at Manu, and Heymann (1990b) noted alarm events of the *S. mystax-S. fuscicollis* mixed groups every 2–3 hours, over half of which were directed towards avian predators. Izawa (1978) witnessed six attacks on *S. nigricollis,* two of which were successful. Tamarins give specific, high-pitched alarm calls and then initiate escape behavior or become silent and immobile upon the appearance of most large, flying objects, including low flying aircraft. Garber (pers. comm.) has observed moustached tamarins to repeatedly chase large birds perched above them in exposed areas of the tree crown.

Predation thus seems to be an important selective force on these small primates, and they use many mechanisms to avoid predators. They are quick and agile animals, normally active in dense foliated areas (Terborgh 1983a, Sussman and Kinzey 1984, Rylands 1986b, 1987, Snowden and Soini 1988, Rylands and Faria 1993). They are cryptic when resting and choose sleeping sites carefully. Sleeping trees of tamarins lack physical connection with surrounding vegetation, a factor that may make detection more difficult and make an approaching predator more noticeable. When moving to a sleeping tree the animals move rapidly and silently and, if disturbed soon after reaching the tree, will choose another site. When reaching the sleeping tree, the monkeys huddle together on rudimentary "nests" (see Dawson 1979:275) or in a dense tangle of leaves or vines. There is also increased vigilance when retiring to the sleeping site (Caine 1987, 1993).

Upon first seeing a tamarin group huddled together at a sleeping site, Dawson (1976) actually thought it was a termite nest and believed this might be an example of crypsis or protective mimicry. Marmosets and tamarins also reveal a remarkable cryptic coloration when clinging to large trunks while feeding on exudates (Fig. 2-21). Coimbro-Filho and Mittermeier (1973) believe that the colors of the lion marmosets have a protective function, and lion tamarins also are very specific in the sleeping sites they choose. Certain types of tree holes are indispensable to this species for nightly protection (Coimbra-Fihlo 1977, Rylands 1993).

Being the smallest anthropoids, the pygmy marmosets are potential prey for an especially large number of predators. Moynihan (1976b) and Soini (1988) suggest that all of their anti-predator devices are designed to avoid attracting attention rather than distracting the predator. They do not mob predators as tamarins do, and they move exceedingly slowly or in quick spurts and then freeze. Their coloration is highly cryptic, and they almost always move in the dark, dense underbrush below the canopy.

Figure 2-21 *S. geoffroyi* feeding on plant exudate, illustrating the cryptic nature of the color pattern of this species. [Photo by Paul Garber]

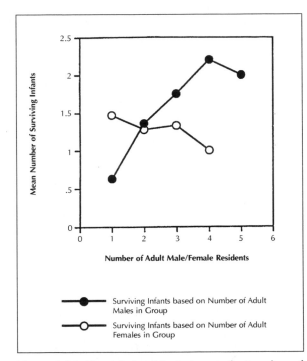

Figure 2-22 The relationship between the number of dependent young per group and the number of adult male and female helpers residing in a group. Groups with more than two adult males had greater success in rearing infants to the juvenile stage of maturation. The number of dependent young did not increase as the number of adult female residents increased. [From Garber 1997]

Like other diurnal primates, marmosets and tamarins live in groups, and the group organization may be influenced to some degree by predation pressure (see Sussman and Kinzey 1984, Caine 1993). When foraging for insects in the dense underbrush or cryptically on large trunks for gum, the group usually is less cohesive, and non-foraging individuals may serve a function scanning for both feeding sites and potential predators. At fruiting and flowering trees, however, individuals are more visible and vulnerable, and group members usually feed in close proximity. It has been suggested that, in some species, individuals play an important role in predator vigilance during feeding (Goldizen 1987, Zullo and Caine 1988, Caine 1993). In fact, in wild tamarins, groups with at least two adult males are more successful in rearing offspring than are other groups (Fig. 2-22)(Sussman and Garber 1987, Garber 1997). Savage et al. (1996) suspect that one reason for this is increased efficiency of predator detection.

Vigilance and sentinel behavior, alarm calling, and mobbing are common cooperative behaviors within both single species and mixed-species groups (Heymann 1990a, Castro 1991, Peres 1993a, Caine 1993, Savage et al. 1996, Buchanan-Smith and Hardie 1997). Caine (1993) believes that predation is one of the major selective pressures leading to many aspects of the unique social system of the callitrichids. For example, not all adults in tamarin and marmoset groups breed (although many adults may be involved in copulatory behavior, thus adding numbers, but not immediate reproductive competitors, to the group), and where two species, coexist they often travel in mixed-species groups (see below).

Callimico is subject to the same predators as the marmosets and tamarins (Pook and Pook 1981). It remains in low, dense vegetation, moves quietly, and has dark, cryptic coloration. If the group is disturbed while in a tree, it climbs down to 1–4 m and moves away by a series of vertical leaps or runs off on the ground. Groups will mob ground predators, such as snakes or the tayra. *Callimico* sleeps and rests in dense vegetation and sometimes in bamboo thickets. It sometimes is found in polyspecific associations with tamarins, which also may reduce the risk of predation (Pook and Pook 1982).

SOCIAL STRUCTURE AND ORGANIZATION

Marmosets and tamarins live in relatively small groups. Group size, from censuses of a number of populations, ranges from 1–19 individuals (Table 2-8). Long term studies suggest that the smaller and larger number of tamarins are temporary phenomena: average group size is 6–7 individuals for *Saguinus,* 6–10 individuals for *Cebuella,* 5–8 individuals for *Leontopithecus,* and 8–12 individuals for *Callithrix.* However, groups of tamarins as large as 13 animals have remained stable over extended periods of time (Neyman 1977, Garber 1988a). *Callimico* also lives in groups of 6 to 9 animals and possibly larger (Pook and Pook 1981).

Despite recent field studies to the contrary, callitrichids have long been regarded by some as being strictly monogamous (Kleiman 1977b, Leutenegger 1980, Redican and Taub 1981, Evans 1983, Evans and Poole 1983). For example, Redican and Taub (1981:208) state, "marmosets and tamarins are known to be organized in monogamous family units." Others have considered marmosets and tamarins to live in extended family groups in which a monogamous pair allows some offspring to remain with the group after they mature (Eisenberg et al. 1972, Epple 1975, Moynihan 1976a). In large part, the study of family groups in the laboratory led to these misconceptions, since long-term field studies have not supported the laboratory findings. In most captive breeding colonies of *Saguinus geoffroyi, S. oedipus, S. fuscicollis, Leontopithecus rosalia, Callithrix jacchus,* and *Callimico goeldii* (Epple 1975a, 1977, Dummond 1971, Hearn 1977, 1978, Rothe 1975) there is only one reproductively active female per group. Subdominant adult females (*C. jacchus*) do not exhibit hormonal changes indicative of an ovarian cycle (Hearn 1977), although in some contexts daughters may not be suppressed to the same degree as unrelated females (Saltzman et al. 1997).

Further, field data on the composition of groups are not inconsistent with this hypothesis since Dawson (1976, 1977), Neyman (1977), Izawa (1978), Stevenson (Stevenson and Rylands 1988), Garber (1993b), Goldizen et al. (1990, 1996) and Rylands (1981) have all found that in virtually all groups only one female gives birth, even though the group may have contained more than one adult female. As discussed below, in some groups of *Callitrhix jacchus* (Digby 1994), *C. flaviceps* (Ferrari and Digby 1996), *Leontopithecus rosalia* (Dietz and Baker 1993), and extremely rarely in *S. fuscicollis* (Goldizen et al. 1996), two females have been observed to successfully give birth in the same group during the same breeding season.

However, there is evidence from field studies in which individual animals were identified that tamarins do not have a monogamous mating system as defined by Wickler and Seibt (1983:46). In her review of monogamy in mammals, Kleiman sim-

Table 2-8 Group Size of Marmosets and Tamarins (Adapted from Various Sources)

Genus and species	Group Size		No. of groups observed	Reference
	Range	Mean		
Saguinus oedipus (Panama)	1–9	3.39	28	Moynihan (1970)
S. oedipus (Panama)	1–19	6.93	71	Dawson (1976)
S. oedipus (Colombia)	3–13	—	6	Neyman (1979)
S. oedipus (Panama)	5–10	7	—	Garber (1980a)
S. oedipus (Panama)	1–8	5.3	21	Lindsay (1980)
S. midas (Amapá, Brazil)	2–6	3.4	8	Thorington (1968)
S. midas (Surinam)	—	6	1	Mittermeier & van Roosmalen (1981)
S. nigricollis (Colombia)	4–8	6.3	10	Izawa (1978)
S. nigricollis (Peru)	—	7	1	Freese et al. (1982)
S. nigricollis (Colombia)	4–12	6.2	10	Moynihan (1976a)
S. labiatus (Peru)	1–13	5.7	7	Freese et al. (1982)
S. labiatus (Peru)	3–8	6.6	27	Castro (pers. comm.)
S. mystax (Peru)	1–16	5.25	374	Castro (pers. comm.)
S. mystax (Peru)	3–11	6.08	12	Garber et al. (1993)
S. mystax (Peru)	3–8	5.2	9	Garber et al. (1984)
S. mystax (Peru)	3–7	5.2	9	Ramirez (1989)
S. fuscicollis (Colombia)	1–7	4.1	21	Moynihan (1976a)
S. fuscicollis (Peru, Bolivia)	2–9	5.0	16	Freese et al. (1982)
S. fuscicollis (Peru)	—	5	—	Terborgh (1983a)
S. fuscicollis (Peru)	1–17	5.74	375	Castro (pers. comm.)
S. fuscicollis (Peru)	2–9	6.8	12	Garber (pers. comm.)
S. fuscicollis (Peru)	4–	10	5.5	Ramirez (1989)
S. fuscicollis (Bolivia)	2–7	—	—	Yoneda (1984b)
S. imperator (Peru)	1–3	2.5	4	Freese et al. (1982)
S. imperator (Peru)	2–8	4	—	Terborgh (1983a)
Leontopithecus rosalia (Brazil)	2–8	3–4	—	Coimbra-Filho & Mettermeier (1973)
Callithrix argentata (Bolivia)	5–6	5.5	2	Freese et al. (1982)
C. jacchus (Brazil)	4–13	11	6	Stevenson & Rylands (1988)
C. jacchus (Brazil)	3–13	8.56	12	Hubrecht (1984)
C. humeralifer (Brazil)	4–13	10	4	Rylands (1981)
C. humeralifer (Brazil)	4–15	11	6	Stevenson & Rylands (1988)
C. penicillata (Brazil)	4–9	6.75	8	Stevenson & Rylands (1988)
Cebuella pygmaeus (Colombia)	10–15	—	—	Hernandez-Camacho & Cooper (1976)
C. pygmaeus (Colombia)	3–6	—	6	Moynihan (1976a)
C. pygmaeus (Peru)	7–9	—	—	Ramirez et al. (1977)
C. pygmaeus (Peru)	2–9	6.4	76	Soini (1982)
Callimico goeldii (Bolivia)	6	—	1	Masataka (1981)
C. goeldii (Bolivia)	8–9	—	1	Pook & Pook (1981)

ilarly defines monogamy as follows, "The concept of monogamy implies exclusivity in mating, i.e., a given male and female will mate only with each other. . . . In mammals, it is usually implied that the mated pair remain together through several breeding seasons" (1977b:39). Since it is often difficult to prove mating exclusivity, "monogamy is generally recognized in the field and captivity by a variety of less stringent characteristics" (1977b:39). According to Kleiman, these include an absence of adult unrelated conspecifics from the pair's home range, territory, or nest and breeding by only one adult pair in a family group (see also Fuentes 1999).

Dawson (1976, 1977) monitored group membership in five groups of *S. geoffroyi* in Panama, and Neyman (1977) did likewise for six groups of *S. oedipus* in Colombia. In both studies, individuals were trapped and marked with color-coded collars. In Panama, group sizes and sex-age class proportions remained relatively stable for 10–15 months, but the particular complement of individuals in groups was unstable. Dawson recorded 41 immigrations and emigrations, 14 disappearances, and one death in the five groups. Losses were recouped by immigration and births. While all age and sex classes emigrated, immature tamarins tended to emigrate more frequently than adults. At least one adult male remained a permanent member of each group throughout the study and four of the five groups each maintained a permanent reproductive female.

In Colombia, Neyman (1977) also observed changes in group composition to be the normal pattern. However, of 23 identified individual tamarins known to enter or leave groups, 22 were adults, including both males and females, and all had dental wear indicating they were not young adults. Judging by nipple condition, at least two females had previously given birth. Savage et al. (1996) report that their study groups of *S. oedipus* were somewhat more stable, nevertheless immigration and emigration of adults of both sexes were common. Males tended to enter groups in the context of death or migration of one or more resident males. Adult females tended to enter groups that already contained a breeding female. The immigrating female generally did not usurp the breeding sovereignty of the resident breeding female. These authors state, "Wild groups [cotton-top tamarins] contained individuals of various ages and both sexes that were unrelated to the reproductively active animals in the group" (Savage et al. 1996: 94). Izawa (1978) also observed changes in group composition in *S. nigricollis* in Colombia, though his animals were not individually marked.

In a four-year study in Peru, Terborgh and Goldizen (1985) found that groups of *S. fuscicollis* with marked individuals only occasionally contained a single pair of adults. During a 37-month period when group compositions were known, the group had one adult female and one adult male only 27% of the time, one adult female and more than one adult male 61% of the time, more than one adult of each sex 8%, and adults of only one sex only 4% of the time. Immigration and emigration of adult males and females occurred commonly, with adults transferring into or out of all seven intensively studied groups. In four two-male groups in which copulations were observed, both males copulated. In three of these, two males were observed mating at about equal frequencies with a single female. In the fourth instance, both adult males copulated with the two adult females in the group. Some of the observed copulations occurred in view of the groups' other male without provoking any sign of aggression. In addition, one group was observed with two parous females and with two litters of young, suggesting that both females had reproduced within the group.

Goldizen et al. (1996) have amassed 13 years of information on patterns of mating and reproduction in saddle-back tamarins (Fig. 2-23). Their data indicate that males and females migrate/disappear from their natal groups between 2.5 and 3.5 years of age. Most documented successful migrations involve transferring to neighboring groups. Males tend to migrate into groups already containing other adult females, whereas females tend to migrate into groups that do not currently contain a breeding female. Several adult females have remained in their natal group and inherited the sovereign breeding position.

Moustached tamarins are characterized by a similar pattern of mating and migration. Garber et al. (1993) monitored group size and migration patterns in *S. mystax* inhabiting an island in northeastern Peru. In this study, 91 individuals residing in 13 social groups were trapped, examined, and marked. Group size averaged seven, and groups normally contained more than one adult male and one adult female. The greatest number of adult males in any group was three, and the greatest number of adult females was four. Based on dental wear, there was evidence of what was called age-related female reproductive sovereignty. In all groups studied, the oldest female in the group was the breeding female. In groups containing nine or more individuals, two females were reproductively active (i.e., two pregnant

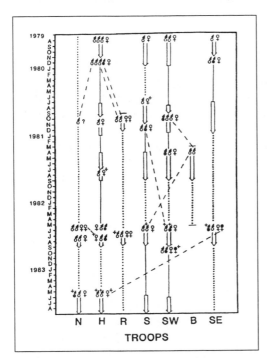

Figure 2-23a Adult composition of seven saddle-backed troops over 5 years. *Double lines* represent compositions observed at least once a month; *single lines* represent groups whose adult compositions did not change over periods when observers were absent from the study site; *dotted lines* represent unknown compositions during prolonged intervals when observers were unable to check the groups, usually during the observers' absences from the site; *dashed lines* indicate transfers between groups. Symbols: ♂ adult male; ♀ adult female; ♂, ♀ animals that had reached adulthood within their natal groups; (+) indicates replacements of adult males and females; ——— troop formation or extinction. [From Goldizen et al. 1996]

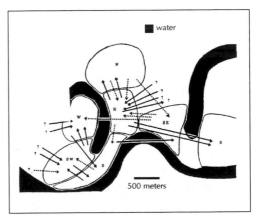

Figure 2-23b Approximate map of the seven territories studied and the intergroup movements of tamarins known to occur during the 7 years of the study. *Solid arrows,* males; *dotted arrows,* females. The letters are territory labels, and the question marks signify that either the exact territory emigrated from or the one immigrated into was not known.

or one pregnant and one lactating); however, in none of these cases did both females produce offspring.

It is likely that behavioral and physiological mechanisms similar to ovulatory suppression or inhibition also may occur in subordinate females that have conceived. Mechanisms of suppression and inhibition are known not only to vary between callitrichid species (ovulation at least in subordinate female *Leontopithecus rosalia* and *Callimico goeldii* does not appear to be physiologically suppressed), but may vary depending on relatedness or familiarity (Abbott et al. 1993, Saltzman et al. 1997), and environmental factors (Savage et al. 1997). In golden lion tamarins, common marmosets, and occasionally saddle-back tamarins, when two females in the same group are reproductively active, they are reported to be mother and daughter.

In tamarins, it appears that patterns of migration take several forms. Although individuals are known to migrate singly, this may be more common in females than in males. In moustached tamarins and golden lion tamarins, for example, paired male migration is common. Females rarely migrate in pairs (Dietz and Baker 1993, Garber et al. 1994, Garber 1994). Moreover, in saddle-back tamarins, females are reported to migrate once, whereas secondary dispersal occurs in adult males. Tamarins also migrate by groups splitting. In the wild, group size can increase rapidly, but groups larger than 13 or more animals are unstable. Garber (1988a) reports that his study group of 13 moustached tamarins split into groups of eight and five immediately after the birth of a new set of twin infants. The group of eight plus two infants remained in the home range, and the group of five, which consisted of both males and females, migrated together out of the area.

For *Leontopithecus rosalia,* Kleiman, Dietz, Baker and colleagues have collected extensive data on migration and mating patterns. Their data on 17 habituated groups studied over a seven-year period (Baker and Dietz 1996, Dietz et al. 1994) indicate that groups typically contain one reproductive female and 1–2 males. Approximately 10% of groups include two breeding females. In two-male groups (which may be comprised of brothers or father-son pairs), both males may copulate with the breeding female, although generally there is a strong dominance hierarchy, and one male is more likely to sire offspring.

As stated above, in golden lion tamarins, males enter established groups singly or in pairs, whereas females migrate individually. There is a strong bias towards male immigration. In some instances, females may inherit the breeding position of their mother; in other cases mother-daughter polygyny occurs. Females may emigrate from their natal group, but opportunities to enter established groups may be severely limited.

At their study site, Baker and Dietz (1996) indicate that the number of immigrating individuals per group per year in *L. rosalia* averages 0.48 (range 0–1.15). Although these authors argue that this is a low rate of immigration, an alternative explanation is possible. Golden lion tamarin groups contain approximately three adults, two of which contribute genes to the next litter (assuming only one male sires both twin offspring). Field data indicate that a group's breeding female generally produces only two offspring per year. If, on average, there is a change in the adult composition of a group by 0.5 each year, then (0.5/3.5 adults) 14% of potential gene pool of that group changes each year. If the immigrant becomes a breeding animal (male or female), then 50% of the gene pool is changed. Thus, in species that are characterized by a small number of breeding animals, even a small change in the number of potential breeders can have a large impact on individual reproductive success and gene frequencies in the local population (Garber et al. in prep).

Long-term data on marmoset social and mating systems are available for *C. jacchus, C. flaviceps,* and *C. humeralifer.* Female marmosets tend to give birth to two sets of twins per year, and group sizes of 9–16 individuals are common. Based on observations of copulations among group members, the mating system of these marmoset species can be described as principally polyandrous. However, polygnous groups of *Callithrix jacchus* have been studied by Digby (1994), and Ferrari (1988) presents data that at least some groups of *C. flaviceps* are best considered monogamous. Some marmoset groups have been reported to contain up to six adult females, although only one female breeds. In all three species, the number of adult males in established groups averages between three and four. Thus, *Callithrix* groups may contain eight or more adults (Ferrari and Digby 1996).

Based on their extremely high birth rate alone, recruitment into marmoset groups is principally due to births (Ferrari and Digby 1996). Immigration has rarely been observed in the wild, whereas emigration/disappearance is more common. In their review of *Callithrix* social systems, Ferrari and Digby (1996) list the confirmed emigration of 12 adults (six males and six females; plus 24 disappearances and only two immigrations) in a total of 131 observation months of *C. flaviceps, C. humeralifer,* and *C. jacchus.* They argue that social stability in marmosets is enhanced by factors associated with both kinship and resource abundance; specifically, that due to their ability to harvest plant exudates, opportunities for feeding competition among members of a large social group are minimized. Once group size approaches 14–16, however, limited breeding opportunities for subordinate group members, and reduced feeding efficiency may result in social instability.

In this regard, Ferrari has observed four adult *C. flaviceps* migrating together. This may be similar to group splitting activities noted in moustached tamarins. It is possible that given their high reproductive output, solitary migrant marmosets have few opportunities to enter established groups. However, group fissioning may allow males and females to form a new group, complete with helpers who can act collectively to establish a territory. Marmosets can subsist in small ranges, especially if they contain productive gum trees, and this may give a splinter group the opportunity to establish itself and become reproductive.

Pygmy marmosets exhibit a social system that is distinct from other callitrichids. Group size in *Cebuella* averages 7–9 individuals, including 1.4 adult males and 1.4 adult females (Soini 1988). Adults of both sexes are often aggressive to same sex conspecifics. This results in relatively early natal migration of subadult and young adult offspring. Two thirds of groups studied by Soini (1988) contained only one fully adult male and one fully adult female, although groups with as many as three adult males have been documented (Garber pers. comm.). Dominant males are reported to form a consort with a breeding female and guard them from other group and extra-group males. Subordinate males have been observed to copulate with the breeding female, but as has been reported in lion tamarins, it is possible that the dominant male sires most offspring. The degree to which particular males or females form an exclusive long-term breeding relationship and the length of reproductive sovereignty remain unknown. Migrations of adult males and adult female pygmy marmosets are reported to be more common than in *Callithrix.*

Like *Callithrix,* female *Cebuella* frequently give birth to two litters per year. Although subadult daughters and unrelated males aid in infant care, pygmy marmosets are unusual in that distance traveled per day is extremely short (<100 meters), and infants are often left unattended while adults forage and excavate gum holes. It is likely that the costs of cooperative infant care differ between callitrichid taxa, and this may play a major role in determining group size, composition, and social interactions.

As in the wild, promiscuous and/or polyandrous matings (one female mating with more than one male) have been reported in captive callitrichid groups. *S. fuscicollis* has been kept successfully in captivity in two-male one-female trios, and in such groups, both males usually copulate with the female (Epple 1975b). Similar observations on *S. fuscicollis* and *S. mystax* were made by E. Menzel (pers. comm.) and Malaga (1981) respectively. Polyandrous matings have also been observed in *S. oedipus* (Hampton et al. 1966).

In summary, in those field studies in which individual tamarins were identified, there was commonly more than one adult of each sex per group, and it seems likely that, at any instant, many of the animals forming a group were not closely related. The social structure was neither a monogamous nuclear family nor an extended family group. In the majority of groups, breeding was not restricted to a single pair of adults. Terborgh and Goldizen (1985) refer to this mating system as cooperative polyandry, in which one female mates with more than one male during a breeding season and all raise her young cooperatively.

In golden lion tamarins, groups also frequently contain more than one adult of each sex. Males tend to migrate in pairs, and there exists a strong male dominance hierarchy. One male has generally been observed to copulate more frequently than others, especially during the female's fertile period. Subordinate female golden lion tamarins do not exhibit physiological ovulatory suppression. In approximately 10% of groups in the wild, two females give birth. In *Callithrix,* immigration is reported to be uncommon, and groups are likely to contain many related adults of both sexes. New groups may form by splitting rather than by individual or paired migration. In both *Callithrix aurita* and *Callithrix jacchus,* two females have been observed giving birth simultaneously in some groups. (Digby and Ferrari 1994, Ferrari et al. 1996). Polyandry and polygamy appear to be the most common mating patterns. In *Cebuella,* the most specialized or derived callitrichid taxa in terms of body size, diet, and ranging patterns, it remains uncertain whether monogamy or polyandry is the most common mating pattern.

Very little is known regarding the natural social and mating system of *Callimico.* There have been no long term studies of Goeldi's monkey in the wild, and the few brief studies provide only limited information (Pook and Pook 1981, 1982, Masataka 1982, Buchanan-Smith 1991 Garber and Rehg 1998). Based on these accounts, wild *Callimico* appears to live in groups of at least 6–9 that contain more than one breeding female. Masataka (1982) reported two nursing infants and two lactating females in a group he observed in the wild, and Pook and Pook (1981) indicate that their main study group contained two juvenile-sized individuals. Patterns of infant caregiving in wild *Callimico* are unknown.

In reviewing callitrichid breeding systems, Garber (1994) and Garber and Leigh (1997) have suggested that the ancestral mating system of tamarins, marmosets, and Goeldi's monkey is small multi-male and multi-female groups. Polyandry in many species is likely to result from high levels of female reproductive competition and the ability of a dominant female to suppress/inhibit breeding in subordinate females. Not only does the dominant female control the reproductive opportunities of subordinate females, but in doing so, she also controls male breeding opportunities by reducing the number of reproductively active females in the population. However, there is some indication that the dominant female may only have a reproductive tenure of 2–4 years (Garber 1997). Cooperative care-giving (see below) in callitrichids plays a major role in increasing the individual reproductive success and individual reproductive output of breeding animals. Although, in certain contexts, the breeding female is dominant to other group members, within group aggression is extremely infrequent (Garber 1997).

Most New World monkeys are characterized by a relatively slow reproductive output and have offspring every 2 or 3 years (Garber and Leigh 1997). This occurs in squirrel monkeys, capuchin monkeys, spider monkeys, sakis, woolly monkeys, and woolly spider monkeys and is not closely related to body size. Exceptions to this slow reproductive output are callitrichids, which can have two litters per year and female titi monkeys and night monkeys, which are reported to give birth to a single offspring once every year (howler monkeys also are fast breeders and have an inter-birth interval of approximately 18 months). In the case of *Aotus* and *Callicebus,* extra-maternal infant care reduces the cost of reproduction to the mother, allowing her to rapidly redirect her energy to the next reproductive event. In this regard, Garber and Leigh (1997) suggest that monogamy in *Aotus* and *Callicebus* represents a very specialized social and mating system designed to increase male and female reproductive output. Callitrichids have also evolved a specialized social and mating system designed to increase reproductive output and reduce the cost to the mother of infant care. Cooperative infant care in tamarins and marmosets is a system in which adult males, adult females, kin, and non-kin help raise offspring born into their social group (Garber 1997).

Cooperative infant care has been described in birds and certain mammals and provides an explanation as to why adults, especially males, help raise offspring they have not sired. Stacey (1979, 1982) describes a social system in acorn woodpeckers (*Melanerpes formicivordes*) similar to that found in some callitrichids. In the woodpeckers, immigration and emigration by adults is common, and data collected on marked individuals indicate that groups are composed largely of unrelated adults of both sexes. In each group, only a single female is usually reproductively active, and she may mate with a number of males, all of which subsequently provide care for the young. Stacey points out that the system, referred to as a communal or cooperative breeding system, is relatively rare but taxonomically widespread among bird species and is found in some social carnivores.

This system is characterized by the presence, in addition to an adult male and female, "of one or more extra individuals, or helpers (Skutch 1961), that participate in the care and feeding of young" (Stacey 1979:53). The presence of helpers in these groups has been shown to have a significant positive effect on infant survivorship. In the case of some tamarins and marmoset species, there is correlational evidence that groups with more adult male helpers may be more successful in raising their young (Garber and Sussman 1987, Koenig and Rothe 1991, Garber 1997).

One might ask why adults would care for unrelated offspring. Several explanations are possible. In the case of subordinate males, helping might provide a critical opportunity for practicing care giving skills that are required to insure the survivorship of their own young when they begin breeding. In the case of reproductively active males, infant care giving may be a courtship behavior exhibited by males to increase their likelihood of mating with the breeding female. Given that females may be lactating and ovulating at the same time, the breeding female can directly assess male parenting skills during the period that she is most fertile.

In several species (golden lion tamarins, saddle-back tamarins, moustached tamarins) there is evidence of paired male migration. Although, in the absence of genetic information, assigning kinship to individuals based on behavior and movement patterns is extremely problematic, in many of these groups it is possible that some of these male pairs are related (father-son, full or half sibs). Care-giving in these cases may involve paternal uncertainty (the breeding female will mate with several males) or inclusive fitness gains associated with helping to raise your kin's offspring. However, any discussion of inclusive fitness must include some estimate of the cost to individual fitness of remaining in the present group as a nonbreeder relative to migrating and breeding successfully in another group. It is likely that, for most callitrichid species, the presence and absence of breeding opportunities in neighboring groups play a more prominent role in natal and secondary dispersal than desire to enhance inclusive fitness.

Thus, as has been described for acorn woodpeckers and other communally breeding avian and mammalian species, it appears that callitrichids generally live in small, multi-male/multi-female groups characterized by cooperative infant care, high levels of female breeding competition, a single breeding female (with certain exceptions), and mating promiscuity. This has also been referred to as cooperative polyandry. It is clearly unlike the monogamous mating system found in *Aotus, Callicebus,* or *Hylobates.* However, it is necessary to stress the variable nature of this breeding and social system; that within a single population or study area, an individual group may be polyandrous and/or polygynous or be composed principally of related or unrelated adults. It is even likely that there may be a set of temporary conditions in which only one male and one female in a group may mate. Overall, however, the social and breeding system of marmosets and tamarins should be referred to as a cooperative breeding system that tends toward polyandrous mating. Stacey (1982) provides excellent evidence that the adaptive strategy of this system is to increase the care, and thus the survival, of offspring.

Group structure of tamarins is further complicated by the fact that, under certain conditions, two or more groups may merge. Large, presumably merged, groups have been observed in *S. midas* (Thorington 1968), *S. geoffroyi* (Moynihan 1970, Dawson 1976, 1979), *S. fuscicollis* (Izawa 1976, Castro and Soini 1977), and *S. nigricollis* (Izawa 1978). These large groups come together for short periods and seem to be attracted by the availability of a temporarily abundant, concentrated food source. Large groups form in areas of overlap of separate smaller groups, with the same smaller units probably forming the merged group (see especially Izawa 1976, 1978, and Castro and Soini 1977).

In some areas, groups of two different species of tamarin unite to form a mixed-species group. For example, *S. fuscicollis* has been observed to live in mixed-species groups with *S. mystax* (Castro and Soini 1977, Garber 1986, 1988a, 1989, 1993b, Heymann 1990a, Castro 1991, Peres 1991), *S. labiatus* (Pook and Pook 1982) and *S. imperator* (Terborgh 1983a). These mixed groups are quite stable. In fact, Terborgh found the two species of tamarins to live in permanent mixed associations consisting of similarly sized small groups of each species (4–5 individuals each). These mixed-species groups remained intact for at least three years and shared and jointly defended a common territory against similar mixed groups.

Due to different locomotor behavior and substrate preferences (discussed earlier), the two species traveled separate but parallel paths. They coordinated movement by exchanging frequent vocalizations. Within the mixed-species group, movements were closely coordinated when visiting fruit trees and more loosely so at other times. This close association was also found in *S. mystax* and *S. fuscicollis* mixed-species groups (Garber 1988a, Castro 1991, Peres 1991). Group sizes for each species ranged from 7–13 individuals (Garber 1988a).

REPRODUCTION

Callitrichids are uniquely specialized among mammals in having dizygotic twins (Fig. 2-24) (except for *Callimico geoldii*), which lie within a common chorion during embryonic development. Although tamarins and marmosets normally bear twins and might be considered obligate twinners (Jaquish 1993), up to 19% single births and up to 30% triplets have been reported in captivity (see table in Hershkovitz 1977:422). There is an indication that triplet and quadruplet births are more frequent in captivity than in the natural habitat(Stevenson and Sutcliffe 1978), but this has not been confirmed.

In captivity, births occur throughout the year, and the most common birth interval (in *Callithrix*) is five months (Stevenson and Rylands 1988), indicating the potential for two sets of twins per year. *Cebuella* may have two breeding peaks per year (Christen 1974), and in the wild, there appear to be two birth peaks per year in both *C. jacchus* and *C. humeralifer* (Stevenson and Rylands 1988). However, in natural populations of *S. oedipus* in Columbia, almost 90% of births occurred between March and June over a six year period, and inter-birth intervals were 332 (53.6 days) (Savage et al. 1997). In *Saguinus geoffroyi,* there is a birth peak at the beginning of the wet season between April and June (Wislocki 1939, Moynihan 1970, Dawson 1976), and there may be a secondary minor birth peak from November to February (Dawson 1976). Birth seasonality is reported for most other species as well. In addition, there is evidence in *S. mystax* and *S. fuscicollis* of seasonal changes in male testes size (Garber et al. 1996a, Garber 1997). Whether this is influenced by abiotic factors of climate or day length or by pheromonal cues of females or other group males remains uncertain. In many multi-male groups of *S. mystax* and *S. fuscicollis,* one male tends to have significantly larger testes than other group males. In *Leontopithecus rosalia,* Dietz et al. (1994) report that males experience up to a 10% increase in body weight (685 g) in the late wet season (May) in order to more successfully compete for mat-

Figure 2-24 Pygmy marmoset with twins. [From Hershkovitz, M. 1977]

ing opportunities. By June, however, male body weight has dropped by 12% (Mean body weight 609 g). These authors suggest, "The seasonal variation in male body mass appears to be explained by male-male competition, not female choice" (Dietz et al. 1994:127).

The gestation period is 148 ± 5 days for *C. jacchus* (Hearn 1977), 135–142 days for Cebuella (Hershkovitz 1977), 140–165 days for *Sagu*inus sp. (Epple 1970, Gengozian et al. 1977, Cross and Martin 1981), 155 days for *Callimico* (Martin 1992) and 129–132 days for *Leontopithecus* (Kleiman 1977a). Thus, the largest and the smallest callitrichids have the shortest gestation lengths. Values for *Cebuella* and *Leontopithecus* are comparable with that of *Aotus,* which has a gestation length of 133 days.

It is usually assumed that callitrichid fathers carry infants most of the time beginning a few days after birth (c.f. Napier 1972, Jolly 1972), as do *Aotus* (Wright 1981) and *Callicebus* (Kinzey 1981). In *Leontopithecus rosalia* and *Callimico,* the mother is the principal carrier for the first 2–3 weeks postpartum. In all species of callitrichids, however, family members other than the father are also allowed to carry infants. Dixson and George (1982) provide a possible endocrinological basis for this behavior. They report that male *C. jacchus* carrying their twin offspring had plasma prolactin levels five times higher than those of males without infants. Prolactin has been implicated in the control of maternal behavior (Zarrow et al. 1971), and this is an indication that males exhibiting strong parental behavior also have high prolactin levels. This also has been proposed by Epple (1975b). Prolactin levels should be measured in other helpers that participate in care of the young to determine whether this is the likely mechanism stimulating care-giving behavior.

HOME RANGE AND RANGING PATTERNS

The notion that all or most species of callitrichids live in exclusively defended territories is an oversimplification of their behavioral ecology. These primates are extremely variable in their ranging patterns—among populations of the same species, as well as among species.

Dawson (1976, 1979) radio-tracked two groups of *Saguinus geoffroyi* in the Rodman Reserve in Panama: one in a lowland area, the other in an upland area. The home range of the lowland group was 26 ha, was actively defended, and 13% of it was shared by four other groups. Inter-group interactions, including vocalization and occasional physical contact, occurred frequently in boundary areas. Group movement within the home range was not random but was influenced by the location of overlap areas and by the fluctuations in availability of certain fruit. On all 26 days in which movements were monitored, the group visited overlap areas. This group thus could be considered territorial. The groups of *S. oedipus* studied by Neyman (1977) in Colombia were also territorial; however, home range sizes were much smaller, and there was a 20–30% overlap of adjacent ranges.

The upland group of *S. geoffroyi* studied by Dawson had a larger home range, which was affected more by seasonal fluctuations than was that of the lowland group. During six months of the wet season, the home range was 32 ha, but in the late wet season, the range included an additional 11 ha. This area was *not* defended but was shared with five other groups. These groups utilized a wide area of overlap, and through spatial and temporal segregation, they defended the integrity of the space around them at a given time, rather than a fixed geographical territory (Dawson 1979:280).

Thus, even nearby populations of the same species of tamarin may have different patterns of ranging and inter-group behavior; some groups are territorial, while others share extensive portions of their home ranges. The fact that, in some tamarin species, groups merge temporarily into larger groups further exacerbates a simple picture of ranging behavior. In fact, Izawa (1978) believes that groups of *S. nigricollis* in Colombia consistently merge and split into what he referred to as "larger groups" or regional populations.

Yet another pattern of home range utilization emerges from Terborgh's study of *S. imperator* and *S. fuscicollis*. As described in the last section, groups of these two species share common home ranges. The groups move along separate but parallel routes throughout the day, keeping in vocal contact. At night, they sleep in different but nearby roosting sites. Associated groups share a common pool of resource trees and jointly defend the boundaries of the shared home range. These mixed-species groups thus are territorial.

In mixed-species troops of *Saguinus mystax* and *Saguinus fuscicollis*, Garber (1988a) found that the location of inter-troop vocal battles and aggressive encounters changed seasonally and were directly associated with the locations of large productive feeding sites. As new trees began fruiting, neighboring troops would range into the same areas. The ability to defend large productive feeding trees from other mixed-species troops played an important role in tamarin feeding and ranging activities. In a related study on single-species groups of moustached tamarins, Garber et al. (1993b) demonstrated that the frequency and severity of inter-group encounters were related to three factors: the presence of productive feeding sites, the particular location in the home range, and whether group females were in estrus. These three factors varied temporally, and this accounted for much of the variation in inter-group interactions.

Home ranges of *Callithrix* (0.5–36 ha) are generally smaller than those of *Saguinus* and larger than those of *Cebuella* (0.1–3.0 ha), although they are quite variable (Ferrari and Digby 1996) (Table 2-9). *Callithrix* groups generally have overlapping ranges and appear not to defend territories (but see Ferrari et al. 1996 concerning one population of *C. aurita*). Stevenson found 17%, 23%, and 52% overlap in each of three groups of *C. jacchus*, and Rylands found 22% overlap in *C. humeralifer* (Stevenson and Rylands 1988). Ferrari (1988) reported 87.5% home range overlap in his study groups of *C. flaviceps*, and Digby (1994) reported 86% home range overlap in her study groups of *C. jacchus*. In this population, home range size was small (3.9 ha) and the density of animals was extremely high (Digby 1994). In another study, *C. jacchus* aggressively defended its main exudate tree but not its entire range (Maier et al. 1982).

In gallery forest where groups occupied long narrow ranges, Lacher et al. (1981) observed overlapping ranges in three groups of *C. penicillata* utilizing the same exudate trees. The groups moved along the stream up and down the gallery forest and seemed to maintain "sliding" home ranges. Marmosets frequently scent-mark exudate holes (Coimbra-Fihlo and Mittermeier 1977, Ramirez et al. 1977, Rylands 1981, Lacher et al. 1981). This behavior has been considered to be territorial (Coimbra-Filho 1972), but the groups studied by Lacher et al. did not avoid holes marked previously by other groups. Marking may be a way of indicating relative time elapsed since a particular exudate source was last utilized and does not appear to have any territorial significance.

Table 2-9 Home Range, Day Range and Density Estimates for Some Callitrichids

Genus and Species	Home Range	Day Range	Density	Reference
Saguinus geoffroyi	10–43	2061	—	Garber 1993b
S. oedipus	8–10	1750	30–180	Neyman 1978
S. oedipus	26–32+	2000	27–36	Dawson 1979
S. imperator	30–120	1420	12	Terborgh 1983a
S. nigricollis	30–50	1000	10–13	Izawa 1978
S. fuscicollis	30–40	1849	—	Garber 1988
S. fuscicollis	30	1220	16	Terborgh 1983a
Leontopithecus rosalia	—	1496	—	Peres 1986
L. chrysomelas	36	1792	—	Rylands 1989
Callithrix humeralifer	28	1500	30	Stevenson & Rylands 1988
C. jacchus	0.5	100–200	700	Stevenson & Rylands 1988
C. jacchus	4.0	704	—	Hubrecht 1985
C. kuhli	10–12	974	—	Rylands 1989
C. penicillata	10	1000	—	Stevenson & Rylands 1988
Cebuella pygmaea	0.3 (0.1–0.5)	—	51–59, 210–227[a]	Soini 1993
Callimico goeldii	30–60	2000	—	Pook & Pook 1981

[a] overall average, river edge only.

Cebuella troops live in very small, nonoverlapping home ranges until the exudate yield is diminished and then move on to new ranges. Thus, the lifetime range of a *Cebuella* troop is a series of successive small home ranges (Soini 1982, Terborgh 1983a). Interactions between groups of *Cebuella* have not been described. Group home ranges and populations density figures are listed in Table 2-9.

Most authors (e.g., Ramirez et al. 1977) agree that density and distribution of marmosets are directly related to density and distribution of exudate trees. However, Terborgh (1983a), noticing the widely scattered distribution of *Cebuella* in southern Peru, believes that more than suitable exudate trees are needed for an adequate home range. Besides feeding resources, these small primates must have suitable dense cover in which to rest and forage for insects and night-time resting sites well protected by vines and foliage. Terborgh also believes that there is a constant need to shift to a new site after one set of exudate trees has been exploited to exhaustion, and this has been confirmed by Soini (1982). Intensive and prolonged exploitation probably imposes a severe burden on the trees, but Terborgh has observed that most trees heal their wounds and survive for years after the *Cebuella* abandon them. There is also a need for an alternative resource base (such as fruit or flowers) during portions of the dry season. Nevertheless, *Cebuella* appears to have adopted the optimal strategy for exploitation of the exudate resource, which is found in concentrated, spatially widely scattered packages (Soini 1982).

In the case of *Callimico,* groups are reported to live in widely separated and non-overlapping areas. It has been suggested that the ecology of *Callimico* is closely tied to areas of secondary and bamboo forest (Izawa and Yoneda 1981), but recent studies have not confirmed this (Christen 1999). No information is available on inter-group or territorial interactions.

Most recorded day ranges of marmosets and tamarins are quite long for such small animals. The average day range of *S. geoffroyi* was 2,061 ± 402 m (Dawson 1979), and a group used about 56% of its home range in any given day. Based on full day follows in which the location of focal animals were recorded every two minutes throughout the day, Garber (1993b) estimated day range in a mixed-species group of *Saguinus mystax* and *Saguinus fuscicollis* to average just over 2,000 m per day. The average day range for *C. humeralifer* was 1,469 ± 193 m over 12 months with a range of 773–2115 m; day range for *C. penicillata kuhli* was about 1000 m (Stevenson and Rylands 1988). In *C. flaviceps,* (Ferrari 1988) and *C. jacchus* (Digby 1994) day ranges were 1223 m and 1243 m, respectively.

In contrast, however, very small day ranges have been reported for some groups of *C. jacchus* and for *Cebuella*. Stevenson reported average day ranges of 100 m and 200 m for each of two groups of *C. jacchus* she studied (Stevenson and Rylands 1988). Terborgh (1983b) observed a group of *Cebuella* to spend most of its time in just four or five trees, and the group studied by Ramirez et al.(1977) spent 80% of its daylight time in a core area comprising only one-third of its 0.3 ha home range.

The ranging patterns of individual marmoset and tamarin species is extremely variable. Some species of tamarins are territorial in only part of their range. The pattern is not species-specific and seems to be dependent on resource distribution. Interrelationships appear to exist between range size, group size, and infant care and development (Digby and Berreto 1996). Most marmosets thus far studied in the wild appear not to be territorial, or at least they are not reported to maintain exclusive ranges or travel to borders of their ranges in any regular pattern.

SUMMARY OF ECOLOGY OF THE CALLITRICHIDAE

In the past, the Callitrichidae have been characterized as squirrel-like both in their locomotor behavior and general ecology. They have also been described as living in monogamous family groups that were strictly territorial. Field studies, however, have given us a very different picture of callitrichid behavior and ecology and a better understanding of the morphological adaptations of this primate family. They have a suite of highly derived morphological features, and they can no longer be regarded as morphologically primitive New World primates.

Tamarins and marmosets are found in a variety of habitat types, and the home range of most species is characterized by a mix of habitats, usually including an abundance of edge. Most activity takes place on thin branches in the cover of the densely foliated middle to lower canopy or in the underbrush. Unlike squirrels, which range through the forest canopy mainly by ascending and descending large vertical trunks, callitrichids move through the forest canopy by running quadrupedally along horizontal branches and leaping between thin terminal supports. Thus, the claws of squirrels are a locomotor adaptation, used in traveling on large vertical and oblique supports; the claw-like nails of the callitrichids are, for the most part, a *postural* adaptation, used mainly for feeding on exudate sources located on large supports.

Squirrels are morphologically adapted to feed on hard nuts. The Callitrichidae eat mainly insects, soft fruit, nectar, flowers, and plant exudates. Unlike squirrels that move to large, horizontal, stable branches to feed, callitrichids forage for insects and fruit in the terminal branches and feed where these items are procured.

Both tamarins and marmosets feed on plant exudates, (though *Callimico* does not, nor does it share a number of the other morphological and behavioral characteristics of tamarins and marmosets). In fact, the Callitrichidae exemplify an adaptive array of plant exudate feeders. *Callithrix* and especially *Cebuella* represent the culmination of this adaptive radiation, with morphological and behavioral features of the dentition for gouging holes to obtain exudates.

The callitrichines live in small groups, generally ranging from 5–12 individuals. Most groups are *not* monogamous extended families. Exchange of members between both neighboring and distant groups occurs regularly. However, reproductive sovereignty may be more stringent, migration may be less important, and groups may be more stable among marmosets than among tamarins. It appears that in all species, there is usually more than one unrelated adult of each sex in a group, and the pattern of mating is flexible but usually promiscuous or polyandrous. Generally, only one female gives birth each season. Twins are the norm, and adult males usually assume the major burden of carrying the infants, but infant care is also shared by other group members. Food also is shared with the infant by group members. This pattern has been referred to as a "communal breeding system." It is found in many species of birds and mammals and seems to be an adaptation for maximizing successful care of the young.

Groups of some species of tamarins merge temporarily, presumably when there are concentrated sources of fruit, and some species are also found in mixed-species groups. Furthermore, some populations are territorial while others share large portions of their home ranges. Marmosets, because they are able to produce the flow of exudates year-round, are less dependent upon seasonal availability of resources than are tamarins. This allows them to have smaller home ranges and to move less throughout the day. It also may allow them to have more stable group membership, though this remains to be shown.

Marmosets and tamarins produce twins and marmosets can do so up to two times per year. *Callithrix* and *Cebuella* births can occur in more than one season by virtue of the ability to exploit exudates year-round. Indeed, the adaptive strategy of the marmosets and tamarins can best be understood by studying the interrelationship of dietary, positional, social, and reproductive features of both morphology and behavior.

BIBLIOGRAPHY

Abbott, D.H., Barrett, J., George, L.M. 1993. Comparative aspects of the social suppression of reproductions in female marmosets and tamarins. Pp. 152–163. In *Marmosets and Tamarins: Systematics, Behaviour, and Ecology.* A.B. Rylands, Ed., Oxford, Oxford University Press.

Baba, M., Goodman, M., Dene, H., Moore G.W. 1975. Origins of the Ceboidea viewed from an immunological perspective. *J. Hum. Evol.* 4:89–102.

Baker, A.J., Dietz, J.M. 1996. Polygyny and female reproductive success in gold lion tamarins, *Leontopithecus rosalia. Anim. Behav.* 46:1067–1078.

Barroso, C.M.L., Schneider, H., Schneider, M.P.C., Sampaio, I., Harada, M.L., Czelusniak, J., Goodman, M. 1997. Update on the phylogenetic systematics of New World monkeys: further DNA evidence for placing marmoset (*Cebuella*) within the genus *Callithrix. Int. J. Primatol.* 18:651–674.

Bartecki, U., Heymann, E.W. 1987. Sightings of red uakaris, *Cacajao calvus rubicundus,* at Rio Blanco Peruvian Amazonia. *Primate Conserv.* 8:34–36.

Bates, H.W. 1864. *The Naturalist on the River Amazon,* Second Edition. London, John Murray.

Bearder, S.K., Martin, R.D. 1980. Acacia gum and its use by bush-babies, *Galago senegalensis* (Primates: Lorisidae). *Int. J. Primatol.* 1:103–128.

Buchanan-Smith, H. 1991. Field observations of Goeldi's monkey, *Callimico goeldii,* in Northern Bolivia. *Folia Primatol.* 57:102–105.

Buchanan-Smith, H., Hardie, S.M. 1997. Tamarin mixed-species groups: an evaluation of a combined captive and field approach. *Folia Primatol.* 68:272–286.

Caine, N.G. 1987. Vigilance, vocalizations, and cryptic behavior at retirement in captive groups of red-bellied tamarins (*Saguinas labiatus*). *Am. J. Primatol.* 12: 241–250.

Caine, N.G. 1993. Flexibility and co-operation as unifying themes in *Saguinas* social organization: the role of Predation pressures. Pp. 200–219. In *Marmosets and Tamarins: Systematics, Behavior, and Ecology.* A.B. Rylands, Ed., Oxford. Oxford University Press.

Caine, N.G., Weldon, P.J. 1989. Responses by red-bellied tamarins (*Saguinas labiatus*) to fecal scents of predatory and non-predatory neotropical mammals. *Biotropica* 21:186–189.

Cartmill, M. 1974. Pads and claws in arboreal locomotion. Pp. 45–83. In *Primate Locomotion.* F.A. Jenkins, Ed., New York, Academic Press.

Carvalho, C.T. de, Carvalho, C.F. de 1989. A organizacao social dos suis-pretos, (*Leontopithecus chrysopygus* Mikan), na reserva em Teodoro Sampaio, Sao Paulo (Primates, Callitrichidae). *Revta. Bras. Zool.* 6:707–717.

Castro, R. 1991. *Behavioral Ecology of Two Coexisting Tamarin Species* (Saguinus fuscicollis nigrifrons *and* Saguinus mystax mystax, *Callitrichidae: Primates*) *in Amazonian Peru.* Ph.D. Thesis. Washington University, St. Louis.

Castro, R., Soini, P. 1977. Field studies on *Saguinus mystax* and other callitrichids in Amazonian Peru. Pp. 73–78. In *The Biology and Conservation of the Callitrichidae.* D.G. Kleinman, Ed., Washington, D.C., Smithsonian Institute Press.

Charles-Dominique, P. 1971. Eco-ethologie des prosimiens du Gabon. *Biol. Gabonica* 7:121–228.

Christen, A. 1974. Fortpflanzungsbiologie und verhalten bei *Cebuella pygmaea* und *Tamarin tamarin. Fortschritte der Verhaltensforschung.* No. 14.

Christen, A. 1999. Survey of Goeldi's monkeys (*Callimico goeldii*) in Northern Bolivia. *Folia Primatol.* 70:107–111.

Christen, A., Geissmann, T. 1994. A primate survey in northern Bolivia, with special reference to Goeldi's monkey, *Callimico goeldii. Int. J. Primatol.* 15:239–273.

Coimbra-Filho, A.F. 1972. Aspectos inéditos do comportamento de sagüis do gênero *Callithrix* (Callitrichidae: Primates). *Rev. Bras. Biol.* 32:505–512.

Coimbra-Filho, A.F. 1976. *Leontopithecus rosalia chrysopygus* (Mikan, 1823) o Mico-Leao do Estado de Sao Paulo (Callitrichidae: Primates). *Silvicultura, Sao Paulo* 10:1–36.

Coimbra-Filho, A.F. 1977. Natural shelters of *Leontopithecus rosalia* and some ecological implications (Callitrichidae: Primates). Pp. 79–89. In *The Biology and Conservation of the Callitrichidae.* D.G. Kleiman, Ed., Washington D.C., Smithsonian Institution Press.

Coimbra-Filho, A.F., Mittermeier, R.A. 1973. Distribution and ecology of the genus *Leontopithecus* Lesson, 1840 in Brazil. Primates 14:47–66.

Coimbra-Filho, A.F., Mittermeier, R.A. 1977. Tree gouging, exudate-eating and the 'short-tusked' condition in *Callithrix* and *Cebuella.* Pp. 105–115. In *The Biology and Conservation of the Callitrichidae.* D.G. Kleiman, Ed., Washington D.C., Smithsonian Institution Press.

Coimbra-Filho, A.F., Rocha N da, C., Pissinatti, A. 1980. Morfofisiologia do ceco e sua correlacao com o tipo odontologico em Callitrichidae (Platyrrhini: Primates). *Rev. Basil. Biol.* 41:141–147.

Coimbra-Filho, A.F., Mittermeier, R.A., Constable, I.D. 1981. *Callithrix flaviceps* (Thomas, 1903) recorded from Minas Gerais, Brazil (Callitrichidae: Primates). *Rev. Bras. Biol.* 41:141–147.

Crandlemire-Sacco, J.L. 1986. *The ecology of saddle-backed tamarins,* Saguinas fuscicollis, of *Southeastern Peru.* Ph.D. Thesis. University of Pittsburgh, Pittsburgh.

Cross, J.F., Martin, R.D. 1981. Calculation of gestation period and other reproductive parameters for primates. *Dodo, J. Jersey Wildl. Preserv. Trust* 18:30–43.

Cruz Lima, E. Da. 1945. *Mammals of Amazonia, Vol. 1, General Introduction and Primates.* Belem, Contributions, Museu Paraense Emílio Goeldi de Historia Natural e Etnografia.

Davis, L.C. 1996. Functional and phylogenetic implications of ankle morphology in Goeldi's Monkey (*Callimico goeldii*). Pp. 133–156. In *Adaptive Radiations of Neotropical Primates.* M.A. Norconk, A.L. Rosenberger, P.A. Garber, Eds., New York, Plenum Press.

Dawson, G.A. 1976. *Behavioral Ecology of the Panamanian Tamarin,* Saguinus opdipus (*Callitrichidae: Primates*). Ph.D. Thesis. Michigan State University, East Lansing.

Dawson, G.A. 1977. Composition and stability of social groups of the tamarin, *Saguinus opdipus geoffroyi,* in Panama: Ecological and bahavioral implications. Pp. 23–37. In *The Biology and Conservation of the Callitrichidae.* D.G. Kleiman, Ed., Washington D.C., Smithsonian Institution Press.

Dawson, G.A. 1979. The use of time and space by the Panamanian tamarin, *Saguinus opdipus. Folia Primatol.* 31:253–284.

Dietz, J.M., Baker, A.J. 1993. Polygyny and female reproductive success in golden lion tamarins, *Leontopithecus rosalia. Anim. Behav.* 46:1067–1078.

Dietz, J.M., Baker, A.J., Miglioretti, D. 1994. Seasonal variation in reproduction, juvenile growth, and adult body mass in golden lion tamarins (*Leontopithecus rosalia*). *Am. J. Primatol.* 34:115–132.

Dietz, J.M., Peres, C.A., Pinder, L. 1997. Foraging ecology and use of space in wild golden lion tamarins (*Leontopithecus rosalia*). *Am. J. Primatol.* 41:289–303.

Digby, L.J. 1994. *Social Organization and Reproductive Strategies in a Wild Population of Common Marmosets* (Callithrix jacchus). Ph.D. Thesis. Univ. of California, Davis.

Digby, L.J., Ferrari, S.F. 1994. Multiple breeding females in free-ranging groups of *Callithrix jacchus. Int. J. Primatol.* 15:389–397.

Digby, L.J., Barreto, C.E. 1996. Paternal care patterns and vigilance in wild cotton-top tamarins (*Saquinus oedipus*). Pp. 173–185. In *Adaptive Radiations of Neotropical Primates.* M.A. Norconk, A.L. Rosenberger, P.A. Garber, Eds., New York, Plenum Press.

Dixson, A.F., George, L. 1982. Prolactin and parental behavior in a male New World primate. *Nature* 299:551–553.

D'Souza, F. 1974. A preliminary field report on the lesser tree shrew (*Tupaia minor*). Pp. 167–182. In *Prosimian Biology.* R.D. Martin, G.A. Doyle, A.C. Walker, Eds., London, Duckworth.

DuMond, F.V. 1971. Comments on the minimum requirements in the husbandry of the golden marmoset (*Leontopithecus rosalia*). *Lab. Prim. News.* 10:30–37.

Eisenberg, J.F. 1977. Comparative ecology and reproduction of new world monkeys. Pp. 13–22 37. In *The Biology and Conservation of the Callitrichidae.* D.G. Kleiman, Ed., Washington D.C., Smithsonian Institution Press.

Eisenberg, J.F., Mucknhirn, N.A., Rudran, R. 1972. The relation between ecology and social structure in primates. *Science* 176:863–874.

Emmons, L.H. 1990. *Neotropical Rainforest Mammals.* Chicago, University of Chicago Press.

Emmons, L.H. 1987. Comparative feeding ecology of felids in a Neotropical rainforest. *Behav. Ecol. Sociobiol.* 20:271–283.

Encarnación, C.F., Heymann, E.W. 1998. Body mass of wild *Callimico goeldii. Folia Primatol.* 69:368–371.

Enders, R.K. 1935. Mammalian life histories from Barro Colorado Island. *Bull. Mus. Comp. Zool.* 78:385–502.

Epple, G. 1970. Maintenance, breeding and development of marmoset monkeys (Callitrichidae) in captivity. *Folia Primatol.* 12:56–76.

Epple, G. 1975a. The behavior of marmoset monkeys (Callitrichidae). Pp. 195–239. In *Primate Behavior, Vol. 4.* L.A. Roseblum, Ed., New York, Academic Press.

Epple, G. 1975b. Parental behavior in *Saguinus fuscicolis* (Callitrichidae). *Folia Prmatol.* 24:221–238.

Epple, G. 1977. Notes on the establishment and maintenance of the pair bond in *Saguinus fuscicolis.* Pp. 231–237. In *The Biology and Conservation of the Callitrichidae.* DG Kleiman, Ed., Washington D.C., Smithsonian Institution Press.

Evans, S. 1983. The pair-bond of the common marmoset, *Callithrix jacchus jacchus:* An experimental investigation. *Anim. Behav.* 31:651–658.

Evans, S., Poole, T.B. 1983. Pair-bond formation and breeding success in the common marmoset, *Callithrix jacchus jacchus. Int. J. Primatol.* 4:83–97.

Faria, D.S. de 1986. Tamnho, composicao de um grupo social e area de vivencia (home-range) do sagui (*Callithrix jacchus*) na mata ciliar do corrego Capetinga, Brasilia, DF. Pp. 87–105. In *A Primatologica no Brasil-2.,* M. De Mello, Ed., Brasilia, Sociedade Brasileira de Primatologia.

Ferrari, S.F. 1988. *The Behaviour and Ecology of the Buffy-Headed Marmoset,* Callithrix flaviceps (*O. Thomas, 1903*). Ph.D. Thesis. University College, London.

Ferrari, S.F. 1991. Preliminary report on a field study of *Callithrix flaviceps*. Pp. 159–171. In *A Primatologia no Brasil-3*. A.B. Rylands, A.T. Bernardes, Eds., Belo Horizonte, Fundacao Bidiversitas.

Ferrari, S.F. 1992a. The care of infants in a wild marmoset (*Callithrix flaviceps*) group. *Am. J. Primatol.* 26:109–118.

Ferrari, S.F. 1992b. "Diet for a Small Primate." *Natural History, NY.*

Ferrari, S.F. 1993. Ecological differentiation in the Callitrichidae. Pp. 314–328. In *Marmosets and Tamarins: Sytematics, Behavior, and Ecology.* A.B. Rylands, Ed., Oxford, Oxford University Press.

Ferrari, S.F., Digby, L.J. 1996. Wild *Callithrix* groups: stable extended families? *Am. J. Primatol.* 38:19–28.

Ferrari, S.F., Correa, H.K.M. Coutinho, P.E.G. 1996. Ecology of the "southern" marmosets (*Callithrix aurita* and *Callithrix flaviceps*): How different how similar? Pp. 157–171. In *Adaptive Radiations of Neotropical Primates.* M.A. Norconk, A.L. Rosenberger, P.A. Garber, Eds., New York, Plenum Press.

Ferrari, S.F., Lopes Ferrari, M.A. 1990. Predator avoidance behavior in the buffy-headed marmoset (*Callithrix flaviceps*). *Primates* 31:323–338.

Ferrari, S.F., Mendes, S.L. 1991 Buffy-headed marmosets 10 years on. *Oryx* 25(2): 105–109.

Ferrari, S.F., Strier, K.B. 1992. Exploitation of *Mabea fistulifera* nectar by marmosets (*Callithrix flaviceps*) and muriquis (*Brachyteles arachnoides*) in south-east Brazil. *J. Trop. Ecol.* 8:225–239.

Fleagle, J.G., Mittermeier, R.A. 1980. Locomotor behavior, body size and comparative ecology of seven Surinam monkeys. *Am. J. Phys. Anthropol.* 52:301–314.

Fonseca, G.A.B., Lacher, T.E., Alves, C., Magalhaes-Castro, B. 1980. Some ecological aspects of free-living black tufted-eared marmosets (*Calltihrix jacchus penicillata*). *Anthropol. Contemp.* 3: 197.

Ford, S.M. 1986. Systematics of the New World Monkeys. Pp. 73–135. In *Comparative Primate Biology. Vol. 1: Systematics, Evolution and Anatomy.* D. Swindler, J. Erwin, Eds., New York, Allen R. Liss.

Freese, C.H., Heltne, P.G., Castro N., Whitesides, G. 1982. Patterns and determinants of monkey densities in Peru and Bolivia, with notes on distribution. *Int. J. Primatol.* 3:53–90.

Galef, B.G., Mittermeier, R.A., Bailey, R.C. 1976. Predation by the tayra (*Eira barbara*). *J. Mammol.* 57:760–761.

Garber, P.A. 1980a. *Locomotor Behavior and Feeding Ecology of the Panamanian Tamarin* (Saguinus oedipus geoffroyi, *Callitrichidae, Primates*). Ph.D. Thesis. Washington University, St. Louis.

Garber, P.A. 1980b. Locomotor behavior and feeding ecology of the Panamanian tamarin (*Saguinus oedipus geoffroyi,* Callitrichidae, Primates). *Int. J. Primatol.* 1:185–201.

Garber, P.A. 1984a. The ecology of the exudate feeding and the importance of plant exudates in the diet of the Panamanian tamarin. *Int. J. Primatol.* 5:1–15.

Garber, P.A. 1984b. Use of habitat and positional behavior in a neotropical primate, *Saguinus oedipus.* Pp. 113–133. In *Adaptations for Foraging in Nonhuman*

Primates: Contributions to an Organismal Biology of Prosimians, Monkeys and Apes. J.G.H. Cant, P.S. Rodman, Eds., New York, Columbia University Press.

Garber, P.A. 1986. The ecology of seed dispersal in two species of callitrichid primate (*Saguinus mystax* and *Saguinus fuscicollis*) in Amazonian Peru. *Behavior* 105 (1–2): 18–34.

Garber, P.A. 1988a. Diet, foraging patterns, and resource defense in a mixed species troop of *Saguinus mystax* and *Saguinus fuscicollis* in Amazonian Peru. *Behavior* 105:18–34.

Garber, P.A. 1988b. Foraging decisions during nectar feeding by tamarin monkeys *Saguinus mystax* and *Saguinus fuscicollis* in Amazonian Peru. *Biotropica* 20:100–106.

Garber, P.A. 1989. Role of spatial memory in primate foraging patterns: *Saguinus mystax* and *Saguinus fuscicollis*. *Am. J. Primatol.* 19:203–216.

Garber, P.A. 1991. A comparative study of positional behavior in three species of tamarin monkeys. *Primates* 32:219–230.

Garber, P.A. 1992. Vertical clinging, small body size, and the evolution of feeding adaptations in the Callitrichidae. *Am. J. Phys. Anthropol.* 88:469–482.

Garber, P.A. 1993a. Feeding ecology and behaviour of the genus *Saguinus*. Pp. 273–295. In *Marmosets and Tamarins: Sytematics, Behavior, and Ecology.* A.B. Rylands, Ed., Oxford, Oxford University Press.

Garber, P.A. 1993b. Seasonal patterns of diet and ranging in two species of tamarin monkeys: Stability versus variability. *Int. J. Primatol.* 14:145–166.

Garber, P.A. 1994. A phylogenetic approach to the study of tamarin and marmoset social systems. *Am J. Primatol.* 34: 199–219.

Garber, P.A. 1997. One for all and breeding for one: cooperation and competition as a tamarin reproductive strategy. *Evol. Anthropol.* 5:187–199.

Garber, P.A. 1998. Within and between site variability in moustached tamarin (*Saguinus mystax*) positional behavior during food procurement. Pp. 61–78. In *Primate Locomotion.* A. Rosenberger, J. Gleagel, H. McHenry, E. Strasser, Eds., New York, Plenum Press.

Garber, P.A., Kitron, U. 1997. Seed swallowing in tamarins: evidence of a curative function or enhanced foraging efficiency. *Int. J. Primatol.* 181:523–538.

Garber, P.A., Leigh, S.R. 1997. Ontogenetic variation in small-bodied New World primates: implications for patterns of reproduction and infant care. *Folia Primatol.* 68:1–22.

Garber, P.A., Moya, L., Pruetz, J.D., Ique, C. 1996. Social and seasonal influences on reproductive biology in male moustached tamarins (*Saguinus mystax*) *Am. J. Primatol.* 38:29–46.

Garber, P.A., Rehg, J.A. 1998. Preliminary field study of positional behavior and habitat preference in *Callimico goeldii. Am. J. Phys. Anthropol.* Suppl 24: 85–86.

Garber, P.A., Rosenberger, A.L., Norconk, M.A. 1996. Marmoset misconceptions. Pp. 87–95. In *Adaptive Radiations of Neotropical Primates.* M.A. Norconk, A.L. Rosenberger and P.A. Garber, Eds., New York, Plenum Press.

Garber, P.A., Sussman, R.W. 1984. Ecological distinctions in sympatric species of *Saguinus* and *Sciureus. Am. J. Phys. Anthropol.* 65:135–146.

Garber, P.A., Encarnacion, F., Moya L., Pruetz, J.D. 1993. Demographic and reproductive patterns in moustache tamarin monkeys (*Saguinas mystax*): Implications for reconstructing platyrrhine mating systems. *Am. J. Primatol.* 29:235–354.

Garber, P.A., Moya, L., Malaga, C. 1984. A preliminary field study of the moustached tamarin monkey (*Saguinas mystax*) in northeastern Peru: questions concerned with the evolution of a communal breeding system. *Folia Primatol.* 42:17–32

Gengozian, N., Batson, J.S., Smith, T.A. 1977. Breeding of tamarins (*Saguinus ssp.*) in the laboratory. Pp. 163–171. In *The Biology and Conservation of the Callitrichidae.* D.G. Kleiman, Ed., Washington D.C., Smithsonian Institution Press.

Goffart, M. 1978. Physiological aspects of *Perodictus potto.* Pp. 179–180. In *Recent Advances in Primatology, Vol. 3, Evolution.* D.G. Chivers, K.A. Joysey, Eds., New York, Academic Press.

Goldizen, A.W. 1987. Tamarins and marmosets: communal care of offspring. Pp. 34–43. In *Primate Societies.* B.B. Smuts, D.L. Cheney, R.M. Seyfarth, R.W. Wrangham, T.T. Struhsaker, Eds., Chicago, University of Chicago Press.

Goldizen, A.W. 1990. A comparative perspective on the evolution of tamarin and marmoset social systems. *Intl. J. Primatol.* 11:63–83.

Goldizen, A.W., Mendelson, J., van Vlaardingen, M. ,Terborgh, J. 1996. Saddle-back tamarin (*Saguinus fuscicollis*) reproductive strategies: evidence from a thirteen-year study of a marked population. *Am. J. Primatol.* 38:57–84.

Hampton, J.K., Jr, Hampton, S.H., Landwehr, B.T. 1966. Observations on a successful breeding colony of the marmoset, *Opdipomidas oedipus. Folia Promatol.* 4:265–287.

Hamrick, M.W. 1998. Functional and adaptive significance of primate pads and claws: evidence from New World anthropoids. *Am. J. Phys. Anthropol.* 106:113–127.

Hearn, J.P. 1977. The endocrinology of reproduction in the common marmoset *Callithrix jacchus.* Pp. 163–177. In *The Biology and Conservation of the Callitrichidae.* DG Kleiman, Ed., Washington D.C., Smithsonian Institution Press.

Hearn, J.P. 1977. The endocrinology of reproduction in the common marmoset *Callithrix jacchus.* Pp. 163–177. In *The Biology and Conservation of the Callitrichidae.* D.G. Kleiman, Ed., Washington D.C., Smithsonian Institution Press.

Hearn, J.P. 1978. Fertility and infertility in the marmoset monkey, *Callithrix jacchus.* Pp. 59–73. In *Biology and Behavior of Marmosets.* H. Rothe, J.H. Wolters, J.P. Hearn, Eds., Gottingen, University of Gottingen Press.

Heltne, P.G. Wojcik, J.F., Pook, A.G. 1981. Goeldi's monkey, genus *Callimico.* Pp. 169–209. In *Ecology and Behavior of Neotropical Primates, Vol. 1.* A.F. Coimbra-Filho, R.A. Mittermeier. Eds., Rio de Janeiro, Academia Brasileira de Ciências.

Hernandez-Camacho, J., Cooper, R.W. 1976. The non-human primates of Colombia. Pp. 35–69 In *Neotropical Primates: Field Studies and Conservation.* R.W. Thorington Jr., P.G. Heltne, Eds., Washington, D.C., National Academy of Sciences.

Hershkovitz, P. 1972. The recent mammals of the neo-tropical region: A zoogeographic and ecological review. Pp. 311–341. In *Evolution, Mammals and Southern Continents.* A. Keast, F. Erk, B. Glass, Eds., Albany, State University of New York Press.

Hershkovitz, P. 1975. Comments on Taxonomy of Brazilian marmosets (*Callithrix:* Callitrichidae). *Folia Primatol.* 24:137–172.

Hershkovitz, P. 1977. *Living New World Monkeys (Platyrrhini), Vol. 1.* Chicago, University of Chicago Press.

Heymann, E.W. 1987. A field observation of predation on a moustached tamarin (*Saguinas mystax*) by an anaconda. *Int. J. Primatol.* 8: 193–195.

Heymann, E.W. 1990a. Interspecific relations in a mixed species troop of moustached tamarins, *Saguinas mystax,* and saddle-backed tamarins, *Saguinus fuscicollis* (Platyrrhini: Callitrichidae), at the Rio Blanco, Peruvian Amazon. *Am. J. Primatol.* 21:115–127.

Heymann, E.W. 1990b. Reactions of wild tamarins *Saguinus mystax* and *Saguinus fuscicollis* to avian predators. *Int. J. Primatol.* 11:327–337.

Hladik, A., Hladik, C.M. 1969. Rapports trophiques entre végétation et primates dans la forêt de Barro Colorado (Panama). *La Terre et La Vie* 23:25–117.

Hladik, C.M. 1970. Les singes du Nouveau Monde. *Science Nat. l'Environ.* 102:1–9.

Howes, F.N. 1949. Vegetable Gums and Resins. Boston, Chronica Botanica Co.

Hubrecht, R.C. 1984. Field observations on group size and composition of the common marmoset (*Callithrix jacchus jacchus*), at Tapacura, Brazil. *Primates* 25:13–21.

Izawa, K. 1976. Group sizes and compositions of monkeys in the upper Amazon basin. *Primates* 17:367–399.

Izawa, K. 1978. A field study of the ecology and behavior of the black-mantled tamarin (*Saguinus nigricollis*). *Primates* 19:241–274.

Izawa, K. 1979. Studies on peculiar distribution pattern of Callimico. *Kyoto University Overseas Research Reports of New World Monkeys* 1:1–19.

Izawa, K., Bejarano, G. 1981. Distribution ranges and patterns of nonhuman priamtes in Western Pando, Bolivia. *Kyoto University Overseas Research Reports of New World Monkeys* 2:1–11.

Izawa K., Yoneda, M. 1981. Habitat utilization of nonhuman primates in a forest of the western Pando, Bolivia. *Kyoto University Overseas Research Reports of New World Monkeys* 2: 13–22.

Janson, C.H., Terborgh, J., Emmons, L.H. 1981. Non-flying mammals as pollinating agents in the Amazonian forest. *Reprod. Biol.* 13:1–6.

Janzen, D.H. 1973a. Sweep samples of tropical foliage insects: Description of study sites, with data on species abundances and size distribution. *Ecology* 54:659–686.

Janzen, D.H. 1973b. Sweep samples of tropical foliage insects: Effects of seasons, vegetation types, elevation, time of day and insularity. *Ecology* 54:659–686.

Janzen, D.H., Schoener, T.W. 1968. Differences in insect abundance and diversity between wetter and drier sites during a tropical dry season. *Ecology* 49:98–110.

Jaquish, C.E. 1993. *Genetic, Behavioral and Social Effects on Fitness Components in Marmosets and Tamarins (Family: Callitrichidae).* Ph.D. Thesis. Washington University, St. Louis.

Jolly, A. 1972. *The Evolution of Primate Behavior.* New York, MacMillan.

Kay, R.F. 1975. The functional adaptations of primate molar teeth. *Am. J. Phys. Anthropol.* 43:195–216.

Kay, R.F. 1994. "Giant" tamarin from the Miocene of Columbia. *Am. J. Phys. Anthropol.* 95:333–353.

Kay, R.F., Madden, R.H., Cefelli, R.L., Flynn J.J. 1997. *Vertebrate palaeontology in the neotropics: the Miocene fauna of La Venta, Columbia.* Washington D.C., Smithsonian Institution Press.

Kinzey, W.G. 1973. Reduction of the cingulum in Ceboidea. Pp. 101–127. In *Craniofacial Biology of Primates.* M.R. Zingeser, Ed., Basel, S. Karger.

Kinzey, W.G. 1979. Marmosets and tamarins. *Science* 203:879.

Kinzey, W.G. 1981. The titi monkeys, genus *Callicebus.* Pp. 241–276. In *Ecology and Behavior of Neotropical Primates, Vol. 1.* A.F. Coimbra-Filho and R.A. Mittermeier., Eds., Rio de Janeiro, Academia Brasileira de Ciências.

Kinzey, W.G. 1997a. History of New World primate field studies. Pp. 743–748. In *History of Physical Anthropology: An Encyclopedia.* F. Spencer, Ed., New York, Garland.

Kinzey, W.G. 1997b. Synopsis of New World Primates (16 Genera). Pp. 169–324. In *New World Primates: Ecology, Evolution and Behavior.* Kinzey, W.G., Ed., New York, Aldine De Gruyter.

Kinzey, W.G., Rosenberger, A.L., Ramirez, M. 1975. Vertical clinging and leaping in a neotropical anthropoid. *Nature* 255:327–328.

Kleiman, D.G. 1977a. Characteristics of reproduction and sociosexual interactions in pairs of lion tamarins (*Leontopithecus rosalia*) during the reproductive cycle. Pp. 181–190. In *The Biology and Conservation of the Callitrichidae.* D.G. Kleiman, Ed., Washington D.C., Smithsonian Institution Press.

Kleiman, D.G. 1977b. Monogamy in mammals. *Q. Ref. Biol.* 52:39–69.

Kleiman, D.G., Hoage, R.J., Green, K.M. 1988. The lion tamarins, genus *Leontopithecus.* Pp. 299–347. In *Ecology and Behavior of Neotropical Primates, Vol. 2.* R.A. Mittermeier, A.F. Coimbra-Filho and G.A.B. da Fonseca, Eds., Washington, D.C., World Wildlife Fund.

Koenig, A., Rothe, H. 1991. Social relationships and individual contributions to cooperative behavior on common marmosets. *Primates* 32:183–195.

Lacher, T.E., Jr., Bouchardet da Fonseca, G.A., Alves, C., Jr., Magalhaes-Castro, B. 1981. Exudate-eating, scent marking and territoriality in wild population of marmosets. *Anim. Behav.* 29:306–307.

Lemelin, P. Grafton, B.W. 1998. Grasping performance in *Saguinus midas* and the evolution of hand prehensility in primates. Pp. 131–144. In *Primate Locomotion: Recent Advances.* E. Strasser, J. Fleagle, A. Rosenberger, H. McHenry, Eds., New York, Plenum.

Leutenegger, W. 1980. Monogamy in callitrichids: A consequence of phyletic dwarfism? *Int. J. Primatol.* 1:95–98.

Lindsay, N.B.D. 1980. A report on a field study of Geoffroy's tamarin, *Saguinus geoffroyi.* Dodo 17:27–51.

Lopes, M.A., Ferrari, S.F. 1994. Foraging behavior in tamarin group (*Saguinus fuscicollis weddelli*) and interactions with marmosets (*Callithrix emiliae*). *Int. J. Primatol.* 15:373–388.

Maier, W., Alonso, C., Langguth, A. 1982. Field observations on *Callithrix jacchus jacchus L. Z. Saugetierkunde* 47:334–346.

Malaga, C. 1981. *Transcript of The First Annual* Saguinus mystax *Conference,* Iquitos, Peru. 13 July.

Martin, R.D., Rivers, J.R.W., Cowgill, U.M. 1976. Culturing mealworms as food for animals in captivity. *Int. Zoo Yrbk.* 16:63–70.

Martin, R.D. 1992. Goeldi and the dwarfs: the evolutionary biology of the small New World monkeys. *J. Hum. Evol.* 22:367–393.

Masataka, N. 1982. A field study on the vocalizations of Goeldi's monkeys (*Callimico goeldii*). *Primates* 23:206–219.

Mittermeier, R.A., Coimbra-Filho, A.F. 1981 Systematics: Species and subspecies. Pp. 29–109. In *Ecology and Behavior of Neotropical Primates, Vol. 1.* A.F. Coimbra-Filho and R.A. Mittermeier. Eds., Rio de Janeiro, Academia Brasileira de Ciências.

Mittermeier, R.A., van Roosmalen, M.G.M. 1981. Preliminary observations on habitat utilization and diet in eight Surinam monkeys. *Folia Primatol.* 36:1–39.

Moynihan, M. 1970. Some behavior patterns of platyrrhine monkeys, II. *Saguinus geoffroyi* and some other tamarins. *Smithsonian Contrib. Zool.* 28:1–77.

Moynihan, M. 1976a. *The New World Primates.* Princeton, Princeton University Press.

Moynihan, M. 1976b. Notes on the ecology and behavior of the pygmy marmoset (*Cebuella pygmaea*) Pp. 79–84. In *Neotropical Primates: Field Studies and Conservation.* R.W. Thorington Jr., P.G. Heltne, Eds., Washington, D.C., National Academy of Sciences.

Muskin, A. 1984. Preliminary observations on *Callithrix aurita* (Callitrichidae: Cebidae). Pp. 79–82. In *A Primatologia No Brasil.* M.T. de Mello, Ed., Brasilia, Sociedade Brasileira de Primatologia.

Napier, J.R., Napier, P.H. 1967. *A Handbook of Living Primates.* New York, Academic Press.

Napier, P.H. 1972. *Monkeys and Apes.* New York, Bantam Books.

Nash, L.T. 1983. Reproductive patterns in galagos (*Galago zanzibaricus* and *Galago garnettii*) in relation to climatic variability. *Am. J. Primatol.* 5:181–196.

Nash, L.T. 1986 Dietary, behavioral, and morphological aspects of gummivory in primates. *Yrbk. Phys. Anthropol.* 29:113–137.

Natori, M. 1986a. Interspecific relationships of *Callithrix* based on dental characters. *Primates* 27: 321–336.

Natori, M. 1986b. Phylogenetic relationships of marmosets (Calltirichidae). *Jinruigaku Zasshi/ J. Anthropol. Soc. Nippon.* 94:247.

Natori, M. 1990. Numerical analysis of the taxonomical status of *Callithrix kuhli* based on measurements of postcanine dentition. *Primates* 31:555–562.

Natorii, M., Shigehara, M. 1992. Interspecific differences in lower dentition among eastern Brazilian marmosets. *J. Mammal.* 73:688–671.

Neyman, P.F. 1977. Aspects of the ecology and social organization of free-ranging cotton-top tamarins *Saguinus oedipus* and the conservation status of the species. Pp. 39–71. In *The Biology and Conservation of the Callitrichidae.* D.G. Kleiman, Ed., Washington D.C., Smithsonian Insititution Press.

Nickle, D.A., Heymann, E.W. 1996. Predation on Orthoptera and other orders of insects by tamarin monkeys, *Saguinus mystax mystax* and *Saguinus fuscicollis nigrifrons* (Primates: Callitrichidae), in north-eastern Peru. *J. Zool. Lond.* 239:799–819.

Norconk, M.A. 1986. *Interaction Between Primates Species in a Near Tropical Forest: Mixed Species Troops of* Saguinas mystax *and* S. fuscicollis *(Callitrichidae)*. Ph.D. Thesis. University of California, Los Angeles.

Pack, K.S., Henry, O., Sabatier, D. 1999. The insectivorous-frugivorous diet of the golden-handed tamarin (*Saguinas midas midas*) in French Guiana. *Folia primatol.* 70:1–7.

Passamani, M. 1995 Field observation of a group of Geoffroy's marmosets mobbing a margay cat. *Folia primatol.* 64:163–166.

Passamani, M. 1998. Activity budget of Goeffroy's marmoset (*Callithrix geoffroyi*) in an Atlantic forest in Southeastern Brazil. *Am. J. Primatol.* 46:333–340.

Passos, F.C., Carvalho, C.T. de. 1991. Importancia de exsudatos na alimentacao do mico-leao preto, *Leontopithecus chrysopygus* (Callitrichidae, Primates). P. 392. In *Resumos. XVIII Congresso Brasileiro de Zoologia*. Salvasor, Universidad Federal da Bahia.

Patterson, B., Pascual, R. 1972. The fossil mammalian fauna of South America. Pp. 247–309. In *Evolution, Mammals and Southern Continents*. A. Keast, F. Erk, B. Glass, Eds., Albany, State University of New York Press.

Penny, N.D., Arias, J.R. 1982. *Insects of the Amazon Forest*. New York, Columbia University Press.

Peres, C.A. 1986a. Golden lion tamarin project. II. Ranging patterns and habitat selection in golden lion tamarins *Leontopithecus rosalia* (Linnaeus, 1766) (Callitrichidae: Primates). *Primatologia no Brasil* 2:223–233.

Peres, C.A. 1986b. Consequences of territorial defense in wild golden lion tamarins, *Leontopithecus rosalia. Primate Report* 14:234.

Peres, C.A. 1989a. Exudate-eating by wild golden lion tamarins, *Leontopithecus rosalia. Biotropica* 21:287–288.

Peres, C.A. 1989b. Costs and benefits of territorial defense in wild golden lion tamarins, *Leontopithecus rosalia. Beh. Ecol. Sociobiol.* 25:287–288.

Peres, C.A. 1991. Seed predation of *Cariana micrantha* (Lecythidaceae) by brown capuchin monkeys in central Amazonia. *Biotropica* 23:262–270.

Peres, C.A. 1993a. Anti-predation benefits in a mixed-species group of Amazonian tamarins. *Folia Primatol.* 61:61–76.

Peres, C.A. 1996 Food patch structure and plant resource partitioning in interspecific associations of Amazonian tamarins. *Int. J. Primatol.* 17:695–723.

Peres, C.A. 1997. Primate community structure at twenty western Amazonian flooded and unflooded forests. *J. Trop. Ecol.* 12:381–405.

Pook, A.G., and Pook, G. 1981. A field study of the socioecology of the Goeldi's monkey (*Callimico goeldii*) in northern Bolivia. *Folia Primatol.* 35:288–312.

Pook, A.G., Pook, G. 1982. Polyspecific association between *Saguinus fuscicollis, Saguinus labiatus, Callimico goeldii* and other primates in north-western Bolivia. *Folia Primatol.* 35:196–216.

Porter, C.A., Czelusniak, J., Schneider, H., Schneider, M.P.C., Sampaio, I., Goodman, M. 1997. Sequences of primate e-globin gene: implications for systematics of the marmosets and other New World primates. *Gene* 205:59–71.

Ramirez, M.F. 1989. *Feeding ecology and demography of the moustached tamarin, Saguinas mystax, in northeastern Peru.* Ph.D. Thesis. New York, City University of New York.

Ramirez, M.F., Freese, C.H., Revilla, J. 1977. Feeding ecology of the pygmy marmoset, *Cebuella pygmaea,* in northeastern Peru. Pp. 91–104. In *The Biology and Conservation of the Callitrichidae.* D.G. Kleiman, Ed., Washington D.C., Smithsonian Insititution Press.

Redican, W.K., Taub, D.M. 1981. Male parental care in monkeys and apes. Pp. 203–258. In *The Role of the Father in Child Development, Second Edition.* M.E. Lamb, Ed., New York, Wiley.

Robinson, C.H. 1980. *Basic Nutrition and Diet Therapy, Fourth edition.* New York, MacMillan.

Rosenberger, A.L. 1978. Loss of incisor enamel in marmosets. *J. Mammal.* 59:207–208.

Rosenberger, A.L. 1979. *Phylogeny, evolution and classification of New World monkeys (Platyrrhini, Primates).* Ph. D. Thesis. City University of New York.

Rosenberger, A.L. 1981. Systematics: the higher taxa. Pp. 9–27. In *Ecology and Behavior of Neotropical Primates, Vol. 1.* A.F. Coimbra-Filho and R.A. Mittermeier. Eds., Rio de Janeiro, Academia Brasileira de Ciências.

Rosenberger, A.L. 1992. Evolution of feeding niches in New World monkeys. *Am. J. Phys. Anthropol.* 88:525–562.

Rosenberger, A.L., Coimbra-Filho, A.F. 1984. Morphology, taxonomic status, and affinities of the lion tamarins *Leontopithecus* (Callitrichidae, Primates). *Folia Primatol.* 42: 149–179.

Rosenberger, A.L., Setoguchi, T., Shiguegara, N. 1990. The fossil record of callitrichine primates. *J. Hum. Evol.* 19:209–236.

Rosenberger, A.L., Stafford, B.J. 1994. Locomotion in captive *Leontopithecus* and *Callimico:* A multimedia study. *Am. J. Phys. Anthropol.* 94:379–394.

Rothe, H. 1975. Some aspects of sexuality and reproduction in groups of captive marmosets (*Callithrix jacchus*). *Z. Tierpsychol.* 37:255–273.

Rowe, N. 1996. *The Pictorial Guide to the Living Primates.* East Hampton, Pagonias Press.

Rylands, A.B. 1979. Observaçoes preliminares sobre o sagüi, *Callithrix humeralifer intermedeius intermedeius* (Hershkovitz, 1977) em Dardanelos, rio Aripuana, Mato Grosso. *Acta Amazonica* 9:589–602.

Rylands, A.B. 1981. Preliminary field observations on the marmoset, *Callithrix humeralifer intermedius* (Hershkovitz, 1977) at Dardanelos, rio Aripuana, Mato Grosso. *Primates* 22:46–59.

Rylands, A.B. 1982. *The behavior and ecology of three species of marmosets and tamarins (Callitrichidae, Primates) in Brazil.* Ph.D. Thesis. University of Cambridge, Cambridge.

Rylands, A.B. 1984a. Ecologia do mico leao, *Leontopithecus chrysomelas,* e o sagui, *Callithrix kuhlii,* na Bahia. *Resumos, XI Congresso Brasileiro de Zoologia, Belem,* pp. 292–293.

Rylands, A.B. 1984b. Exudate-eating and tree-gouging by marmosets (Callitrichidae, Primates). *Leeds Philos and Lit. Soc.* Pp. 155–168.

Rylands, A.B. 1986a. Ranging behavior and habitat preference of a wild marmoset group, *Callithrix humeralifer* (Callitrichidae, Primates). *J. Zool. London (A)* 210:489–415.

Rylands, A.B. 1986b. Infant-carrying in a wild marmoset group, *Callithrix humeralifer:* Evidence for a polyandrous mating system. Pp. 131–144 In *A Primatologia no Brasil, II,* M.T. de Mello, Ed,. Campinas, Sociedade Brasileira de Primatologia.

Rylands, A.B. 1987. Primate communities in Amazonian forests: their habitats and food resources. *Experientia* 43: 265–279.

Rylands, A.B. 1989. Sympatric Brazilian callitrichids: The black tufted-ear marmoset, *Callithrix kuhlii,* and the golden-headed lion tamarin, *Leontopithecus chrysomelus. J. Hum. Evol.* 18: 679–695.

Rylands, A.B. 1993. The ecology of the tamarins, *Leontopithecus:* some intrageneric differences and comparisons with other callitrichids. Pp. 296–313 In *Marmosets and Tamarins: Sytematics, Behavior, and Ecology.* A.B. Rylands, Ed., Oxford, Oxford University Press.

Rylands, A.B. 1996. Habitat and the evolution of social and reproductive behavior in Callitrichidae. *Am. J. Primatol.* 38:5–18.

Rylands, A.B., Coimbra-Filho, A.F., Mittermeier, R.A. 1993. Systematics, geographic distribution, and some notes on the conservation status of the Calltirichidae. Pp. 11–77. In *Marmosets and Tamarins: Systematics, Behavior, and Ecology.* A.B. Rylands, Ed., Oxford, Oxford University Press.

Rylands, A.B., de Faria, D.S. 1993. Habitats, feeding ecology and home range size in the genus *Callithrix.* Pp. 262–272. In *Marmosets and Tamarins: Systematics, Behavior, and Ecology.* A.B. Rylands, Ed., Oxford, Oxford University Press.

Saltzman, W., Schultz-Darkin, N.J., Abbott, D.H. 1997. Familial influences on ovulatory function in common marmosets (*Callithrix jaccus*). *Am. J. Primatol.* 41:159–177.

Sarich, V.M., Cronin, J.E. 1980. South American mammal molecular systematics, evolutionary clocks, and continental Drift. Pp. 399–421. In *Evolutionary Biology of the New World Monkeys and Continental Drift.* R.L. Ciochon, A.B. Chiarelli, Eds., New York, Plenum Press.

Savage, A., Giraldo, L.H., Soto, L.H., Snowdon, C.T. 1996. Demography, group composition, and dispersal in wild cotton-top tamarins (*Saguinus oedipus*) groups. *Am. J. Primatol.* 38:85–100.

Savage, A., Shideler, S.E., Soto, L.H., Causado, J., Ciraldo, L.H., Lasley, B.L., Snowdon, C.T. 1997. Reproductive events of wild cotton-top tamarins (*Saguinus oedipus*) in Colombia. *Am. J. Primatol.* 43:329–337.

Savage, A., Snowden, C.T. Giraldo, L.H., Soto, L.H. 1996. Parental care patterns and vigilance in wild cotton-top tamarins (*Saguinus oedipus*). Pp. 187–199. In *Adaptive Radiations of Neotropical Primates*. M.A. Norconk, A.L. Rosenberger, P.A. Garber, Eds., New York, Plenum Press.

Schneider, H., Rosenberger, A.L. 1996. Molecules, morphology, and platyrrhine systematics. Pp. 3–19. In *Adaptive Radiations of Neotropical Primates*. M.A. Norconk, A.L. Rosenberger, P.A. Garber, Eds., New York, Plenum Press.

Skutch, A.F. 1961. Helpers among birds. *Condor* 63:198–226.

Sleeper, B. 1997. *Primates: The Amazing World of Lemurs, Monkeys, and Apes*. San Francisco, Chronicle Books.

Smith, R.J., Jungers, W.L. 1997. Body mass in comparative primatology. *J. Hum. Evol.* 32:523–559.

Snowdon, C.T. and Soini, P. 1988. The tamarins, genus *Saguinus*. Pp. 223–298. In *Ecology and Behavior of Neotropical Primates, Vol. 2*. R.A. Mittermeier, A.F. Coimbra-Filho, G.A.B. da Fonseca, Eds., Washington, D.C., World Wildlife Fund.

Soini, P. 1982. Ecology and population dynamics of the pygmy marmoset, *Cebuella pygmaea*. *Folia Primatol.* 39:1–21.

Soini, P. 1987a. Ecology of the saddle-backed tamarin *Saguinus fuscicollis illigeri* on the Rio Pacaya, northeastern Peru. *Folia Primatol.* 49:11–32.

Soini, P. 1987b. *Ecology of Cebuella. Int. J. Primatol.* 8:437.

Soini, P. 1988. The pygmy marmoset, Genus *Cebuella*. Pp. 79–129. In *Ecology and Behavior of Neotropical Primates, Vol. 2*. R.A. Mittermeier, A.F. Coimbra-Filho, G.A.B. da Fonseca, Eds., Washington, D.C., World Wildlife Fund.

Soini, P. 1993. The ecology of the pygmy marmoset, *Cebuella pygmaea:* some comparasons with two sympatric tamarins. Pp. 257–261. In *Marmosets and Tamarins: Systematics, Behavior, and Ecology*. A.B. Rylands, Ed., Oxford, Oxford University Press.

Stacey, P.B. 1979. Kinship, promiscuity, and communal breeding in the acorn woodpecker. *Behav. Ecol. Sociobiol.* 6:53–66.

Stacey, P.B. 1982. Female promiscuity and male reproductive success in social birds and mammals. *Am. Nat.* 120:51–64.

Stallings, J.R. 1988. *Small mammal communities in an Eastern Brazilian park*. M.A. Thesis. University of Gainsville, Florida.

Stallings, J.R., Mittermeier, R.A. 1983. The black-tailed marmoset (*Callithrix argentata melanura*) recorded from Paraguay. *Am. J. Primatol.* 4:159–163.

Stevenson, M.F., Rylands, A.B. 1988. The marmoset monkeys, Genus *Callithrix*. Pp. 131–222. In *Ecology and Behavior of Neotropical Primates, Vol. 2*. R.A. Mittermeier, AF Coimbra-Filho G.A.B. da Fonseca, Eds., Washington, D.C. World Wildlife Fund.

Stevenson, M.F., Sutcliffe, A.G. 1978. Breeding a second generation of common marmosets *Callithrix jacchus jacchus. Int. Zoo Yrbk.* 18:109–114.

Sussman, R.W., Kinzey, W.G. 1984. The ecological role of the Callitrichidae: A review. *Am. J. Phys. Anthropol.* 64:419–444.

Sussman, R.W., Phillips-Conroy, J.E. 1995. A survey of the distribution and density of the primates of Guyana. *Int. J. Primatol.* 16: 761–791.

Szalay, F.S., Delson, E. 1979. *Evolutionary History of the Primates.* New York, Academic Press.

Takai, M., Anaya, F. 1996. New specimen of the oldest platyrrhine, *Bransiella boliviana* from Salla, Bolivia. *Am. J. Phys. Anthropol.* 99:301–317.

Terborgh, J. 1983a. *Five New World Primates: A Study in Comparative Ecology.* Princeton, Princeton University Press.

Terborgh, J. 1985. The ecology of Amazon primates. Pp. 284–304. In *Amazonia.* G.T. Prance, T.E. Lovejoy, Eds., New York, Pergamon Press.

Terborgh, J. 1986. Keystone plant resources in the tropical forest. Pp. 330–344. In *Conservation Biology.* M.E. Soule, Ed., Sunderland, MA, Sinauer.

Terborgh, J., Goldizen, A.W. 1985. On the mating system of the cooperatively breeding saddle-back tamarin (*Saguinus fuscicollis*). *Behav. Ecol. Sociobiol.* 16:293–299.

Terborgh, J., Stern, M. 1989. The surreptitious life of the saddle-backed tamarin. *Am. Sci.* 75:260–269.

Thorington, R.W., Jr. 1968. Observations of the tamarin, *Saguinus midas. Folia Primatol.* 9:95–98.

Tovar, N.V. 1994. Activity patterns of *Saguinus nigricollis hernandezi* at the Tinigua National Park, Colombia. *Field Studies of New World Monkeys, La Macarena, Colombia.* 9:23–31.

Uvarov, B. 1966. *Grasshoppers and Locusts: A Handbook of General Acridology, Vol. 1.* Cambridge, Cambridge University Press.

Waser, P.M., Wiley, R.H. 1980. Mechanisms and evolution of spacing in animals. Pp. 159–223. In *Handbook of Behavioral Neurobiology, Vol. 3: Social Behavior and Communication.* P. Marler, J.G. Vandenbergh, Eds., Plenum, New York.

Webb, S.D. 1978. A history of savanna vertebrates in the New World. Part II. South America and the great faunal interchange. *Ann. Rev. Ecol. Syst.* 9:393–426.

Wickler, W., Seibt, U. 1983. Monogamy: An ambiguous concept. Pp. 33–50. In *Mate Choice.* P. Bateson, Ed., Cambridge, Cambridge University Press.

Wilson, A.C. 1987. The Callitrichidae and Callimiconidae: Cooperatively breeding primates. Pp. 34–43. In *Primate Societies.* D.L. Cheney, R.M. Seyfarth, B. Smuts, T.T. Struhsaker, R.W. Wrangham, Eds., Chicago, University of Chicago Press.

Wilson, C.G. 1977. Gestation and reproduction in golden lion tamarins. Pp. 191–192 In *The Biology and Conservation of the Callitrichidae.* D.G. Kleiman, Ed., Washington D.C., Smithsonian Insititution Press.

Winter, M. 1978. Investigation of the sequence of tooth eruption in hand reared *Callithrix jacchus.* Pp. 109–124. In *Biology and Behavior of Marmosets.* H. Rothe, J.H. Wolters, J.P. Hearn, Eds., Gottingen, University of Gottingen Press.

Wislocki, G.B. 1939. Observations on twinning in marmosets. *Am. J. Anat.* 64:445–483.

Wright, P.C. 1981. The night monkeys, Genus Aotus. Pp. 211–240. In *Ecology and Behavior of Neotropical Primates, Vol. 1.* A.F. Coimbra-Filho, R.A. Mittermeier. Eds., Rio de Janeiro, Academia Brasileira de Ciências.

Yoneda, M. 1981. Ecological studies of *Saguinus fuscicollis* and *Saguinus labiatus* with reference to habitat segregation and height preference. *Kyoto University Overseas Research Reports of New World Monkeys* 2:43–50.

Yoneda, M. 1984a. Comparative studies on vertical separation, foraging behavior and traveling mode of saddle-backed tamarins (*Saguinus fuscicollis*) and red chested moustached tamarins (*Saguinus labiatus*) in northern Bolivia. *Primates* 25:414–442.

Yoneda, M. 1984b. Ecological study of the saddle-backed tamarin (*Saguinus fuscicollis*) in Northern Bolivia. *Primates* 25:1–12.

Zarrow, M.X., Gandelman, R., Denenberg, V.H.H. 1971. Prolactin: Is it an essential hormone for maternal behavior in the mammal. *Horm. Behav.* 2:243–354.

Zullo, J., Caine, N.G. 1988. The use of sentinels in captive groups of red-bellied tamarins. *Am. J. Primatol.* 14:455.

CHAPTER 3

Cebidae

INTRODUCTION

The relationships between the higher taxonomic groups of New World monkeys have not been determined precisely, and thus, there are a number of alternative classifications at the family and subfamily level (e.g., Cabrera 1958, Hershkovitz 1977, Rosenberger et al. 1991, Mittermeier et al. 1988, Ford and Davis 1992, Rylands 1995, Schneider and Rosenberger 1996). In this chapter and the next, I follow the classification presented by Fleagle (1999) because of its simplicity and convenience in relation to the behavior and ecology of these animals. Besides the Callitrichidae, this classification includes two families, four subfamilies, and eleven extant genera (see Volume I, Chapter 2). In this chapter, I focus on the Cebidae. In Chapter 4, I discuss the Atelidae. It is likely, however, that the Cebidae is not a monophyletic group. For example, a number of authors believe that *Saimiri* may be more closely related to the Callitrichidae than to *Cebus,* and that *Callicebus* may be linked with the Pithecinae. Discussion of alternative classifications can be found in Schneider and Rosenberger (1996), Fedigan et al. (1996a), and Kinzey (1997a).

The Cebidae and Atelidae range in size from around 1 kg (*Callicebus* and *Aotus*) to 15 kg (*Brachyteles*) (Tables 3-1, 4-1). The dental formula is 2:1:3:3/2:1:3:3, and all digits have flat nails. The tail is long (except in *Cacajao*) and prehensile in some genera. Normally, a single young is born who is carried by the mother from birth. These monkeys occur throughout the tropical forested regions of America, from southern Mexico to southeastern Brazil and northern Argentina. They are best represented in the Amazonian forests where as many as 22 monkey species can be found living sympatrically in some localities (Mittermeier and Coimbra-Filho 1977). Most genera have a wide distribution but a few are quite restricted in geographic range.

Subfamilies of the Cebidae are Cebinae and Aotinae. Cebinae is represented by two genera, *Cebus* (capuchin monkeys) and *Saimiri* (squirrel monkeys). *Cebus* includes four species: *C. albifrons, C. capucinus, C. olivaceus,* and *C. apella.* Some recognize a fifth species, *C. kaapori,* and other groups currently designated as subspecies may be separated as species when more data are available (Rylands 1995, Ford and Hobbs 1996). Capuchins are relatively small animals and have prehensile tails (Fig. 3-1). They have a wide geographic distribution in Central and South America (Fig. 3-2). *C. capucinus* is the only species that occurs in Central America, ranging from Belize to northern Colombia. *C. olivaceus* and *C. albifrons* are found in northern South America, but the latter species has a larger geographical range and occurs to the west of the range of *C. olivaceus. C. albifrons* inhabits a vast area of the upper Amazon basin, extending south to northern Bolivia. The above three species are allopatric. The fourth species of capuchins, *C. apella,* has the largest range of any New World monkey, occurring from extreme northern South America to northern Argentina. It is sympatric with *C. olivaceus* and especially *C. albifrons* over large areas.

The classification of *Saimiri* has been the subject of recent revision using data from pelage variation, geographic distribution, biochemistry, chromosomes, skull and dentition, and behavior (Costello et al. 1993, Fedigan et al. 1996a, Boinski and Cropp 1999, Boinski 1999a). Three species are recognized: *S. sciureus* and *S. boliviensis* in South America and *S. oerstedii* in Central America. Unpublished molecular data indicate that another species, *S. ustus,* also may exist in South America (Boinski 1999a). Squirrel monkeys are smaller than capuchins (Table 3-1) and do not have prehensile tails (Fig. 3-3). *S. oerstedii* is widely distributed from western Panama to southern Costa Rica. The distribution of South American species is illustrated in Fig. 3-4.

The subfamily Aotinae includes *Aotus* and *Callicebus.* As with many South American primate taxa, work is currently in progress on the classification of *Aotus* (Hershkovitz 1983, Mittermeier et al. 1988, Kinzey 1997a). Here, I will use a simplified taxonomy including only one genus and species, *A. trivirgatus. Aotus* is the only nocturnal anthropoid. It is about the same size as *Saimiri* and, like the squirrel monkey, does not have a prehensile tail (Fig. 3-5). The owl monkey has a wide distribution from Panama in Central America south to Argentina and Paraguay, and possibly in some parts of the Guianas (Fig. 3-6).

Figure 3-1 *Cebus* [Photo by R.W. Sussman]

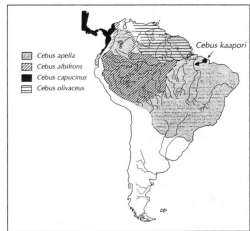

Figure 3-2 Map of distributions of species of *Cebus* [adapted from Ford & Hobbs 1996]

Table 3-1 Taxonomy Common Names, and Weight of Cebidae

Species	Common Name	Weight	N	Body Weights* Weight	N
Family: Cebidae					
Subfamily: Cebinae					
Cebus albifrons	White-fronted capuchin	3.18	26	2.29	15
C. capucinus	White-throated capuchin	3.68	16	2.54	10
C. olivaceus	Olive or Wedge-capped capuchin	3.29	28	2.52	10
C. apella	Tufted capuchin	3.65	51	2.52	38
Saimiri scuireus	S. American squirrel monkey	.779	11	.680	7
S. oerstedii	C. American squirrel monkey	.897	11	.680	7
Subfamily: Aotinae**					
Aotus trivirgatus	Night monkey, owl monkey	.813	20	.736	17
Callicebus moloch	Dusky titi monkey	1.02	10	.956	19
C. torquatus	Yellow-handed titi monkey	1.28	15	1.21	21
C. personatus	Masked titi monkey	1.27	5	1.38	7

* Smith & Jungers 1997 (see references therein)
** simplified classification

Until recently, three species of *Callicebus* were recognized: *Callicebus moloch, C. torquatus,* and *C. personatus.* In 1990, Hershkovitz revised the taxonomy to include 13 species in four species groups: *C. torquatus* group, *C. moloch* group (which includes *C. personatus*), *C. donacophilus* group, and *C. modestus* group. Titi monkeys are small with long non-prehensile tails (Fig. 3-7). They are widely distributed in the Amazon basin, and *C. personatus* is found in the coastal forests of southeastern Brazil (Fig. 3-8). The geographic ranges of several species of the *C. moloch* group overlap with those of *C. torquatus* (Kinzey 1997a).

Figure 3-3 *Saimiri* [From Sleeper 1997]

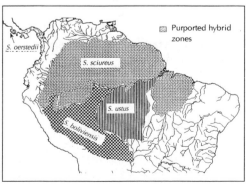

Figure 3-4 *Saimiri* distribution [From Boinski 1999a]

Figure 3-5 *Aotus* [Photo by R.W. Sussman]

Figure 3-6 *Aotus* distribution [From Wolfheim 1983]

Figure 3-7 *Callicebus* [From Rowe 1996]

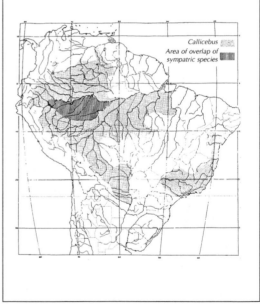

Figure 3-8 *Callicebus* distribution [From Kinzey 1997a]

THE ECOLOGY OF THE CEBIDAE

Among the Cebidae, certain species of *Cebus* and *Callicebus* are congeneric sympatrics. Otherwise, congeneric species are allopatric (Kinzey and Gentry 1979). From available evidence, it seems that among the cebids, most species within a genus fill similar ecological roles and, generally, can be considered ecological equivalents.

In the vast tropical rain forests of northern South America, referred to as Amazonia, many genera and species of ceboids are found to coexist. Not all of these taxa have been studied in the same forest, for the same length of time or intensity, nor with the same methodology. However, enough information exists to determine their general habitat preferences and to examine how they are able to coexist. In this chapter, I will draw from a number of studies carried out in different forests and compare and contrast the ecological role of each genus. Differences that are known to exist between allopatric species of the same genus will be noted.

Until the late 1960's, almost all systematic research of Neotropical primates had been conducted on Barro Colorado Island (BCI) (see Kinzey 1997b). This island is a biological reserve now maintained by the Smithsonian Institution (see Leigh et al. 1982). It was formed in 1914 during the building of the Panama Canal and was declared a biological reserve in 1923. It has an area of 155 km^2 and *Cebus capucinus, Aotus trivirgatus, Saguinus oedipus,* and *A. palliata* naturally occur on the island; *Ateles geoffroyi* was introduced in 1960 (Eisenberg and Kuehn 1966).

Only during the 1970's did information become available from other regions of Central and South America. By 1977, behavioral or ecological field research had only been conducted on 17% of the 64 then recognized species of New World primates, 23% had been surveyed or observed incidentally, and 60% remained unstudied (Baldwin et al. 1977). By the mid-1990's, all genera of Neotropical monkeys had been studied to a greater or lesser degree, and there has been an emergence of studies by native Latin American scientists. See Norconk et al. (1996), Fedigan et al. (1996a), Kinzey (1997a,b), and Boinski (1999a) for lists of recent field research.

THE COMPARATIVE ECOLOGY OF THE CEBINAE

Habitat Selection

Cebus and *Saimiri* are widely distributed in the Neotropics and are found in many kinds of forest habitat. In fact, they occupy a greater variety of habitats than any other New World monkey.

The geographic range of *Cebus* is second only to that of *Alouatta*. Capuchins inhabit virtually every type of forest in the Neotropics. *Cebus* is found in deciduous forests, in every type of humid forest, in seasonally flooded forests and dry forests, in swamp forests, in isolated forest patches, in areas of secondary growth, and also will cross open ground between forest fragments (Freese and Oppenheimer 1981). *C. apella* (Fig. 3-9a, the brown capuchin) is especially adaptable and has a larger geographic range than any other species of New World monkey (Eisenberg 1989). In parts of Amazonia, *C. apella* is sympatric with *C. albifrons* or *C. olivaceus*. *Saimiri* is also very adaptable and is generally found in the same types of forest as *Cebus*, although it is less likely to be found in primary forest and prefers secondary and successional stages of forest growth (Fig. 3-9b) (Fig. 3-10) (Sussman and Phillips-Conroy 1995, Kinzey 1997a, Wallace et al. 1998). Capuchins and squirrel monkeys often are seen in mixed-species associations (Terborgh 1983, Boinski 1989a, Podolsky 1990, Mendes Pontes 1997).

Mittermeier and van Roosmalan (1981) included three cebines in a quantitative study of the use of forest types by eight sympatric monkey species in Surinam. The species were *Saguinus midas, Pithecia pithecia, Chiropotes satanas, Saimiri sciureus, Alouatta seniculus, Ateles paniscus, Cebus apella,* and *Cebus nigrivittatus* (= *C. olivaceus*). All of the species, except *Saimiri*, were most frequently seen in

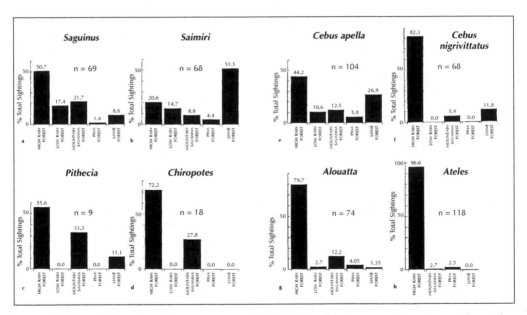

Figure 3-9b *Saimiri* [Photo by R.W. Sussman]

Figure 3-9a *Cebus apella* [From Sleeper 1997]

Figure 3-10 Utilization of the five forest types in the Voltzberg study area. **a** *Saguinus midas midas.* **b** *Saimiri sciureus.* **c** *Pithecia pithecia.* **d** *Chiropotes satanas chiropotes.* **e** *Cebus apella.* **f** *Cebus nigrivittatus.* **g** *Alouatta seniculus.* **h** *Ateles paniscus paniscus.* [From Mittermeier & van Roosmalen 1981]

high forest (Fig. 3-10). The squirrel monkey was found most often in liane forest. *Cebus apella* was the least specialized in habitat choice, followed closely by *Saimiri*. *C. olivaceus,* on the other hand, was highly dependent upon high rain forest, as was *Ateles*. The use of edge habitats by each of these species is illustrated in Fig.

3-11. Besides *Saguinus,* only *Saimiri* and *C. apella* used edge extensively, although *Pithecia* and *Alouatta* were seen in edges over 15% of the time.

Locomotion and Use of Forest Strata

Mittermeier and van Roosmalen (1981) also compared the use of forest strata between the above species. *Saimiri* was seen mainly in the understory (Fig. 3-12). However, squirrel monkeys can be found at all levels of the forest but are usually associated with densely foliated areas. The two *Cebus* species were quite similar to each other in their use of forest strata, using the lower to mid-canopy and understory.

Cebus and *Saimiri* utilize all levels of the forest, and *Cebus* will visit the ground to forage, drink, or occasionally during travel. For example, in Costa Rica, white faced capuchins

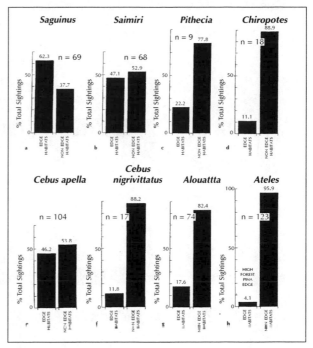

Figure 3-11 Utilization of edges in the Voltzberg study area. **a** *Saguinus midas midas.* **b** *Saimiri sciureus.* **c** *Pithecia pithecia.* **d** *Chiropotes satanas chiropotes.* **e** *Cebus apella apella.* **f** *Cebus nigrivittatus.* **g** *Alouatta seniculus.* **h** *Ateles paniscus paniscus.* [From Mittermeier & van Roosmalen 1981]

spent 2.5% of their time on the ground, with males using ground more frequently than females (Rose 1998). No South American monkey species can be considered terrestrial. *Saimiri* uses the understory more extensively than *Cebus apella* or *Cebus olivaceus,* and the two *Cebus* species spend more time in the middle and upper canopy in Surinam (Mittermeier and van Roosmalen 1981). However in Manu National Park, Peru, Terborgh (1983) found that crown diameter differentiated the behavior of the monkeys far better than did tree height or level. While feeding on fruit, *Saimiri* fed in trees with crowns of the largest diameter (mainly fig trees). While insect foraging, squirrel monkeys often used the understory, but more importantly, they foraged in densely foliated areas. *C. apella* generally utilized trees with small crown size, mainly because of this monkey's concerted use of palms (see below). *Cebus albifrons* was much like *Saimiri,* generally utilizing tall trees with crowns larger than 15 meters in diameter while eating fruit but coming lower in the canopy while eating insects.

Both capuchins and squirrel monkeys are mainly arboreal quadrupeds. *C. apella* uses more quadrupedal locomotion (86%) and less leaping and climbing (17%) than does *C. capucinus* (54% and 41%, respectively) (Gebo 1989, 1992). *Saimiri* locomotion also involves predominantly quadrupedal walking and running (Fleagle and Mittermeier 1980, Fleagle et al. 1981, Boinski 1989b). Fleagle et al. (1981) found that 55% of observed locomotor bouts were walking or running, 45% leaping, and

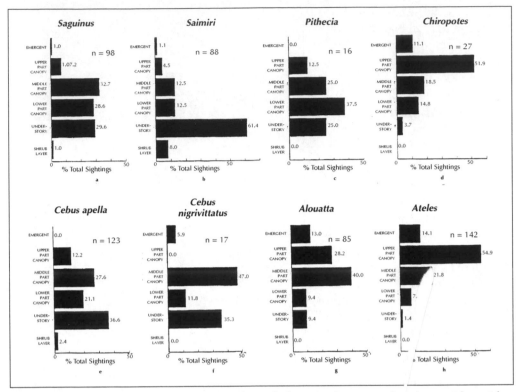

Figure 3-12 Utilization of forest strata in the Voltzberg study area. **a** *Saʒuinus midas midas.* **b** *Saimiri sciureus.* **c** *Pithecia pithecia.* **d** *Chiropotes satanas chiropotes.* **e** *Cebus apella apella.* **f** *Cebus nigrivittatus.* **g** *Alouatta seniculus.* **h** *Ateles paniscus paniscus.* [From Mittermeier & van Roosmalen 1981]

only 3% climbing. Squirrel monkeys are agile and are able to move through the smallest branches with dexterity and speed. The long nonprehensile tail is used mainly for balance (although infants can support their weight with their tails) (Fig. 3-13). Squirrel monkeys infrequently use suspensory postures, and usually only during feeding. The positional behavior of *Saimiri* is highly flexible, and this is related to its seasonal adaptability in foraging behavior (Boinski 1987a, 1989b, Kinzey 1997a).

Cebus monkeys have a prehensile tail, which evolved independently from that in the Atelinae (Rosenberger 1983). Overall, the tail is used in 36% of locomotor and postural activities and in 60% of foraging and feeding observations (Bergeson 1996, 1998). The rate of prehensile tail use is most common near the trunk and in the tree periphery. However, *Cebus* rarely suspends itself solely by the tail and uses its tail in high tension postures. It often uses an inverted bipedal suspensory posture (Fig. 3-14), most frequently when feeding on fruits, particularly palm fruits near the tree trunk. This posture also provides access to many other resources near the trunk, such as invertebrate fauna and vines. In the inverted bipedal posture the hands remain free. This plays a significant role in the destructive feeding habits of *Cebus,* allowing them to efficiently rip apart and search branches for prey (Bergeson 1996, 1998).

Figure 3-13 *Saimiri* using tail for balance. Tail is not prehensile. [Photo by R.W. Sussman]

Figure 3-14 *Cebus* using prehensile tail in a bipedal suspensory posture. [From Rowe 1996]

Diet

Cebus and *Saimiri* are mainly frugivorous in quantity of food ingested but include a relatively large proportion of insects in their diets. Insect consumption varies with environment and season. *Saimiri* spends 75–80% of its time foraging for insects (Fig. 3-15) (Mittermeier and van Roosmalan 1981, Terborgh 1983, Boinski 1988), and during the dry season, it resorts to complete insectivory for as much as a week at a time (Terborgh 1983, Janson and Boinski 1992). Squirrel monkeys are feisty little creatures, constantly on the move. They search for insects continuously—uncurling leaves, breaking twigs, and investigating foliage. Little time is spent manipulating the environment, rather a quick search is made—squirrel monkeys usually spend only 2–4 minutes in any one tree while insect foraging (Thorington 1968, Janson and Boinski 1992).

Prey species are typically slow or immobile and cryptic and are flushed from their hiding places. Caterpillars and various pupae are the most frequently eaten prey but some grasshoppers and other mobile prey are taken (Baldwin and Baldwin 1981, Janson and Boinski 1992). When an insect is uncovered, the monkeys quickly and agiley pounce on their prey. Caterpillars are often protected by stinging spines or unappetizing hairs and *Saimiri* uses skillful techniques in consuming them (Boinski and Fragaszy 1989). While foraging for insects, the individuals of a *Saimiri* group are spread over a wide area. Vertebrates, such as frogs, birds, lizards, and bats make up a very small fraction (< .30%) of the diet (Janson and Boinski 1992).

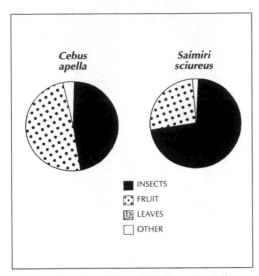

Figure 3-15 Time spent feeding on different foods by *C. apella* and *S. sciureus*. [Adapted from Fleagle 1999]

About 20% of the diet is made up of plant material, mainly soft, berry-like, ripe fruit. *Saimiri* generally feed on smaller and softer fruit than does *Cebus* (Janson and Boinski 1992). This is related to its smaller size and less strong mandibles. Flowers, buds, nuts, and nectar are eaten when the supply of fruit is low. Squirrel monkeys eat a highly diversified assortment of fruit, sampling many more species than are consumed in quantity. The diversity of fruit in the diet is related to the availability of preferred berry-like, ripe fruit. For example, in Costa Rica, *S. oerstedii* ate fruit from 45 species of 20 plant families, whereas Peruvian *S. sciureus* ate over 150 species from 42 families (Mitchell et al. 1991). Where available, large trees with wide crown diameters are the preferred site for fruit eating, and this corresponds with the squirrel monkey's predilection for figs. However, in more disturbed sites squirrel monkeys are adept at using smaller sized trees (Boinski 1988).

At the Manu site, figs accounted for over 50% of fruit eating in all months but one (Terborgh 1983, 1986). During the dry season, large trees in fruit are rare and figs become even more important, sometimes making up as much as 77% of the diet and over 90% of the fruit eaten. During this time, 80% of *Saimiri* food may come from 2–3 large, widely scattered trees. It is during this period of the dry season, when there are no figs available, that squirrel monkeys must spend from dawn to dusk foraging for insects. While fruit feeding, *Saimiri* groups are often in mixed species associations with groups of *Cebus*.

Like *Saimiri*, *Cebus* relies on ripe fruit for the bulk of its calories and on animal prey (mainly insects) for protein. Hladik and Hladik (1969) estimated that insects made up 20% of the dry weight of the capuchin diet. Actual time spent foraging is much greater, with at least half of the day at some sites spent manipulating substrates and ingesting prey (Fig. 3-15) (Terborgh 1983, Robinson 1986, Janson 1990a, Rose 1998). Capuchins move a great deal within a day, and foraging for insect prey generally takes place as individuals move between fruit trees (Robinson 1986). The proportion of fruit and insects in the diet varies with *Cebus* species, location, and season (Freese and Oppenheimer 1981, Robinson 1986, Chapman 1987, Chapman and Fedigan 1990, Janson and Boinski 1992, Miller 1996, Rose 1998), and with age and sex (Fragaszy and Boinsky 1995). Nevertheless, the importance of fruit in the diet of *Cebus* is evident. At several locations, ripe fruit comprises the top ranked item (46–81% of the diet) followed by animal foods (17–33%) and small amounts of vegetative matter such as pith and flowers (1–15%) (Oppenheimer 1968, Hladik and Hladik 1969, Robinson 1986, Chapman 1987, Rose 1998).

Cebus monkeys are very adaptable, and in marginal habitats and seasons of scarcity, their diets can become very specialized; they can become almost entirely frugivorous or insectivorous (Chapman 1987). Rose (1998) found that the time white-faced capuchins spent feeding on invertebrates in Costa Rica varied from 25% in the dry season to 50% in the wet season. In dry forests scarce in fruit, capuchins can survive almost entirely on bromiliads (Brown and Zunino 1990) or become seed predators (Peres 1991, Galetti and Pedroni 1994). This dietary flexibility corresponds with the wide geographic distribution of capuchins and with the number of habitats they are able to inhabit. Capuchins have exceptional manual dexterity and the ability to be extractive foragers, thus enabling them to use a number of foods that other species cannot access (Fragaszy et al. 1990, Janson and Boinski 1992, Rose 1998). Group tradition and individual variation in preferences also play a role in dietary flexibility (Chapman and Fedigan 1990, Rose pers. comm.).

Unlike squirrel monkeys, capuchins are slow, meticulous foragers, often spending over 20 minutes at one location (Fig. 3-16). They search diligently and strenuously—ripping off dead bark, rolling logs, breaking branches, splitting hollow vines and thorns, and searching through dead leaves and the dead bases of palm fronds (Thorington 1968, Freese and Oppenheimer 1981, Robinson 1986, Janson and Boinski 1992). While foraging for insects, group members are often spread over a wide area.

Capuchins eat a wide array of prey including ants, termites, wasps, cicadas, grasshoppers, spittle bugs, and some species of Coleoptera. Freese (1977) observed that larvae, especially of Lepidoptera (caterpillars), made up most of the wet season diet of *C. capucinus* and other insects were eaten more during the dry months at his site. The use of caterpillars is probably related to availability. Rose (1998), for example, found that they accounted for 25% of the feeding time in the wet season at Santa Rosa, but in some months, when they were very abundant, they accounted for over 50% of the feeding time. However, Janson and Boinski (1992) note that capuchin monkeys mainly eat social insects (e.g., ants, wasps, and termites) (Table 3-2). These insects, though individually small, live in colonies that con-

Figure 3-16 *Cebus* hammering on hard nut. [From Freese and Oppenheimer 1981]

tain a combined mass of protein much larger than individual prey items. Capuchins may be at the extreme upper size limit of non-specialized insectivores and, like virtually all strictly insectivorous mammals over 2 kg, must rely heavily on social insects as prey (Janson and Boinski 1992).

Cebus also eats a small proportion of vertebrate prey, accounting for .45–2.5% of its diet (Chapman and Fedigan 1990). This includes birds and bird eggs, lizards, squirrels, bats, and coatis (Fig. 3-17) (Oppenheimer 1968, Robinson 1986, Fedigan 1990, Janson and Boinski 1992, Rose 1997, 1998). There are also reports of *Cebus* monkeys killing and possibly eating titi monkeys (see Freese and Oppenheimer 1981). In some ways, capuchin predation on vertebrates resembles that observed in chimpanzees (see theoretical insert).

Table 3-2 Taxonomic Breakdown (%) of Prey Items Large Enough to be Positively Identified During Capture.

Prey taxon	*Cebus apella*	*Cebus albifrons*	*Saimiri sciureus*
Vertebrates	6	6	4
Frog	1	1	1
Lizards	2	4	3
Birds	2		1
Mammals	1		
Eggs	1	1	
Orthoptera	5	14	34
Lepidoptera	17	12	50
Larvae	4	6	30
Pupae	11	7	18
Adults	2		2
Hymenoptera	42	48	4
Ants	39	37	3
Wasps	3	11	1
Isoptera	8	5	1
Coleoptera	8	8	2
Larvae	6	7	
Adults	2	2	2
Miscellanea	14	7	5
Galls	1	1	2
Hemiptera	1	1	1
Millipedes		1	
Snails	12	5	2
Total no. of identified prey	178	178	175

[From Terborgh 1983]

At Manu, Terborgh (1983) found different patterns of foraging during the wet and dry seasons in sympatric *C. albifrons* and *C. apella*. Foraging also differed radically during periods of fruit scarcity (March–July). Generally, abundant fruit was by far the preferred resource, and both species of *Cebus* selected a wide variety of fruits. During this time of plenty, there was a great deal of overlap in the types of fruits eaten by both species of *Cebus* and by *Saimiri*. During dryer months when fruit was scarce, dietary choices diverged and the monkeys concentrated on a few species of plants (Table 3-3).

During the five months of the dry season, 63–97% of the diet of both species of *Cebus* was accounted for by figs and palms with a minor supplement of floral nectar. Just as with squirrel monkeys, figs were an extremely important dry season resource for these monkeys. It is the techniques they use to exploit palms, however, that distinguished the *Cebus* monkeys from sympatric species and from each other. During the critical period of fruit scarcity, *C. apella* became a specialist at exploiting a number of species of palms, using them in an impressive number of ways: for insect foraging, for the fleshy parts of the fruit, for the seeds, for the pith of petioles, for the apical meristem (heart of palm), and for immature flowers. At Manu, palms are uniformly and densely distributed, with the two principal types (*Astrocaryum* and *Scheelea*) having densities of 39 and 25 per hectare.

The nuts of *Astrocaryum* mature in April and are abundantly available during the May–June period of greatest fruit

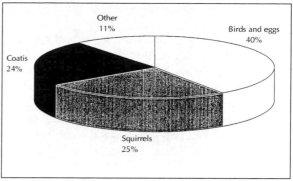

Figure 3-17 Types of vertebrate prey eaten by *C. capucinus* at Santa Rosa [From Rose 1997]

scarcity. Both *Cebus* species use palm nuts at this time, and nuts become the major food item in June. However, the two monkeys use different techniques to exploit palms. *C. apella* is relatively large, with strong jaw muscles, and simply crushes the hard intact nut with a single bite; although it may sometimes soften the outer shell by banging the nut against a trunk (Struhsaker and Leyland 1977). *C. apella* searches for nuts in the trees and ferrets them out of the crevices. Although heaps of these nuts are available on the ground, *C. apella* does not utilize them, probably because they are parasitized by bruchid beetles.

C. albifrons is not able to crush the intact nut and must depend on this parasite in order to utilize the nuts. For this monkey, opening an *Astrocaryum* nut requires strategy and persistence. Most nuts found on the ground are infected by the beetles; therefore, only those already opened but not completely eaten are worthwhile to this capuchin. Thus, *C. albifrons* spends long hours during June on the ground trying to find a suitable nut, often rejecting 20 or more in the process. The selection process is diligent; first a smell, then a bite or tap against a branch or another nut to test for hardness, then if the nut passes these tests, the monkey carries it to a low branch for opening. There it bashes the nut vigorously against the branch

**Table 3-3 Differential Use of Food Resources
During the Early Dry Season (May–July).**

Species	Early Dry Season Feeding Habits
Cebus apella	Heavy use of *Scheelea* and intact *Astrocaryum* nuts, supplemented with pith, meristmeatic tissue of palms, and figs when available.
Cebus albifrons	Concentrated feasting on figs when available, alternating with laborious exploitation of bruchid-infested *Astrocaryum* nuts.
Saimiri sciureus	Concentrated feasting on figs when available, alternating with periods of pure insectivory.
Saguinus imperator	Exploitation of a sequence of resources that are too diffuse to be of major significance to larger monkeys: *Celtis iguanea* (April–August). *Combretum assimili* (July, early August), *Quararibea cordata* (August).

[From Terborgh 1993]

or another nut and begins to bite it with its premolars—if unsuccessful, the whole process begins again.

During June, *C. albifrons* spends three times longer feeding on these nuts per day than *C. apella* (130 minutes/day vs. 45 minutes/day), spending 5–10 minutes for each successfully opened nut and often getting only a half eaten endosperm for its trouble. Because of this, when figs are available, they are the most preferred food of *C. albifrons*. *Astrocaryum* nuts are a reliable resource, but because of the difficulty in exploiting them, they are a last resort for this monkey. However, the size and strength of *C. apella* allows it to utilize the products of palms with relative ease, and it has much less difficulty during the dry months (Terborgh 1983, Janson 1986a,b).

As do many other primates, *Cebus* monkeys modify the reproductive success of many trees by acting as pollinators and especially seed dispersal agents. The seeds are dispersed away from the parental tree. This decreases seed predation, increases spread of the species to new sites, and helps accelerate gene flow. The most important means of dispersal by monkeys is the ingestion of seeds and defecation of the intact seed at some distant spot (a process termed 'endozoochory') (see articles in Lambert and Garber 1998). Hladik and Hladik (1969) found that the seeds of a number of plants eaten by capuchins had higher germination rates and/or germinated earlier than non-ingested seeds. *Cebus* is also a pollination agent for some species of plants. Although capuchins are destructive to some flowers, others are not destroyed. *Cebus* has been observed pollinating at least three genera of plants: *Ochroma* (Oppenheimer 1968, 1977), *Combretum* (Prance 1980, Janson et al. 1981), and *Maibea* (de Assumpção 1981).

Oppenheimer (1977) observed three major types of insect infestations at BCI: defoliation of certain species of large canopy trees by caterpillars, removal of sap from understory trees by spittle bugs, and destruction of seeds by grubs. Capuchins harvest all of these insects in intense feeding bouts and greatly reduce insect populations. They thereby reduce the amount of damage done to vegetation. Other animals on BCI also help control insect populations but, Oppenheimer believes, to a smaller extent than do capuchins.

Cycles of Activity

As stated earlier, there is a relationship between body size and amount of time spent eating insect or plant material. A relationship also exists between these two factors and the amount of time needed to procure and digest food and to rest. Because of the limited number of insects an animal can capture in a given amount of time, assimilation rates, and the small size of insects, obligate insectivores are necessarily small. Among birds, the maximum size is around 200 g (Terborgh 1980) and among mammals slightly larger (Charles-Dominique 1975, Terborgh 1983).

Larger forms are omnivorous, include vertebrate prey in their diets, and/or feed on social insects, in which the unit of prey is not the individual but the colony. Most primates are omnivores (Harding and Teleki 1981, Terborgh 1983, Sussman 1987, Martin 1990), and generally, as body size increases the proportion of insects in the diet decreases and that of plant material increases (cf. Kay 1984, Harvey et al. 1987, Janson and Boinski 1992). Insects are relatively easy to digest but difficult to find and capture, whereas plant material, especially leaves, can be ingested at a more rapid rate than it can be processed. Thus, we would expect insect eating primates to be relatively small and to spend a great deal of time foraging and less time resting. *Saimiri* and *Cebus* fit these expectations, spending 70–80+% of the time travelling and feeding and from 20–25% resting and in social activity, including vigilance behavior (Fig. 3-18) (Freese and Oppenheimer 1981, Terborgh 1983, Robinson 1986, Mitchell 1990, Rose 1998).

Just as overall activity is constrained by body size and diet, so is the daily cycle of activity. Insect food is easy to digest but comes in small "packets." Primates depending on these resources alternate short periods of foraging and feeding with short rest periods. *Cebus* and *Saimiri* feed on fruit immediately upon leaving the night sleeping area and then shift to insect foraging (though some fruit is also taken during this time) (Fig. 3-19). Foraging for insects continues, interspersed with periods of rest, during the middle portion of the day. Late in the afternoon, at some sites, there is another peak of fruit feeding just before the animals retire for the night. There is a tendency for resting to peak in mid-day when ambient temperatures are high, but under conditions of food scarcity, midday rest periods are not observed (Baldwin and Baldwin 1972, 1981, Freese and Oppenheimer 1981, Terborgh 1983, Robinson 1984a, Rose 1998).

The patterns described above are complicated by a number of cyclical factors that occur throughout the year, such as seasonal changes in availability and quantity of resources, seasonality of births, cycles of day length, and seasonal patterns of rainfall and temperature (see for example Robinson 1984a). However, seasonal deviations from the above patterns of activity seem to result in only minor variations on the patterns necessitated by body size and dietary mode (see Gaulin and Gaulin 1982, Terborgh 1983, Robinson 1986).

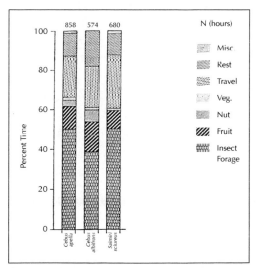

Figure 3-18 Activity budgets of *C. apella, C. albifrons* and *S. sciureus* at Manu National Park, averaged over all samples. Numbers at top of columns are the total contact hours for each species. The miscellaneous category includes grooming, play, intraspecific aggression, sexual behavior, and territorial activity. [From Terborgh 1983]

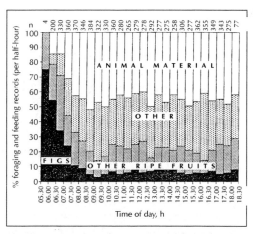

Figure 3-19 Diurnal variation in diet of *Cebus* lumping all foraging records taken during systematic sampling between November 1977 and December 1978. 'Other' refers to other plant material or unidentified objects. n = Number of foraging records, in which a capture was noted, in each half-hour. [From Robinson 1986]

Predation

Birds of prey are the most common predators of the arboreal Neotropical primates, and the smaller primates are exposed to a greater amount of danger than larger ones (Hart 2000). Only the largest raptors, such as the harpy eagle (4000–4500 g), can be of any danger to large monkeys (Fig. 3-20). Terborgh (1983) suggests that aerial predators constitute the only serious daytime threat to Neotropical arboreal monkeys, but there are a number of reports of predation on these monkeys by other predators. Night sleeping sites are selected to minimize the chances of surprise attack by nocturnal predators.

Figure 3-20 The harpy eagle—a major predator of monkeys. [Photo by R.W. Sussman]

Saimiri is among the smallest of the cebids and yet, because these monkeys are constantly active, they are conspicuous to aerial predators and not always alert to them. They give alarm calls to most medium to large flying predatory birds and have been observed being preyed upon by several raptors (Boinski 1986, Mitchell 1990, Boinksi in press). In fact, troops in Costa Rica and Peru were subject to a diurnal predator attack every 6–7 days. Five confirmed predations by raptors were observed in Costa Rica and four in Peru (Mitchell et al. 1991). Squirrel monkeys mob and vocalize at dogs, snakes, tayras, and cats (Freese and Oppenheimer 1981) and are

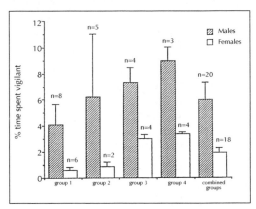

Figure 3-21 Time spent in vigilant behavior by male and female *C. capucinus*. [From Rose 1994a]

preyed upon by tayras (Galef et al. 1976), ocelots (Mitchell 1990), and larger cats (Emmons 1987). Predator protection is probably afforded by living in large groups and in mixed-species groups especially with *Cebus*.

Cebus monkeys have a well-developed predator alarm system, and the alpha males spend a great deal of time scanning the environment (Fig. 3-21) (see below). The alarm bark of capuchins is quite distinct and immediately responded to by conspecifics as well as other species of monkey and also birds. Capuchins are larger than squirrel monkeys and are probably predated upon by fewer species of raptor. However, in Peru, Terborgh (1983) observed two unsuccessful attacks on *Cebus* by harpy eagles, and Eason (1989) observed attacks on mixed species groups of *Cebus* and *Saimiri.* In a study of harpy eagles in Guyana, *Cebus* was the second most common prey in nest remains and by far the most common monkey species in this eagles' diet, others being *Alouatta, Pithecia,* and *Chiropotes* (Rettig 1978, see also Fowler and Cope 1964). An average of one capuchin was caught every 25 days and there was no selection by age of the monkeys. Chapman (1986) reports a capuchin being eaten by a boa constrictor.

Capuchins have been observed giving alarm reactions to ocelots, boa constrictors, and caimans (Freese and Oppenheimer 1981). In fact, Rose (1997, 1998) reports that they initially respond very quickly to anything that might be a predator and give alarm calls to an enormous range of both potentially dangerous and "harmless" things. However, they are normally able to assess the level of danger in short order, and usually only persist to give alarm calls and mob animals that are potential predators.

Social Structure and Organization

Group size in *Saimiri* varies in different areas and seems to correlate with forest condition. Groups of 10–300+ animals have been reported (Table 3-4), but those over 100 represent temporarily combined groups (Baldwin and Baldwin 1981, Terborgh 1983, Mitchell et al. 1991). Most commonly, groups average between 20–75 individuals (Boinski 1986, Robinson and Janson 1987, Boinski in press), which are the largest groups of any Neotropical primate (Kinzey 1997a). Larger groups are more common in large, undisturbed forests and smaller ones in smaller, disturbed areas and where squirrel monkeys are hunted (Baldwin and Baldwin 1981). Large group size may be an anti-predator adaptation for this small monkey (Boinski 1988). *Saimiri* groups are multi-male in structure.

Groups are cohesive, with members usually in close proximity, (within 50–100 meters) sometimes climbing over one another or sitting close together (Baldwin and Baldwin 1972, Klein and Klein 1975). This is especially so when the group is moving or at a concentrated food source. However, sometimes individuals can be widely dispersed (Boinski 1991), especially when foraging for insects. Squirrel monkeys use a specialized vocalization to coordinate group movements (Boinski 1991, 1996). While insect foraging, the monkeys are constantly moving and changing positions and may be facilitating one another by flushing insect prey (Thorington 1968, Klein and Klein 1975). Groups are often followed by small hawks and other birds, which catch insects the monkeys stir up while foraging (Thorington 1968, Janson 1975, Boinski and Scott 1988).

Different types of social organization have been described by various researchers. In early short-term studies, a sexually segregated pattern of social organization was reported in Bolivian and Peruvian populations (Baldwin 1968, 1971, Baldwin and Baldwin 1972, 1981, Coe and Rosenblum 1974, Strayer et al. 1975). Squirrel monkeys from Guyana, on the other hand, were not reported to segregate by sex (Mendoza et al. 1978). In these groups, adult males were the most cohesive group members, and other animals oriented towards them. The social organization was sexually integrated. In Peruvian and Bolivian groups, males were often displaced and chased by females, and females were more responsible for the nature of group structure than were the males. The opposite was reported in Guyanese *Saimiri* (Mendoza et al. 1978).

More recent, long-term studies have resulted in a different and more detailed characterization of squirrel monkey social organization. Indeed, as stated by Boinski (1999a, 1999b), morphological similarities between the various populations of squirrel monkeys appear to mask considerable divergence in social organization. In the Central American squirrel monkeys that have been studied, females have

Table 3-4 Group Size, Home and Day Range Size, and Population Density in Capuchins and Squirrel Monkeys

Species & Site	Avg. Group Size (N)	Home Range (HA)	Day Range (meters)	Pop. Density (#/km)	Source
Saimiri oerstedii					
Costa Rica	35–65	200	—	36	Mitchell et al. 1991;
Peru	45–75	250–500	—	6	Boinsky 1999
Panama	23	—	2500–4200	130	Baldwin & Baldwin 1981
S. sciureus					
Peru	35	>250	—	50	Terborgh 1983
Colombia	25–35	65–130	—	50–80	Klein & Klein 1975
Colombia	42–54	33–44	700–2300	175	Bailey (in Robinson & Janson 1987)
Cebus albifrons					
Colombia	35	115	—	—	Defler 1979
Peru	15	>150	1500–2000	24	Terborgh 1983
C. capucinus		60–300	900–4300		Fedigan et al. 1996b
Santa Rosa (1983–92)	18 (18)	X = 147	X = 3000	7.5	Rose 1998
BCI	15 (2)	80	—	—	Freese & Oppenheimer 1981
"	20 (4)	—	—	—	Mitchell 1990
C. olivaceus					
Venezuela	20 (10)	257	2100	40	Robinson 1988
C. apella					
Colombia	16	>260	1000–3000	—	Izawa 1980
Peru	10	80	2100	40	Terborgh 1983

egalitarian and undifferentiated social interactions, show no dominance hierarchies, and are not spatially aggregated (except for mother and young offspring). Furthermore, females transfer between groups (Boinski 1987a,b,c, 1989, 1999a, 1999b, Mitchell et al. 1991, Boinski and Mitchell 1994). Males, on the other hand, maintain close social and spatial associations with their birth cohort but not with females and infants (Boinski 1994a, Boinski and Mitchell 1994). There is little agonism within groups, and males show high levels of predator vigilance and deterrence behavior (Boinski 1994a, in press). Reproductively mature males also cooperate in mobbing females during the mating season, temporarily immobilizing them while taking turns sniffing their genitals (Boinski 1988). Most males maintain residence in their natal group with their birth cohort, eventually attaining reproductive positions. In some cases, however, male age cohorts leave the group and together usurp the reproductive cohort in another group. Boinski and Mitchell (1994) characterize this as among the most egalitarian primate social organizations, especially among large, multimale groups.

Peruvian *S. boliviensis* has a different type of social organization. In groups studied by Terborgh (1983) and Mitchell (1990, Mitchell et al. 1991, Boinski 1999a, 1999b) females form stable, probably kin-based, alliances and coalitions and a female dominance hierarchy. Females also are philopatric in these groups. At the age of 4–5 years, males migrate, first into all-male bachelor groups and then into mixed-sex groups. Male-male relations are agonistic, and adult males form a clear hierarchy. Adult males continue to migrate every one to two years. All adult females in these groups are dominant to males, and males are harassed and kept at the group periphery by adult females. Unlike Costa Rican males, these males do not exhibit anti-predator vigilance or deterrence.

Finally, in a recently initiated field study of Surinamese *S. sciureus,* Boinski (1999a, 1999b) has documented that these monkeys exhibit a markedly different social behavior from Costa Rican and Peruvian squirrel monkeys. In this population, both sexes form a single linear dominance hierarchy, with most males dominant to females. Males form coalitions and are moderately closely affiliated, whereas females do not. (Other differences between these three species are listed in Table 3-5.)

Boinksi and Mitchell (1994) and Boinski (1999a, 1999b) argue that differences between Costa Rican, Peruvian, and Surinam male and female affiliative behavioral patterns are, to some degree, related to the different dispersal patterns of males and females. As in many other primates and other mammals, stronger affiliative patterns usually develop between individuals of the sex that is philopatric. The difference between the pattern of having more general aggression and female hierarchies in *S. saimiri* and a contrasting egalitarian social structure and lack of agonism in *S. oerstedii* is hypothesized to relate to the distribution of resources in the sites in which the species were studied (Mitchell et al. 1991, Boinski 1996). In the Peruvian site, food patches are discrete, of high quality, and defensible; whereas in Costa Rica, patches are tiny and probably too small to be worth defending. In Surinam, Boinski (in press) predicts that the dense clusters of the palms and other fruits that the squirrel monkeys eat lead to food competition between pairs of

Table 3-5 Summary of Life History and Phylogenetically-Informative (Genetically-based) Traits for the Three *Saimiri* Species and the Outgroup *Cebus apella*. For Each Trait Separately, the Pair of Squirrel Monkey Species for Which Closer Affinities Can Be Assigned Are Indicated in Bold Face.

Trait	*S. oerstedii*	*S. sciureus*	*S. boliviensis*	*Cebus apella*
GENERAL LIFE HISTORY				
Body weight (g)	**F < 600; M 750**	**F 635; M 740**	F 751; M 992	F 2,700; M 3,500
Group size	40–65	15–50	45–75	10–16
Typical fruit patch harvested	small, low density	small, extremely dense	large, moderate density	small, extremely dense
Aggressive within-group fruit competition (events/hr)	extremely low (0.004)	extremely high (1.50)	high (0.286)	extremely high (exact rates not available)

continued on next page

Table 3-5 *continued*

Trait	*S. oerstedii*	*S. sciureus*	*S. boliviensis*	*Cebus apella*
ADULT SOCIAL BEHAVIOR IN CAPTIVITY				
Social aggression by females	**rare**	**uncommon**	extremely common	common
Social aggression by males	rare	**common**	**common**	common
Male-female social behavior	egalitarian and **males integrated into group**	males dominant, **males integrated into group**	females dominant, spatially segregated to the group periphery by intense aggression from females	males dominant and **integrated into group**
ADULT SOCIAL BEHAVIOR IN WILD				
Female-female social aggression	**rare**	**uncommon**	extremely common	common
Female-female affiliative coalitions	**not detected**	**not detected**	present, kin based	present, kin based
Male-male social aggression	rare	**common**	**common**	common
Male-male affiliative coalitions	present	present	present	present[b]
Male-female social relations	egalitarian and **males integrated into troop**	males dominant, **males integrated into troop**	females dominant, males excluded by females and peripheral to troop	males dominant and integrated and into troop
Female troop residence	**emigrate before first mating season**	**probably emigrate**[a]	natal	natal
Male troop residence	**usually natal**	**probably natal**[a]	emigrate with coalition members to all-male troop, later attempt to transfer into mixed-sex troop	emigrate
Maled defense of immature troop members from predators	**vigorous**	**vigorous**	absent	vigorous
All-male troops	**absent**	**absent**	present	absent
Intratroop birth synchrony	**2 weeks**	**< 1 week**	2 months	4 months

[a] Field work in 1995 and 1996 by Boinski strongly indicates that in Surinam *S. sciureus* males are philopatric and females emigrate; these observations are now being replicated in a long-term field study

[b] Although *C. apella* in Peru are not reported to exhibit male-male social bonds, male *C. apella* in Argentina do form affiliative coalitions (M. Di Bitetti, pers. comm.)

[From Boinski 1999]

individuals and determine access only to a specific clump of fruit and not the entire tree crown (Fig. 3-22).

Thus, *S. saimiri* and *S. boliviensis* group members are expected to be involved in direct feeding competition with one another, though differently within the two species, whereas *S. oerstedi* are not. However, it remains to be seen whether these differences are species-specific or directly related to ecological variables since populations of the same species in differing habitats have not been studied. Boinski (1999a, 1999b) believes that ecological distinctions and differences are consistent throughout the ranges of the three species. This could be one of the better models of the relationships between ecology and social structure, and future studies should be designed to test these relationships.

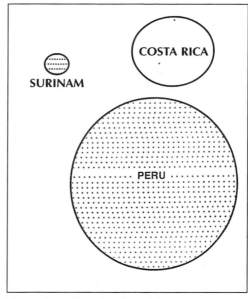

Figure 3-22 Distribution of food resources in three areas in which different species of squirrel monkeys are found. [From Boinski 1999b]

Breeding and births are seasonal among *Saimiri,* seldom exceeding two months in duration (Baldwin and Baldwin 1981, Boinski 1987c, 1992). The annual mating season usually occurs during the dry season (Harrison 1973, Fleming 1973, Baldwin and Baldwin 1981). During mating season, adult males become spermatogenic, more socially active, and highly excitable. In some populations, they gain weight (at least 20% of body weight) which produces a "fatted" appearance in the upper torso, arms, and shoulders (Fig. 3-23) (Dumond 1968, Kinzey 1997a). However, this is not a necessary condition for mating to occur (Baldwin 1970).

In Costa Rica, sexual receptivity in females was synchronized, with each female being receptive for one or two days each season (Boinski 1987b,c, 1992). Most females give birth every year. This is the most seasonally restricted reproductive cycle of any Neotropical primate (Boinski 1987c). While receptive, females, often several at a time, search out certain males with which to mate, first choosing the largest of the fatted males. There is no competition for females by males, and mate selection appears to be mainly a female prerogative. Smaller males in Boinski's study groups only had opportunities to mate when larger ones became exhausted and rejected female solicitations. How this pattern

Figure 3-23 Fatted squirrel monkey male. [Photo by S. Boinski]

coincides with male mobbing of receptive females (Boinski 1988) remains to be explained.

Boinski (1987b, 1992) speculates that synchrony of mating and birth is related to high predation pressure and the increased vigilance when several mothers are present. The males that become most enlarged are usually those that have lived in the group for long periods, are consistently vigilant throughout the year, and are the most likely to intervene against predators. In *S. sciureus* females, birth synchrony was not pronounced and females give birth every other year (Mitchell 1990). It appears that predation pressure is not as great on this population (Boinski 1999a).

Gestation has been estimated at 145–182 days (Baldwin and Baldwin 1981, Boinski 1987c). Females give birth to a single infant; twinning has not been reported in *Saimiri*. Infants first cling ventrally to the mother and at around two weeks move to her back. During weeks 5–7, the infant begins to leave the mother to explore the environment. From 2–4 months, it becomes more independent, entering into peer group play. Infants are usually weaned at around six months of age (Baldwin and Baldwin 1981, Boinski 1992), but Mitchell (1990) reports that weaning did not take place until 18 months in her Peruvian population. Adult size is reached at 16–24 months. However, females are considered fully adult at around 2.5 years of age and males at around 4–5.5 years (Baldwin and Baldwin 1981).

Squirrel monkeys have a complex set of communicative signals involving postural displays and a number of distinct vocalizations. The most common nonverbal signals are the urine-washing display, which may indicate sexual condition, and the genital display, which is used in dominance interactions (Fig. 3-24). Specific vocalizations are important for communicating a number of messages. For example, the "chuck" vocalization is used to facilitate cohesion among widely dispersed group members. It also provides information on the caller's identification and specific foraging activity (Boinski and Mitchell 1992, Boinski 1996). Allogrooming is uncommon in these monkeys. Communicative behavior is described in greater detail in Baldwin and Baldwin (1981), Boinski and Mitchell (1995), and Boinski (1996).

As in *Saimiri,* Cebus lives in multimale groups but group size is generally small. Groups are usually between 6–35 individuals, with *C. apella* forming slightly smaller groups (Table 3-4) (Fedigan et al. 1985, 1996a, Massey 1987, Robinson and Janson 1987). Just as in squirrel monkeys, capuchin groups may intermingle in some contexts (Hernandez-Camacho and Cooper 1976, Terborgh 1983). In those groups censused, females outnumber males, and there is an equal number of young and adult animals. Groups are cohesive; however, since insect foraging is a long, concentrated, and

Figure 3-24 Squirrel monkey urine marking. [From Rowe 1996]

an individual activity, and since most feeding trees are small, individuals are often widely scattered when foraging. They are frequently 50–100 meters apart for hours at a time and congregate only at larger trees (Thorington 1968, Oppenheimer 1968, Phillips 1995, Rose 1998). When dispersed, group members use frequent vocalizations to maintain contact (Boinski 1993, Boinski and Campbell 1995, Phillips 1995).

Changes in group membership are common, although there seems to be a core of individuals that remain in the group for relatively long periods of time. Generally, males disperse from their natal group and females are philopatric (Freese and Oppenheimer 1981, Robinson and Janson 1987, Izawa 1992, Fedigan 1993). However, females split-off and begin new groups (Oppenheimer 1969, Moore 1984, Izawa 1992), and some females have been observed to transfer from one group to another. In fact, this may be more common than generally thought (Rose 1998, Manson et al. 1999).

Probably associated with female philopatry, females form affiliations with one another and groom, interact, and sit together more frequently than do males; female affiliations appear to be based on matrilineal kinship (Fig. 3-25) (O'Brien 1990, 1991, 1993, Fedigan 1993, Izawa 1994, Perry 1996a). Males interact, agonistically and affiliatively, equally across both sexes. They are also more vigilant for potential predators, other groups, and for migrating males (Robinson 1981a, 1988, Terborgh 1983, Chapman 1986, Fragaszy 1986, 1990, De Ruiter 1986, van Schaik and Noordwijk 1989, Boinski 1993, Rose and Fedigan 1995, Perry 1997, Rose 1998). Females rarely take part in intergroup interactions or in group defense (Fedigan 1993, Perry 1996b, but see Rose 1994a). Fedigan (1993) suggests that females are more preoccupied with factors internal and males toward those external to the group.

Cebus groups have relatively stable dominance hierarchies (Robinson and Janson 1987, Perry 1997, 1998) that may be dependent upon matrilineal kinship (O'Brien 1993, Fedigan 1993), a characteristic uncommon among Neotropical primates (Anderson 1996). In many populations, the alpha female, and sometimes other high ranking females, rank immediately below the alpha male, but other females generally rank below adult males (Robinson 1981a, Robinson and Janson 1987, Fedigan 1993).

There is variation in the male dominance structure in different populations or species of capuchins. In some populations of *C. capucinus*, *C. olivaceus*, and *C. apella*, the role of the alpha male is of a central nature; he often intervenes in agonistic bouts, protects the group against major threats, controls access to food resources, and is actively chosen by females for mating (Freese and

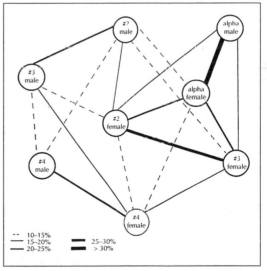

Figure 3-25 Patterns of association among members of a *Cebus* group. Thickness of lines indicates average percent of proximity scores within each dyad, adjusted to reflect the percentage of time that each male was present in the group. Proximity scores exceeding 10% only are included. [From Rose 1998]

Oppenheimer 1981, Bernstein 1966, Robinson 1981a, Janson 1984, 1986b, Robinson and Janson 1987, O'Brien 1993, Rose 1998). The dominant male is usually the largest and possibly oldest adult male in these groups. Robinson (1988) believes that most *C. olivaceus* groups have an age-graded social system, containing only one fully adult male and other subadult and non-breeding males.

In contrast, males in *C. capucinus* groups generally exhibit low agonism towards each other, and some actively affiliate with one another. Dominance relations are based on social strategies and not age and size, and females solicit and mate with lower-ranking males (Fedigan 1993). This form of male dominance also may be found in *C. albifrons* (Janson 1986a,b), although there is greater cooperation and affiliation among *C. albifrons* than among *C. apella* males. Thus, in these two species, the social structure is multimale, and although there is an identifiable alpha male, he is not always conspicuously favored in social interactions with females nor the sole reproductively active male (Fedigan 1993, Perry 1997).

Rose (1998) describes the dominance interactions among *C. capucinus* in some detail. Female ranks are based on social strategies, whereas male ranks appear to be more related to age and, in particular, size. Alpha males are usually, though not always, the largest in the group. Alpha males also are usually prime adult males, with older and younger (subadult) males being lower ranking. Dominant males tend to reinforce their rank through actual physical aggression to a greater extent than females. Support from others is probably important for both sexes but more so for females; a very young or old, decrepit female can be high ranking if she has social support. Alliances and coalitions are common, especially among females. Ranks for both sexes are quite stable, but demographic change can create temporary upheaval (Rose 1998, Manson et al. 1999).

Social interactions between adults mostly involve grooming (Freese and Oppenheimer 1981), which clearly serves a social as well as a hygienic role (O'Brien 1991, 1993, Perry 1996a, 1997, Rose 1998, Manson et al. in press). In most studies of capuchins, very few aggressive interactions have been observed (Fedigan 1993), and in both captive studies of *C. albifrons* and field studies of *C. capucinus,* agonistic encounters occupied only 1% of an individual's time (Bernstein 1965, Rose 1998). In the wild, the majority of these agonistic encounters are threats and occasionally chases—physical aggression is rare (but see below). In *C. albifrons* and *C. capucinus,* adult males within the same group associate strongly with each other, cooperate in group defense, look for lost males, and sometimes transfer together (Fedigan et al. 1996b, Perry 1998). Rank grows out of respect or acceptance rather than out of fear, with older and larger animals occupying the highest ranks (Freese and Oppenheimer 1981).

Occasionally, among *C. capucinus,* isolated episodes of aggression can be very serious, especially among males, and some result in crippling injuries (Rose 1998). This seems to be mostly associated with alpha males trying to evict subadult males from the group. Males very rarely physically attack or injure females other than in the context of male takeovers. Adult males sometimes invade groups and fight with resident males, often injuring (even fatally) these males and also injuring females and infants in the process (Rose and Fedigan 1995, Fedigan et al. 1996b, Rose 1998). Females rarely engage in physical aggression, but an important exception is in the context of dominance rank upheavals.

As stated above, in some *Cebus* populations individuals mate promiscuously whereas in others it appears that the alpha male does most of the mating (Robinson and Janson 1987, Fedigan 1993). Females also often engage in non-conceptive mating (e.g., during pregnancy or early lactation) (Perry 1997, Manson et al. 1997). There is a birth peak for 4–5 months during the dry season, but capuchins mate and give birth year round (Freese and Oppenheimer 1981, Robinson and Janson 1987, Fedigan and Rose 1995). Female *C. apella* come into estrus every 18–20 days, and gestation lasts between 153 and 180 days (Hamlett 1939, Wright and Bush 1977, Fragaszy 1990). Births are single and interbirth intervals are around two years (Fedigan and Rose 1995, Manson et al. 1997, Fragaszy and Adam-Curtis 1998). *C. capucinus* and *C. apella* young up to six weeks ride obliquely across their mothers shoulders. By 9–12 weeks, infants begin to move off the mother (Freese and Oppenheimer 1981, Fragaszy 1990). By 5–6 months, over 50% of the young *Cebus* activities are independent. Nursing lasts for at least a year and, intermittently, up to two years (Fragaszy and Adam-Curtis 1998, Rose pers. comm.). Average life history traits of *C. Capucinus* are given in Table 3-6.

Young capuchins are often carried by other group members, especially juveniles but also adult males (Freese and Oppenheimer 1981, Robinson 1981a, Robinson and Janson 1987, Rose 1998), and they often approach and nurse from adult females besides their mothers (O'Brien 1988, O'Brien and Robinson 1991, Perry 1996a). There may be a great advantage for infants to be able to allonurse, since infants often are widely separated from their foraging mothers (Perry 1996a). Grooming and play are important means of interaction for young *Cebus* (Oppenheimer 1973). Females reach sexual maturity at 5–6 years of age; males exhibit some sexual behavior about the same time but do not reach full adult size until they are 8–10 years (Oppenheimer 1968, Robinson and Janson 1987, Fedigan et al. 1996b, Fragaszy and Adam-Curtis 1998, Rose pers. comm.). Capuchins have been known to live to 48 years of age in captivity (Abate 1984).

Cebus monkeys have a rich array of communicative gestures and postures, though olfactory communication may be more important in capuchins and other Neotropical monkeys than in Old World monkeys (Sussman 1992, Fedigan et al. 1996a). Capuchins are noisy monkeys and may be able to communicate information about categories of predators as has been found in African vervet monkeys (Norris 1990, Fedigan et al. 1996a). Communication patterns of *C. apella* differ in a number of ways from the other three species (see Freese and Oppenheimer 1981). A detailed description of *Cebus* communication is given in Freese and Oppenheimer (1981) and Boinski (1993, 1996, Boinski and Campbell 1995).

Table 3-6 Average Life History Traits of Capuchin Monkeys

Female Weight (kgs)	2.28
Male Weight (kgs)	3.23
Mean Adult Weight	2.75
Fem/Male Wgt (Sex Dim)	.71
IBI (months)	26.4
Gestation (days)	162
Gestation (months)	5.4
Weaning Age (months)	12–24
Estrous Cycle (days)	22
Menarche (months)	54
Age First Birth (months)	60

[From Fedigan and Rose, pers. comm.]

Both squirrel monkeys and capuchins have variable patterns of intraspecific group spacing. The home ranges of some groups of squirrel monkeys overlap only slightly, while others share up to 90% of their home range (Thorington 1968, Baldwin and Baldwin 1981). There are no reports of intergroup agonistic encounters. The Baldwins (1972) observed squirrel monkey groups moving as close as 100 meters for a total of at least 30 hours; on one day two groups closely coordinated their movements for 5.5 h maintaining 75–150 m spacing but mutually avoided intermingling.

Unlike *Saimiri,* groups of *Cebus* have been observed actively defending home range boundaries, which included almost their entire range (i.e., being territorial). In *C. capucinus,* mainly adult males are involved in vocal displays and chases during intergroup conflicts (Oppenheimer 1968, 1882, Perry 1996b). In Costa Rica, Perry observed intergroup encounters (lasting 15–60 minutes) to occur at a rate of one per week. Only males took part in 39 of 44 encounters, and they were the main antagonists in all 44. No physical contact was seen. However, also in Costa Rica, Freese (Freese and Oppenheimer 1981) never observed contact between groups of *C. capucinus* even though ranges overlapped extensively and groups often used the same resources at different times. In later studies at the same site, aggressive intergroup encounters were observed to occur quite frequently (Fedigan 1993, Rose 1994a, Rose 1998). Rose (pers. comm.) believes that this might be due to rapid population increase of these monkeys at the site, which grew by 60% between 1983 and 1992 (Fedigan et al. 1996b).

Similar variations in intergroup interactions have been observed in other species. In Peru, Terborgh (1983) observed inter-group intolerance and vocal battles between *C. albifrons* males, but at his study site, there was almost total range overlap. In Colombia, however, Defler (1982) observed aggressive territorial defense with little range overlap in *C. albifrons* but tolerance and extensive overlap in *C. apella.*

Cebus and *Saimiri* Mixed-Species Associations

Mixed-species groups (or polyspecific associations) of *Saimiri* and *Cebus* are common. In some cases these associations last for many days, and the two taxa may spend over half their time together. Usually, they intermingle peaceably, although occasionally a large capuchin male may chase one or the whole group of squirrel monkeys out of a fruit tree. But the squirrel monkeys are not intimidated for long and soon move back into the tree.

After preliminary studies, some authors hypothesized that *Cebus* takes the active role in maintaining these associations and is the main benefactor (Baldwin and Baldwin 1971, Klein and Klein 1973, Freese 1977). However, Terborgh (1983) found that *Saimiri* followed and were attracted to *Cebus.* During slow meandering travel, squirrel monkeys often led mixed group progressions, but if they were not followed by the capuchins, they circled back. *Cebus* always led direct and fast movement to specific fruit trees. Further, if a *Cebus* group stopped at a fruit source not normally used by *Saimiri* (such as palm fruit), the latter would go off on independent foraging excursions, returning frequently to check on *Cebus.* The reverse was not true; *Cebus* groups would never wait for distracted *Saimiri.* Furthermore, in Manu, squirrel monkeys actively searched for capuchin groups. Groups of *Saimiri* covered much more area when travelling alone than when in mixed groups (twice as far per hour) and would immediately join a *Cebus* group upon hearing its vocalizations. *Cebus,* on the other hand, traveled 40% more when accompanied by *Saimiri.*

If *Saimiri* is actively maintaining these polyspecific associations, what are the benefits of these interactions? One benefit to both *Saimiri* and *Cebus* might be a reduction in their vulnerability to predators because of the greater number of animals able to spot predators. However, Terborgh (1983) believes that *Saimiri* has the greatest advantage, since capuchins have a well developed predator alarm system. In Manu, capuchin alpha males are constantly alert and frequently scan the environment. *Cebus* alarm barks cause an immediate reaction in *Saimiri* as well as in other monkeys and neighboring birds. Terborgh (1983:171) states:

> . . . *the response of* Saimiri *to* Cebus *alarms is generally much stronger than their response to their own calls.* Saimiri *often give alarm 'peeps,' occasionally even in chorus, without provoking much reaction from the* Cebus. *The* Saimiri *may run or fling themselves out of the tree in panic, while the* Cebus *merely look up or continue their feeding.*

During seasons when *Saimiri* and *Cebus* are utilizing similar fruit sources, *Saimiri* may be gaining a further though slighter advantage. Capuchins have smaller home ranges, and the ranges of squirrel monkeys include more than one capuchin group. By following capuchins, squirrel monkeys may benefit from the capuchins better knowledge of the smaller areas. Terborgh believes that *C. albifrons* may take advantage of *C. apella* in much the same way, since these two species are often seen in mixed groups during the dry season when they both utilize palm nuts. Thus, *Saimiri* is the beneficiary of mixed species associations. *Cebus,* on the other hand, has an energetic burden of increased travel, and as Terborgh (1983:186) states, "by all appearances, the attitude of *Cebus* is one of passive resignation to the presence of an accompanying throng of *Saimiri.*"

Ranging Behavior

Cebus and *Saimiri,* as would be expected in omnivorous primates, have relatively large home and day ranges (Table 3-4). Terborgh (1983) compared ranging behavior of *C. apella, C. albifrons,* and *S. sciurius* and found that a detailed analysis of ranging patterns led to a better understanding of the ecological distinctions between these sympatric forms. *C. apella* groups have a relatively small home range (approximately 70 hectares) and generally use the central part of this range, only occasionally going to the perimeters. Throughout the year, the home range contains a relatively abundant and concentrated supply of utilized resources. During the wet season, a great variety of tree species are in fruit and this capuchin intensively uses a central core area of its range. During the dry season, it concentrates on two abundant and evenly distributed species of palm (see section on diet). Although more visits are made to the perimeter of the home range during this time, the group constantly returns to the central core area of its home range.

C. albifrons uses widely scattered, patchily distributed resources and has a much larger home range (over 150 hectares) than *C. apella.* The white-fronted capuchin constantly moves, covering large portions of its home range as it travels from one fruit concentration to another. For example, although the two species of *Cebus* travel about the same distance each day, in 16 days *C. albifrons* visited 33% more hectares than *C. apella* did in 211 days. Squares in the central portion of the *C. apella* home range were visited every two or three days, whereas *C. albifrons* did not visit major sections of its home range for weeks at a stretch.

C. albifrons specializes in exploiting temporary resource concentrations, constantly searching for these resources over a large area. *Saimiri* is even more specialized in exploiting highly concentrated, patchy resources and has longer day ranges and larger home ranges (over 250 hectares) than *Cebus.* Terborgh (1983) suggests that fig trees are the epitome of such resources and that *Saimiri* is a fig eater *par excellence.* A large fig tree with ripe fruit will attract five *Saimiri* groups at once. The groups might remain in the vicinity for as long as the fruit lasts (up to ten days), making daily foraging excursions from this tree. This focus on figs makes *Saimiri* even more nomadic than *C. albifrons*. When one tree has been exhausted, the group may travel several days and cover many kilometers in search of another. All three species forage for insects while moving between fruit resources, and Terborgh believes that the ranging patterns are primarily conditioned by the need to maintain an adequate intake of fruit, especially throughout the dry season.

THE ECOLOGY AND BEHAVIOR OF AOTINAE

Callicebus

The first field study of *Callicebus* was carried out by Mason (1965, 1966, 1968) in central Colombia. More recently, field research concentrating on titi monkeys has been conducted in Peru and Brazil by Kinzey and his students and colleagues (e.g., Kinzey 1978, Kinzey et al. 1977, Kinzey and Wright 1982, Kinzey and Becker 1983, Wright 1984, 1989, see also Easley 1982) and in Colombia by Robinson (1977, 1981b). Year long studies of *C. personatus* have recently been completed in Brazil by Müller (1995, 1996) and by Heiduck (1997). A number of researchers have made short term observations of *Callicebus* during surveys or studies of other species. See Robinson et al. (1987b), Kinzey (1997a) and Müller (1996) for further references.

Habitat and Locomotion

Kinzey and Gentry (1978) argue that where their ranges overlap, *Callicebus moloch* and *C. torquatus* occupy very different habitats and may be "habitat isolates" (Fig. 3-26 a & b). *C. moloch* occupies inundated forests, especially in areas where it is sympatric with *C. torquatus* and *Saimiri*. In a protected reserve (Estacion Biologic Callicebus-EBC) near Iquitos, Peru, Kinzey believes that *C. moloch* is found in forests located on lower ground than *C. torquatus* and may be adapted specifically to forests located on "white sand" soils. These are generally poor soils and the vegetation associated with them has reduced productivity, a lower rate of turnover, and shares a number of other characteristics (Janzen 1974, Stark et al. 1980). Neither Easley (1982) nor Defler (1994), however, were able to confirm this habitat selection in the two *Callicebus* species groups.

   C. moloch is found mainly in areas of dense vegetation including low forest, thickets, and bamboo thickets, and in dense canopy forest, often where lianas are frequent (Kinzey 1981). It also often is found in inundated forests and along river banks (Moynihan 1976, Soini 1972). Moynihan (1976:81) describes *C. moloch* as "the nearest thing to a real swamp monkey in the New World." It spends most of its time in the lower levels of the forest; however, it will often move into the high canopy to feed. *C. torquatus* lives in more open canopy forests and is not usually found in dense vegetation. It is found in "tall mature forest, or mixed forest with many tall and large trees, on well drained ground" (Moynihan 1976:81) and rarely in vine tangles or thickets. *C. torquatus* spends about 70% of its time in the canopy or emergent layers of the forest (Easley 1982). *Callicebus personatus* lives in a wide diversity of habitat types from sea level to over 1000 m, in primary as well as secondary vegetation. Kinzey (1981) regards this as the most adaptable species.

   C. torquatus spends less than 10% of the time on the ground, the rest mainly on large or medium sized horizontal supports. It locomotes and feeds on medium

Figure 3-26a *C. moloch.* [From Rowe 1996]   **Figure 3-26b** *C. torquatus.* [From Rowe 1996]

and terminal branches, rather than larger vertical or horizontal supports (Kinzey et al. 1977, Easley 1982). Most locomotion is quadrupedal walking. Feeding is done above-branch quadrupedally or while sitting. In fact, Easley found *C. torquatus* to spend over 60% of its time sitting. *C. torquatus* spends most of its time in the middle strata of the forest (15–25 m high) but feeds mostly in the emergent layer. When in the understory feeding on berries or insects, this species often uses a vertical clinging and leaping locomotor pattern, although this represents a very small proportion of time. While feeding, *C. torquatus* sometimes uses a suspensory posture. *C. moloch* spends more time in the lower forest strata and utilizes branches of smaller diameter than *C. torquatus* (Kinzey 1981, Wright 1985, Crandlemire-Sacco 1988). It frequently sleeps in a dense vine tangle, whereas *C. torquatus* sleeps on an open, large branch. *C. personatus* also sleeps in the open on large branches; however, other information on its locomotion and posture is not available. In titi monkeys, the tail is not prehensile. It is used mainly for balance and in social tactile communication in a characteristic tail-twining posture (Fig 3-27).

Diet

Both *C. torquatus* and *C. moloch* are mainly frugivorous, but the major proportion of the protein of each is obtained from different sources. These differences can be related to a number of other behavioral and morphological differences between the two monkeys. Both titi species feed on fruit between 70–75% of the time (Kinzey 1977, 1978, Easley 1982, Wright 1985). However, *C. torquatus,* the yellow-handed titi, obtains most of its protein from insects (15–20% of observed feeding bouts) and eats few leaves (4–9%). In some sites, it also eats a large quantity of immature seeds. In Colombia, for example, during periods of low fruit availability, *C. torquatus* was observed feeding on seeds for 27% of the time (Palacios et al. 1997). *C. moloch,* the dusky titi, obtains most of its protein from leaves (20% of feeding observations) and eats few insects (about 4%). Although this species spent an average of 44 minutes per day searching for insects at Wright's study site, capture rates were low (6–8 small insects per day) (Wright 1996).

From available data, it seems that the pattern of fruit exploitation of *C. torquatus* and *C. moloch* may be quite similar. In a 12 month period, Easley (1982) found that *C. torquatus* ate 57 species of fruit. However, 14 species accounted for approximately 75% of the fruit species eaten and six species made up over 50% of the diet. Kinzey (1977, 1978) found that *C. torquatus* ate 55 species of fruit; 16 of them for 80% of the time and spent half the time feeding on six species in a combined period of six months. He also noted that for any short

Figure 3-27 Tail twining in the titi monkey. [From Wright 1994]

period, three to six species accounted for approximately 60% of fruit-feeding time. *C. moloch* also spends a great deal of its feeding time eating few species of fruit (Kinzey 1981). Both *Callicebus* species sample a large number of species of fruit in small quantity, but a small number of fruit species make up a great proportion of the diet.

Easley (1982) believes that, at EBC, one species of palm, *Jessenia polycarpa,* may be the most important fruit staple in the diet of *C. torquatus* and that the distribution and phenology of these palm trees are important determinants of its ranging behavior (Fig. 3-28). *Jessenia polycarpa* is the most commonly eaten fruit, accounting for almost a quarter of the fruit eaten over the year. It is also the only fruit species available and fed upon in every month of the year, with different trees coming into fruit in a serial fashion. Most other species are in fruit for very short periods of time. *J. polycarpa* is scattered, relatively abundant, and evenly distributed within the home range of *C. torquatus* groups, while the rest of the resources utilized are scarce and unpredictable. Easley believes that, at EBC, the territorial behavior of the yellow-handed titi may be related to the distribution of this dependable and stable resource.

The major difference between the diets of *C. torquatus* and *C. moloch* is not in the fruit portion of the diet but in the respective exploitation of insects and leaves. As stated above, *C. torquatus* obtains most of its protein from insects. It feeds mainly on large, slow insects such as grasshoppers, praying mantis, arachnids, and larvae but also eats some social insects, such as ants, flying insects, and beetles (Kinzey 1977,

Figure 3-28 Titi monkey feeding on *Jessinia* fruit. [From Easley 1982]

Easley 1982). This titi monkey eats very little leafy material and only young leaves and shoots.

The non-frugivorous portion of the diet of *C. moloch* is composed mainly of leaves and both mature and immature leaves are eaten (Kinzey and Gentry 1979). It especially consumes leaves of vines and bamboo (Terborgh 1983, Wright 1985). Terborgh believes that its use of vine leaves may be particularly significant, because vines tend to produce new leaves continuously whereas most tropical trees only produce periodic flushes of new leaves. *C. personatus*, like *C. moloch*, supplements a predominantly fruit diet with leaves (Kinzey and Becker 1983, see also Müller 1996, Heiduck 1997) (Fig. 3-29). Food choice in this species, as in many other frugivores, has been shown to be directly related to the abundance of food items, and thus, opportunistic foraging appears to be the optimal strategy (Heiduck 1997). Crandlemire-Sacco (1988) studied *C. brunneus* (= *C. moloch*) living sympatrically with *Saguinus fuscicollis* and found that they shared few plant and animal foods and had different foraging styles and habitat preferences.

As discussed in Volume 1, Chapter 1, many morphological features, especially of the gut tract and dentition, can be related to dietary preferences. The physical properties of foods have been a primary factor in the evolutionary selection of many of these features. Kay (1973) has shown that molar form, especially the length of shearing crests, can be related to the major foods processed by a primate. He defines a "primary specialization" as one of three types of food—insects, fruit, or folivorous materials—that comprise 45% or more of the diet. The molars of both *C. torquatus* and *C. moloch* are those of a frugivore. However, Kinzey (1978) found that other features of the molars of the two species are related to the sources of dietary protein processed. In *C. torquatus*, the talonid basin (Fig 3-30a) is longer and deeper on the lower molars than it is on *C. moloch*. This is an adaptation for crushing and grinding relatively hard foods and chitinous insects. *C. moloch*, on the other hand, has longer shearing crests (the cristid obliqua, Fig 3-30b) on the first two lower molars than *C. torquatus*, even though the latter's overall length of the

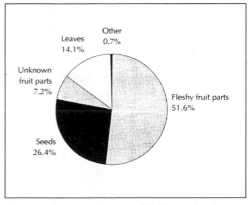

Figure 3-29 Proportions of different food types in the diet of *C. personatus*. [From Heiduck 1997]

Figure 3-30a Bucco-occlusal view of second lower molar of *Callicebus moloch,* showing the relatively longer, sharply angled cristid obliqua and the constricted talonid basin.

Figure 3-30b Bucco-occlusal view of second lower molar of *Callicebus torquatus,* showing the relatively shorter, less sharply angled cristid obliqua and the broad, unconstricted talonid basin.

molars is greater (Kinzey 1978). Increased length of the cristid obliqua has been related to a folivorous diet in primates (Kay 1975). Dietary differences, especially with regard to insect and leaf eating, can also be related to differences in activity cycles and ranging patterns of these two species.

Cycles of Activity

The daily activity patterns of *C. torquatus* and *C. moloch* reflect their dietary propensities. Both species spend over 50% of the day resting, awaken early (about 0600 hours), and feed for approximately the same amount of time. How-

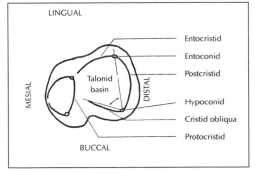

Figure 3-30c Occlusal diagram of second lower molar of *Callicebus,* showing features mentioned in the text. The double arrow designates the angle of the cristid obliqua. [From Kinzey 1978]

ever, the distribution of activities of the two species throughout the day differs significantly. *C. torquatus* feeds more or less continuously with short rests between feeding but without a long break for resting. Fruit feeding, which peaks in early morning, mid-morning, mid-afternoon, and late afternoon is interspersed with insect and leaf eating throughout the day (Easley 1982, Kinzey and Becker 1983). By 1600 hours, two hours before sunset, *C. torquatus* begins resting and grooming in its night sleeping tree, and by 1700 hours, the monkeys begin to rest for the night. They sleep in the canopy, about 25 meters high, on large horizontal branches and choose different sleeping sites each night (Kinzey 1981, Easley 1982).

C. moloch has an activity pattern more similar to folivorous primates. The dusky titi has two major feeding peaks, one in the morning and one in the late afternoon (Fig. 3-31). There is a long afternoon resting period. After the late afternoon feeding period, spent feeding mostly on leaves, the animals move to their sleeping site for the night (Kinzey 1978). The sleeping sites of *C. moloch* are vine tangles far below the top of the canopy, about 15 meters high (Robinson 1977, Kinzey 1981, Wright 1985), and *C. moloch* often returns to the same sleeping sites (Mason 1968,

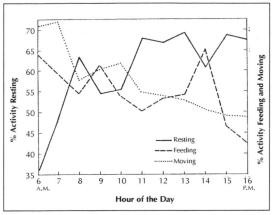

Figure 3-31 Activity cycles of *C. torquatus:* graph of the relative frequencies of resting, feeding, and moving IAR's by hour of the day. Resting frequencies are represented by the scale on the left; feeding and moving by the scale on the right. Note that the graph is compressed for visual purposes; resting is actually the most frequent activity at all hours of the day. [From Easley 1982]

Kinzey 1981). *C. personatus,* being more folivorous, has peaks of feeding and resting similar to those described for *C. moloch.* However, the sleeping sites of *C. personatus* are in the open on large branches above the canopy as are those of *C. torquatus* (Kinzey and Becker 1983).

Predation

Observations of predation on *Callicebus* are rare. Freese (see Kinzey et al. 1977) reports sighting a large predatory bird catching a titi monkey, and Wright (1982) observed *Callicebus* being attacked three times by predatory birds and once by an ocelot in 900 hours of observation. The night sleeping sites are probably chosen for predator protection, as well as for social reasons (see below). The open, large branches used by *C. torquatus* and *C. personatus* allow the monkeys to see approaching predators, whereas *C. moloch* sleeps in dense vine tangles. However, Wright (1982) observed that only 8 of 26 sleeping trees of *C. moloch* provided cryptic sleeping sites. During the day, group members synchronize activities and both *C. moloch* and *C. torquatus* are generally very cryptic in coloration and while moving and resting (Wright 1982, Easley 1982, Terborgh 1983, Crandlemire-Sacco 1988). Resting during the day is done in dense vegetation in the mid-canopy (Terborgh 1983). Wright (1982) believes that, at least at Manu, *Callicebus* diurnal activity stresses predator avoidance, whereas the night sleeping positions are relatively unprotected because nocturnal, arboreal predators at this site are not a threat.

Social Structure and Organization

Callicebus has a classic "family" or "pair-bonded" group structure including an adult female and male and their immature offspring (see Fuentes 1999). Group size ranges from 2–6 individuals (Table 3-7). It is assumed that the bond between the adult pair is relatively permanent (Wright 1996, Kinzey 1997a). The main study group of *C. torquatus* at EBC was followed discontinuously from 1974 to 1981 and was presumed to contain the same adult pair throughout this period (Easley 1982). During nighttime sleeping and day resting, group members sleep huddled together with their tails entwined. Grooming seems to be an important social activity, occurring especially during day resting periods and, in *C. torquatus* and *C. personatus,* before sleeping at night roosting sites. Group activity is synchronized, aggressive interactions are extremely rare, and there appear to be no dominance hierarchies within the group (Kinzey 1981).

Home ranges between groups of conspecifics do not overlap (3-32). All three species exchange "loud calls" between neighboring groups; however, the function

Table 3-7 Group Size, Composition, Home and Day Range Size, and Population Density among *Aotus* and *Callicebus*

Species & Site	Group Size (N)	Group Composition				Home Range (ha)	Day Range (m)	Population Density (#/km)	Source
		Adult M	Adult F	Juv	I				
Callicebus moloch									
Colombia	3.2 (8)	(2.0)		0.5	0.6	0.5	580	400	Mason 1968
Colombia	3.1 (18)	(2.2)		0.4	0.5	3.7	—	57	Robinson 1977
Peru	4.2 (7)	1.0	1.0	1.2	1.0	8.0	670	20	Wright 1984
C. personatus									
Brazil	3.7 (15)	1.0	1.0	0–3	0–1	4.7	700	—	Kinzey & Becker 1983
Brazil	"nuclear family" (2)					24.0	1000	17	Müller 1995
C. torquatus									
Colombia	4.0 (5)	(2.1)		0.9	1.0	14.2	—	32	Defler 1983
Peru	3.9 (15)	1.0	1.0	0–3	0–1	18.0	820	20	Easley 1982, Kinzey 1986
Aotus trivergatus									
Peru	4.5 (9)	1.0	1.0	1.5	1.0	10.0	710	40	Wright 1985
Paraguay	3.1 (21	0						14	Stallings 1984

of these calls is different between the species. *C. moloch* males give loud calls almost every morning to identify the locality of the group. If the group is near a boundary or close to another calling group, the female joins the male in calling. The resulting "duet" stimulates the two groups to approach the boundary and to interact (Robinson 1981b). In 160 days, Robinson (1981b) observed 121 interactions between *C. moloch* groups. The interactions involve elaborate and extended displays in which calling, chasing, and rushing occur, but rarely do animals make contact (Mason 1968, Robinson 1979a). Thus, *C. moloch* loud calls, and especially duets, can be considered distance-decreasing signals between groups (that is, they cause groups to move closer together) and groups are territorial.

Groups of *C. torquatus* and *C. personatus,* on the other hand, do not approach one another after exchanging loud calls. Solo male calls and duets are given either spontaneously or in response to neighboring groups. However, groups do not respond by moving towards one another. Calls are given from well within the home range, and animals do not interact at boundaries. Loud calls in these two species help groups to maintain distance between one another, and thus, intergroup interactions are avoided (Kinzey and Becker 1983, Kinzey and Robinson 1983). In over 1000 hours of observations, no ritualized boundary encounters have been observed between neighboring groups of *C. torquatus.* These patterns of intergroup spacing appear to be directly related to the ranging patterns of the species (see below).

During mating season, Moynihan (1966) reports that *Callicebus* copulates much more frequently than any other New World monkey. Births are seasonal, occurring between November and March (Kinzey 1997a), and a single offspring is born. The length of the estrus cycle is 17–21 days (Sassenrath et al. 1980). In captivity, the mean interbirth interval is 318 ± 19 days (n = 60), and the length of the gestation period is estimated as 124–136 days (Jantschke et al. 1995). Within 48 hours of birth, the male generally begins to carry the infant (Wright 1984, 1990, Jantschke et al. 1995). The infant only moves onto the female to nurse. Infants begin to move on their own between 2.5–3.5 months but are still partially carried by the male until 4–6 months of age. Furthermore, adult male care of the young extends into juvenile stages of development (Kinzey 1981, Jantschke et al. 1995). Weaning occurs sometime between 4–6 months. Sexual maturity is probably attained between 3–4 years of age (Kinzey 1981). Subadults leave the natal group at around three years of age, and their departure is abrupt and without any precipitous agonistic activities (Kinzey 1981, Wright 1996).

Ranging Behavior

There is very little overlap of home ranges of conspecific groups (Fig. 3-32). As stated above, *C. moloch* groups actually have agonistic displays at boundaries that are often stimulated by distance decreasing loud calls. *C. torquatus* and *C. personatus* avoid contact at boundaries by exchanging distance maintaining or increasing calls. If the benefits of exclusive use of space among species are similar, the likelihood of defending boundaries should be higher in species with long day range length relative to home range area (Waser 1976). This relationship holds true for *C. moloch* and *C. torquatus* (Kinzey and Robinson 1983). The day range length of these two species is approximately the same: approximately 580 m for *C. moloch* (Mason 1968, Kinzey 1981) and 820 m for *C. torquatus* (Kinzey 1986) (Table 3-7). However, the home ranges of *C. moloch* (6–12 ha; Wright 1986) are smaller than those of *C. torquatus* (10–15+ ha; Easley 1982, Defler 1983, Easley and Kinzey 1986,

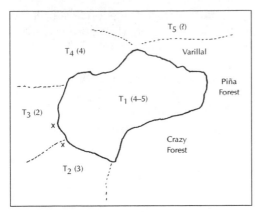

Figure 3-32 Locations of *C. torquatus* groups adjacent to the territory of T₁. Number in parentheses indicates number of individuals in each group. X = location of active border confrontations with neighboring groups T₂ and T₃. Confrontations with groups T₄ and T₅ were not observed. [From Easley 1982]

Palacios et al. 1997). Groups of *C. personatus* have home ranges of 5–24 ha and average day ranges of 695–1000 m (Kinzey and Becker 1983, Müller 1995, 1996). At Müller's site, this species had a population density of $17/km^2$.

Why do *Callicebus* groups maintain exclusive use of space? As we have seen so far, very few primate species show this pattern of intergroup spacing. Generally, it is assumed that animals divide space in this manner if they use evenly distributed, predictable, and self-renewing resources and thus are able to utilize their home range more or less evenly (Pyke et al. 1977). Since *C. moloch* and *C. torquatus* use leaves and insects, respectively, as sources of protein, it is not very likely that these resources are directly related to their exclusive use of space.

Easley (1982) observed that *C. torquatus* depends upon two different types of fruit: seasonal fruit, which is patchily distributed and unpredictable and relatively constant and predictable fruit, such as *J. polycarpa*. He believes that protecting home range boundaries around seasonally utilized, unpredictable resources would be quite risky. Establishment of boundaries on the basis of the number of *J. polycarpa* trees necessary to provide adequate year-long production would be much more ecologically sound.

J. polycarpa trees are evenly distributed within the home range of groups at EBC. The study group of *C. moloch* made a complete circuit of its home range every 6–10 days, traveling through most quadrants of its range on each circuit. There were no dramatic seasonal differences in the way the group occupied its range. Thus, both seasonally available fruit resources and *J. polycarpa* trees in fruit could be constantly monitored. Insects and leaves were harvested opportunistically, and the distribution of these resources did not seem to have much influence on the yellow-handed titi monkeys daily ranging patterns.

The group of *C. torquatus* studied by Kinzey, and subsequently by Easley, also gradually shifted its boundaries over a seven-year period (1974–1980). The group had shifted its range to the northeast (Fig. 3-33) while its home range size remained relatively constant from year to year. The observed sizes for four different sampling periods (20,20,14 and 18.5) are not significantly different from the mean of 18 ha.

Although able to provide only circumstantial evidence, Easley and Kinzey (1986) suggest that this shift of range boundaries is related to the establishment of new territories for offspring. Since offspring of pair-bonded groups necessarily leave the natal group, an adaptive advantage may be gained by providing some offspring with a "known" area. Similar tolerance of offspring near or within the home range of gibbon parents has been reported (Chivers et al. 1975, Tenaza 1975, Tilson 1981). Gibbons live in pair-bonded groups with exclusive home ranges (see Volume 3). Charles-Dominique (1977) also has reported a case where a *Perodicticus potto* mother shifted her home range, allowing the establishment of a new range for her female offspring. Similar observations have been made on a number of other species of mammals and birds (see Waser and Wiley 1980 for a review).

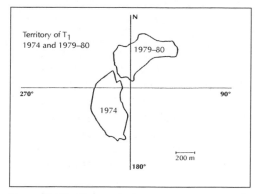

Figure 3-33 Change in home range over study period by *C. torquatus.* [From Easly 1982]

AOTUS

Very few studies have been done on *Aotus.* Moynihan (1964) studied the behavioral patterns of *Aotus* in captivity, and Thorington et al. (1976) released a young captive male on BCI and radio-tracked it for nine days. After this latter study, the authors concluded that it probably would be impossible to conduct a study of the night monkey without using radio-tracking. Wright, however, conducted a 400 hour study in a primary tropical forest in Peru (Wright 1978, 1979) and an 18 month study of *Callicebus* and *Aotus* in Peru and Paraguay (Wright 1984, 1985, 1986, 1989, 1990, 1994, 1996). Both studies were achieved without the use of radio tracking. It is often difficult to find a study site in which it is possible to make detailed observations of arboreal-living primates, especially nocturnal ones. Surveying for a good field site is one of the most important prerequisites of a successful project. Other studies have now been conducted in northeastern Peru (Aquino et al. 1990, Aquino and Encarnacion 1994) and in Bolivia (Garcia and Braza 1989).

Habitat and Locomotion

Aotus has one of the most extensive geographical ranges of any Neotropical primate species (Fig. 3-3), from Panama to northern Argentina and from lowland forests at sea level to over 3000 m in the Andes. It is a small monkey, about 800–1250 g and there is no marked sexual dimorphism. Night monkeys do not have prehensile tails (Fig. 3-34). *Aotus* is basically quadrupedal and moves on the tops of branches, but detailed analysis of its locomotion and substrate use is not available. It is found in all strata of the forest, from near the ground to the top of the canopy (Mohnihan 1964, Durham 1975, Wright 1978, Kinzey 1997a) but rarely uses the ground

Figure 3-34 *Aotus.* [From Wright 1994]

(Wright 1981). In comparison to *Callicebus moloch, Aotus* prefers to feed in large trees (>11 m in diameter) (Wright 1996). It is found in a wide range of forest habitats, including primary and secondary forests and forest remnants.

Diet

Aotus is basically a fruit eater that supplements its diet with flowers and nectar, young leaves, and insects. From stomach contents, Hladik and Hladik (1969) estimated the diet as follows: 65% fruit; 30% foliage (including shoots, young leaves, pith, buds flowers, and sap); and 8% animal prey. However, Wright (1982, 1989) observed *Aotus* to feed almost exclusively on fruit during the wet season (Fig. 3-35).

Many of the fruits used by *Aotus* at night are used by the larger monkey species during the day. *C. moloch,* a similar sized monkey, is often chased out of large fruit trees by these larger species and must move into the understory to feed or utilize fruits when they are unripe (Kinzey 1981, Wright 1981, 1989). During the dryer months at Manu, the night monkey ate mainly from large-crowned, superabundant sources, such as figs and *Brosimum,* and on floral nectar. In fact, in July, approximately 90% of the diet consisted of nectar. During the dry season, the diet of *Aotus* is very similar

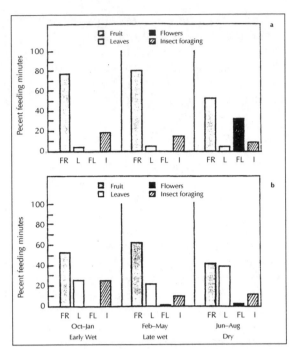

Figure 3-35 (a) Diet of *Aotus* in Peru, October 1980–August 1981, including estimates of insect-foraging and leaf-eating, which are based on analyses of feces collected. **(b)** Diet of *Callicebus moloch* in Peru, October 1980–August 1981. Note that leaf-eating increases during June–August, a period of fruit scarcity. [From Wright 1994]

to that of *Eulemur mongoz* in Madagascar. At Manu, the night monkey feeds on the flowers of *Combretum fruticosum* and *Quariribea cordata* (Janson et al. 1981). Much like the flowers utilized by *E. mongoz* and by marsupials in Australia, these flowers have characteristics adapted for non-flying mammal pollinators (see Volume 1, Chapter 5). The amount of insect and leaf material in the diet was not determined by Wright (1982, 1989) but was thought to be quite negligible, though more insects are eaten by *Aotus* than by sympatric *Callicebus moloch* (Wright 1996). Based on fecal samples, Wright found that five times more insects were ingested by the night monkey each day than by the titi.

Activity Cycle

Aotus is the only species of anthropoid active at night. It descends from its sleeping tree 15 minutes after sunset and returns just before dawn (Thorington et al. 1976, Wright 1978). Sometime during the middle of the night, it usually has one or two rest periods (Fig. 3-36). The amount of rest during the evening depends upon the season, the availability of fruit, and upon the fullness of the moon. Night monkeys are more active during the wet season when more fruit is available and during nights of full moon when locomotor and feeding activity and the number of intergroup agonistic encounters increases (Wright 1981). In the southernmost portion of its range, however, *Aotus* has been observed to be active and foraging during the day (Mann 1956, Rathbun and Gache 1987). Wright (1985, 1989) believes that diurnal activity in this population is related to competitive release (from larger, frugivorous monkeys) and an absence of diurnal predators. However, Garcia and Braza (1987) suggest that these monkeys are active during the day because of low night temperatures.

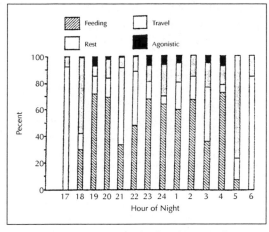

Figure 3-36 Average hourly distribution of activity of *Aotus* group A, for 34 nights. [From Wright 1996]

In most localities, daytime sleeping sites are in cryptic locations, such as holes in hollow trunks or bushes or trees with dense vegetation (Thorington et al. 1976, Moynihan 1976, Wright 1981, 1989). Wright's focal group in Peru returned to one of three sleeping sites, located within 30 m of each other, for a period of nine weeks and was seen again in one of the sites twenty months later (Wright 1981). Aquino and Encarnación (1986, 1994) found that the primary factors in sleeping site selection were protection from predators, easy access, shelter from adverse weather, and sufficient space.

Predation

Wright (1982, 1989, 1996) argues that one of the major advantages of a nocturnal activity pattern in *Aotus* may be predator avoidance. The night monkey spends most of its time in the high canopy and travels quickly and noisily in the tall trees. It also feeds high in the canopy, often on exposed, conspicuous flowers during periods when the trees are leafless (Janson et al. 1981). When frightened, *Aotus* actively mobs the potential danger whereas the similar sized, diurnal *Callicebus* flees and hides. During 1000 hours of observation, Wright (1982) saw no predatory attacks on the night monkey. The only nocturnal predatory birds in the Manu study site are owls, which may be too small to prey upon *Aotus* but have yet to be studied in detail (Fig. 3-37) (Wright 1996).

Social Structure and Organization

Aotus lives in family groups with an adult pair and their offspring, most often 2–4 individuals (Table 3-7) (Moynihan 1964, Heltne 1977, Wright 1978, 1986, 1996, Rathbun and Gache 1977, Green 1978). Larger groups have been observed but these seem to be unstable, merged associations of more than one group at superabundant food sources (Moynihan 1964, Durham 1975, Rathbun and Gache 1977). Unlike diurnal species living in pair-bonded groups, *Aotus* groups do not maintain exclusive use of their home ranges and there is extensive overlap of range boundaries. Intergroup agonistic encounters, previously thought to be territorial in nature (Moynihan 1964, 1976), more likely function to maintain group integrity and to allow overlapping groups to share limited resources on a time-sharing basis. This is similar to the social structure and organization found in the nocturnal *Eulemur mongoz* (Volume 1, Chapter 5, Sussman and Tattersall 1976). Within the group, activity and movement are very cohesive, with group members seldom more than 10 m apart (Wright 1978). Both allogrooming and agonistic encounters between group members are extremely rare, and Wright (1981, 1994) could discern no dominance hierarchy within the group. In Peru, playing behavior was observed between subadult, juvenile and father in one study group on moonlit nights during months when abundant fruit was available (Wright 1984, 1994).

At present, little is known about the breeding cycle of Aotus. There does not seem to be a breeding season in captivity, though in Peru there is a birth peak during the rainy season (Wright 1986). Hunter et al. (1979) report a gestation period of 133 days. The mean age of first

Figure 3-37 Owl that may be potential predator of *Aotus*. [From Wright 1994]

birth in captivity is 3.5 yrs (Gozalo and Montoya 1990). Single births are the rule but twins also have occurred on rare occasion (see Wright 1981). As in *Callicebus*, the *Aotus* infant is carried by the male. The development of an infant has been studied by Wright (1981, 1984). In this study, carrying by the male in a captive group began slowly, but by three weeks of age, the infant spent over 80% of its time on the back of the male. By three months of age, the captive infant already spent most of the time alone (71%), riding on the male for only 26% of the time and spending 3% of its time on the female while nursing. By five months, the young animal rode on the father only in stressful situations. Nursing continued until the infant was nine months old. Sexual maturity is reached at about 2–2.5 years of age. Subadults leave the natal group during their third year (Wright 1986, 1996) without any apparent agonistic behavior prior to departing (Robinson et al. 1987).

Ranging Behavior

Aotus groups have short night ranges and small home ranges. Wet season ranges averaged 829 m per night and in the dry season ranges averaged 252 m (Wright 1978). This probably indicates that night monkeys spend more time on fewer resources during the dry season and spend more time resting (see Wright 1981). The travel of *Aotus* is described as goal directed, from one fruit (or flower) tree to the next (Wright 1982). The home range of nine groups averaged 9.2 ha (range=8–10 ha) (Wright 1982). Data on population densities are given in Table 3-7.

THEORETICAL INSERT

Hunting and Tool Use by Capuchins and Models of Early Hominid Evolution

Meat eating by baboons and chimpanzees has long been of great interest to anthropologists and human biologists because of analogies drawn to theorized hunting behavior of early humans. Baboons and chimpanzees are the primates most often used in developing models of early hominid behavior (for recent examples, see Wrangham and Peterson 1996, Stanford 1999, Ghiglieri 1999; see also Sussman 1999). Vertebrate predation by *Cebus* monkeys generally has been ignored in these models, possibly because parallel behaviors in a highly arboreal, small, New World monkey would not enhance these theories. Yet, many similarities exist in the hunting rates and patterns of these and other primates (Butynksi 1982, Fedigan 1990, Rose 1994, 1997, 2001, Rose and Marshall 1996). For example, Fedigan (1990) has observed one Costa Rican group of capuchins to attempt to capture vertebrate prey once every 12 hours with 91% of the attempts successful. This yields a rate of one capture every 15 hours, which is among the highest capture rates for any primate population.

In some cases, a single monkey pounces on a victim, such as a bird or lizard. Other prey, such as adult squirrels, are often chased by several group members, with one or more individuals pursuing the prey, sometimes in relay fashion. The squirrel is frequently caught when it falls to the ground. These chases are highly coordinated and can last up to five minutes (Rose 1997). This type of relay chase has been described in baboons and chimpanzees (see Volume 3). In Costa Rica, more vertebrate prey are taken during the dry season, which corresponds to the birth season for many of the prey species. Furthermore, adult males account for significantly more chases, captures, and consumption than would be expected from their numbers in the group (Robinson 1986, Fedigan 1990, Table 3-8), but females and juveniles often join in the consumption of vertebrate prey, generally a practice referred to as food-sharing in baboons and chimps. Stalking pursuit used by chimpanzees has not been observed in capuchins.

Are these unexpected patterns of behavior in this New World omnivore? Fedigan (1990) and Rose (1997) believe not, and I concur. Given the availability of different food items eaten by a relatively large omnivore, under certain circumstances it might be expected that vertebrate prey would be relatively more available and less energetically costly than less nutritious plant material and hard to find, small insects. As stated by Fedigan (1990:201):

> . . . we would expect that high rates of vertebrate predation would occur when a set of circumstances arises such that the ease of obtaining vertebrate protein reaches levels where the net energy yield per unit of foraging time is greater than for other food types.

In capuchins, the method of searching for invertebrates is conducive to flushing small vertebrate prey. The group most successful at capturing vertebrates in Costa Rica is in the most marginal habitat. Circumstances during the late dry season, including lower fruit and insect availability and the coincidence of the primary nesting period of three of the most common vertebrate prey—parrots, squirrels, and coatis (Janzen 1983), appear to make hunting for vertebrates a seasonally

Table 3-8 Vertebrate Predation by Group of Capuchin Monkeys at Santa Rosa from January to June 1986: Participation by Age/Sex Class and Types of Prey Taken

	Lizards	Adult	Eggs, birds	Bats nestlings	Squirrels	Coatis	Incidents in which each age/sex class participated %	Age/sex class ever seen to participate %
Adult males (n = 7)								
Chase	3	—	—	—	6	—	100	86
Capture	3	1	—	—	3	2	88	71
Consume	3	1	2	—	5	4	88	100
Adult females (n = 6)								
Chase	—	—	—	—	2	—	38	33
Capture	—	—	—	—	—	—	12	0
Consume	—	—	1	—	2	1	29	50
Juveniles (n = 7)								
Chase	—	—	—	—	1	—	50	29
Capture	—	1	—	2	—	—	12	29
Consume	—	3	—	2	5	5	35	100
Total incidents	3	2	3	1	6	2	17	
Carcasses	3	2	?	2	4	6		

Total group size including infants = 26
[From Fedigan 1990]

worthwhile endeavor for this group. Vertebrate prey become easier to capture at the same time alternate food sources are more difficult to find.

Why do males hunt more and females less? Fedigan (1990) presents three nonexclusive possibilities: (1) Sexual dimorphism: the weight of female capuchins is 70% that of males, and canines are 77% of male size. Prey size is relatively large in relation to the monkeys, and this 25–30% difference in male size could be a major factor in the ability to successfully capture prey. (2) Males forage more on the ground (12% vs. 1%), and certain prey are captured more successfully on the ground. (3) Finally, and perhaps more importantly, females spend most of their adult lives pregnant, lactating, and carrying infants. Hunting for vertebrate prey may be more risky, precarious, and energetically costly for females, especially since dominant males have priority of access to food and can easily take these energy-expensive food items from females.

Rose (1994b) tested these hypotheses and found that the heavier and stronger males did spend more time foraging on or near the ground where they ate larger and more mobile prey, mainly vertebrates and large invertebrates. Females fed more on small invertebrates and larvae. Males also did more strenuous foraging, extracting prey from beneath bark or in tree crevices. Pregnant and lactating females rested more and focused on food that required less energy in capture and little handling. Thus sexual dimorphism and reproductive state did predict sex differences in foraging behavior (Rose 1994b).

Cebus monkeys are highly manipulative, have excellent manual dexterity, and are very exploratory. It is interesting that, along with their pattern of vertebrate hunting, they also are more similar to apes and more proficient than other monkeys in using tools (McGrew and Marchant 1997, Visalberghi 1977, see also other papers in Visalberghi and McGrew 1997 for a summary of comparisons between capuchins and chimpanzees). Visalberghi (1990) reviews tool use in capuchins. They have been observed using stones to crack nuts, shells to crack open oysters, a branch to club a snake, and sticks to probe, dig, groom, and to throw at passers-by. Just as with chimpanzee tool use, it has been hypothesized that capuchins use tools in contexts similar to those hypothesized for early hominids (Westergaard and Suomi 1995). It certainly seems that the ecological, behavioral, and morphological context may be more important in developing models of early hominid evolution than simply relying on taxonomic relationships. I will return to this subject in Volume 3.

BIBLIOGRAPHY

Abate, V. 1984. Bobo, 48-year-old laboratory-maintained cebus. *Lab Animal* 13: cover, 5.

Anderson, J.R. 1996. Chimpanzees and capuchin monkeys: cognitive cognition. Pp. 23–56. In *Reaching into Thought: The Minds of the Great Apes*. A.E. Russon, K.A. Bard, S.T. Parker, Eds., Cambridge, Cambridge University Press.

Aquino, R., Puertas P., Encarnacion F. 1990. Supplemental notes on population parameters of northeastern Peruvian night monkeys, genus *Aotus* (Cebidae). *Am. J. Primatol.* 21:215–221.

Aquino, R., Encarnacion F. 1986. Characteristics and use of sleeping sites in *Aotus* (Cebidae: Primates) in the Amazon lowlands of Peru. *Am. J. Primatol.* 11: 319–331.

Aquino, R., Encarnacion F. 1994. Owl monkey population in Latin America: field work and conservation. Pp. 59–96. In *Aotus: The Owl Monkey*. J.F. Baer, R.E. Weller, I. Kakoma, Eds., New York, Academic.

Baldwin, J.D. 1968. The social behavior of adult male squirrel monkeys (*Saimiri sciureus*) in a seminatural environment. *Folia Primatol.* 9:281–314.

Baldwin, J.D. 1970. Reproductive synchronization in squirrel monkeys (*Saimiri*). *Primates* 11:317–326.

Baldwin, J.D. 1971. The social organization of a semifree-ranging troop of squirrel monkeys (*Saimiri sciureus*). *Folia Primatol.* 14:23–50.

Baldwin, J.D., Baldwin, J.I. 1971. Squirrel monkeys (*Saimiri*) in natural habitats in Panama, Colombia, Brazil, and Peru. *Primates* 12:45–61.

Baldwin, J.D., Baldwin, J.I. 1972. The ecology and behavior of squirrel monkeys (*Saimiri oerstedi*) in a natural forest in western Panama. *Folia Primatol.* 18:161–184.

Baldwin, J.D., Baldwin, J.I. 1981. The squirrel monkeys: *Saimiri*. Pp. 277–330. In *Ecology and Behavior of Neotropical Monkeys. Vol. 1.* A.F. Coimbra-Filho, R.A. Mittermeier, Eds., Rio de Janeiro, Academia Brasileira de Ciências.

Baldwin, L.A., Patterson, T.A., Teleki, G. 1977. Field research on callitrichid and cebid monkeys: an historical, geographical, and bibliographical listing. *Primates* 18:485–507.

Bergeson, D. 1996. *The Positional Behavior and Prehensile Tail Use of* Alouatta palliata, Ateles geoffroyi, *and* Cebus capucinus. Ph.D. Thesis. Washington University, St. Louis.

Bergeson, D. 1998. Patterns of suspensory feeding in *Alouatta palliata, Ateles Geoffroyi,* and *Cebus capucinus.* Pp. 45–60. In *Primate Locomotion: Recent Advances.* E. Strasser, J. Fleagle, A. Rosenberger, H. McHenry, Eds., New York, Plenum.

Bernstein, I.S. 1965. Activity patterns in a *Cebus* monkey group. *Folia Primatol.* 3:211–224.

Bernstein, I.S. 1966. Analysis of a key role in a capuchin (*Cebus albifrons*) Group. *Tulane Studies Zool.* 13:49–54.

Boinski, S. 1986. *The Ecology of Squirrel Monkeys in Costa Rica.* Ph.D. Thesis. University of Texas, Austin.

Boinski, S. 1987a. Habitat use by squirrel monkeys (*Saimiri oerstedii*) in Costa Rica. *Folia Primatol.* 40:151–167.

Boinski, S. 1987b. Mating patterns in squirrel monkey (*Saimiri oerstedii*). Implications for seasonal sexual dimorphism. *Behav. Ecol. Sociobiol.* 21:13–21.

Boinski, S. 1987c. Birth synchrony in squirrel monkeys (*Saimiri oerstedii*) in Costa Rica. *Behav. Ecol. Sociobiol.* 21:393–400.

Boinski, S. 1987d The status of *Saimiri oerstedii citrinellus* in Costa Rica. *Primate Conserv.* 8:67–72.

Boinski, S. 1988. Sex differences in the foraging behavior of squirrel monkeys in a seasonal habitat. *Behav. Ecol. Sociobiol.* 23:177–186.

Boinski, S. 1989a. The positional behavior and substrate use of squirrel monkeys: ecological implications. *J. Hum. Evol.* 18:659–677.

Boinski, S. 1989b. Habitat use in squirrel monkeys (*Saimiri oerstidii*) in Costa Rica. *Folia Primatol.* 49:159–167.

Boinski, S. 1991. The coordination of spatial position: A field study of the vocal behaviour of adult female squirrel monkeys. *Anim. Behav.* 41:89–102.

Boinski, S. 1992. Monkeys with inflated sex appeal. *Nat. Hist.* July: 42–49.

Boinski, S. 1993. Vocal coordination of troop movement among white-faced capuchin monkeys, *Cebus capucinus. Am. J. Primatol.* 30:85–100.

Boinski, S. 1994a. Affiliation patterns among male Costa Rican squirrel monkeys. *Behaviour* 130:191–209.

Boinski, S. 1994b. The Costa Rican squirrel monkey: Waltzing to extinction. *Am. J. Primatol.* 33 (3):196–197.

Boinski, S. 1996. Vocal coordination of troop movement in squirrel monkeys (*Saimiri oerstedi* and *Saimiri sciureus*) and white-faced capuchins (*Cebus capucinus*). Pp. 251–269 In *Adaptive Radiations of Neotropical Primates.* M.A. Norconk, A.L. Rosenberger, P.A. Garber, Eds., New York, Plenum.

Boinski, S. 1999a. Geographic variation in behavior of a primate taxon: stress responses as a proximate mechanism in the evolution of social behavior. Pp. 95–120. In *Geographic Variation in Behavior: Perspectives on Evolutionary Mechanisms.* S.A. Foster, J.A. Endler, Eds., Oxford, Oxford University Press.

Boinski, S. 1999b. The social organization of the squirrel monkeys: implications for ecological models of social evolution. *Evol. Anthropol.* 8:101–112.

Boinski, S. in press. Saimiri. *Illustrated monographs of Living Primates,* Institut voor Ontwikkelingsopdrachten, The Netherlands.

Boinski, S., Campbell, A.F. 1995. Use of trill vocalizations to coordinate troop movement among white-faced capuchins: second field test. *Behaviour* 132:875–901.

Boinski, S., Cropp, S.J. 1999. Disparate data sets resolve squirrel monkey (*Saimiri*) taxonomy: implications for behavioral ecology and biomedical usage. *Int. J. Primatol.* 20: in press.

Boinski, S., Fragaszy D.M. 1989. The ontogeny of foraging in squirrel monkeys, *Saimiri oerstedi. Anim. Behav.* 37:415–428.

Boinski, S., Mitchell, C.L. 1992. Ecological and social factors affecting the vocal behavior of adult female squirrel monkeys. *Ethology* 92:316–330.

Boinski, S., Mitchell, C.L. 1994. Male residence and association patterns in Costa Rican squirrel monkeys (*Saimiri oerstedii*). *Am. J. Primatol.* 34:157–169.

Boinski, S., Mitchell, C.L. 1995. Wild squirrel monkey (*Saimiri sciureus*) "caregiver" calls: contexts and acoustic structure. *Am. J. Primatol.* 35:129–137.

Boinski, S., Scott, P.E. 1988. Association of birds with monkeys in Costa Rica. *Biotropica* 20 (2):136–143.

Brown, A.D., Zunino, G.E. 1990. Dietary variability in *Cebus apella* in extreme habitats: Evidence for adaptability. *Folia Primatol.* 54:187–195.

Butynski, T.M. 1982. Vertebrate predation by primates: a review of hunting patterns and prey. *J. Hum. Evol.* 11:421–430.

Cabrara, A. 1958. Catálogo de los mamiferos de America del Sur. *Revista del museo Argentino Ciencias Naturales "Bernadino Rivadavia"* 4:1–307.

Chapman, C.A. 1986. Boa constrictor predation and group response in white-faced cebus monkeys. *Biotropica* 18:171–172.

Chapman, C.A. 1987. Flexibility in diets of three species of Costa Rican Primates. *Folia Primatol.* 49:90–105.

Chapman, C.A., Fedigan, L.M. 1990. Dietary differences between neighboring *Cebus capucinus* groups: local traditions, food availabiltiy or responses to food profitability? *Folia Primatol.* 54:177–186.

Charles-Dominique, P. 1975. Nocturnal primates and diurnal primates: an ecological interpretation of these two modes of life by analysis of the higher vertebrate fauna in tropical forest ecosystems. Pp. 69–88. In *Phylogeny of the Primates: a multidisciplinary approach.* W.P. Luckett, F.S. Szalay, Eds. New York, Plenum.

Charles-Dominique, P. 1977. *Ecology and Behaviour of Nocturnal Primates.* New York, Columbia University Press.

Chivers, D.J., Raemakers, J.J., Aldrich-Blake, F.P.G. 1975. Long-term observations of siamang behavior. *Folia Primatol.* 23:149.

Coe, C.L., Rosenblum, L.A. 1974. Sexual segregration and its ontogeny in squirrel monkey social structure. *J. Hum. Evol.* 3:551–561.

Costello, R.K., Dickinson, C., Rosenberger, A.L., Boinski, S., and Szalay, F.S. 1993. Squirrel monkey (Genus *Saimiri*) taxonomy; a multidisciplinary study of the biology of species. Pp. 77–210. In *Species, Species Concepts, and Primate Evolution.* Kimbel W.H., Martin L.B., Eds., New York, Plenum.

Crandlemire-Sacco, J. 1988. An ecological comparison of two sympatric primates: *Saguinus fuscicollis* and *Callicebus moloch* of Amazonian Peru. *Primates* 29:465–475.

de Assumção, C.T. 1981. *Cebus apella* and *Brachyteles arachnoides* (Cebidae) as potential pollinators of *Mabea fistulifera* (Euphorbiaceae). *J. Mammal.* 62:386–388.

De Ruiter, J. 1986. The influence of group size on predator scanning and foraging behaviour of wedged-faced capuchin monkeys (*Cebus olivaceus*). *Behaviour* 98:240–258.

Defler, T.R. 1979. On the ecology and behavior of *Cebus albifrons* in northern Columbia, 1: Ecology. *Primates* 20:475–490.

Defler, T.R. 1982. A comparison of intergroup behavior in *Cebus albifrons* and *C. apella*. *Primates* 23:385–392.

Defler, T.R. 1983. Some population characteristics of *Callicebus torquatus lugens* (Humboldt, 1812) (Primates: Cebidae) in eastern Colombia. *Lozania (Acta Zoologica Colombiana)* 38:1–9.

Defler, T.R. 1994. *Callicebus torquatus* is not a white-sand specialist. *Am. J. Primatol.* 33:149–154.

DuMond, F.V. 1968. The squirrel monkey in a seminatural environment. Pp. 87–145. In *The Squirrel Monkey.* L.A. Rosenblum, R.W. Cooper, Eds., New York, Academic.

Durham, N.M. 1975. Some ecological, distribtional, and group behavioral features of Atelinae in southern Peru; with comments on interspecific relations. Pp. 87–101. In *Socioecology and Psychology of Primates.* R.A. Tuttle, Ed., The Hague, Mouton.

Easley, S.P. 1982. *Ecology and Behavior of* Callicebus torquatus. Ph.D. Thesis. Washington University, St. Louis.

Easley, S.P., Kinzey, W.G. 1986. Territorial Shift in the yellow-handed titi monkey. *Am. J. Primatol.* 11:307–318.

Eason, P. 1989. Harpy eagle attempts predation on adult howler monkey. *Condor* 91:469–470.

Eisenberg, J.F. 1989. *Mammals of the Neotropics. Volume 1. The Northern Neotropics.* Chicago, Chicago University Press,.

Eisenberg, J.F., Kuehn, R. 1966. The behavior of *Ateles goeffroyi* and related species. *Smith. Misc. Coll.* 151:1–63.

Emmons, L.E. 1987. Comparative feeding ecology of felids in a Neotropical rain forest. *Behav. Ecol. Sociobiol.* 20:271–283.

Fedigan, L.M. 1990. Vertebrate predation in *Cebus capucinus:* Meat eating in a Neotropical monkey. *Folia Primatol.* 54:196–205.

Fedigan, L.M. 1993. Sex differences and intersexual relations in adult white-faced capuchins, *Cebus capucinus*. *Int. J. Primatol.* 14:853–877.

Fedigan, L.M., Fedigan, L., Chapman, C. 1985. A census of *Alouatta palliata* and *Cebus capucinus* monkeys in Santa Rosa National Park, Costa Rica. Brenesia 23:309–322.

Fedigan, L.M., Rosenberger, A.L., Boinski, S., Norconk, M.A., Garber, P.A. 1996a. Critical issues in cebine evolution and behavior. Pp. 219–228. In *Adaptive Radia-*

tions of Neotropical Primates. M.A. Norconk, A.L. Rosenberger, P.A. Garber, Eds., New York, Plenum.

Fedigan, L.M., Rose, L.M., Avila, R.M. 1996b. See how they grow: tracking capuchin monkey populations in a regenerating Costa Rican dry forest. Pp. 289–307. In *Adaptive Radiations of Neotropical Primates*. M.A. Norconk, A.L. Rosenberger, P.A. Garber, Eds., New York, Plenum.

Fleagle, J.G. 1999. *Primate Adaptation and Evolution*. New York, Academic Press.

Fleagle, J.G., Mittermeier, R.A. 1980. Locomotor behavior, body size and comparative ecology of seven Surinam monkeys. *Am. J. Phys. Anthropol.* 52:301–314.

Fleagle, J.G., Mittermeier, R.A., Skopec, A.L. 1981. Differential habitat use of *Cebus apella* and *Saimiri sciureus* in central Surinam. *Primates* 22:361–367.

Fleming, T.H. 1973. The reproductive cycles of three species of opossums and other mammals in the Panama Canal Zone. *J. Mammal.* 54:439–455.

Ford, S.M., Davis, L.C. 1992. Systematics and body size: Implications for feeding adaptations in New World monkeys. *Am. J. Phys. Anthropol.* 88:415–468.

Ford, S.M., Hobbs, D.G. 1996. Species definition and differentiation as seen in the postcranial skeleton of *Cebus*. Pp. 229–249. In *Adaptive Radiations of Neotropical Primates* M.A. Norconk, A.L. Rosenberger, P.A. Garber, Eds., New York, Plenum.

Fowler, J., Cope, J. 1964. Notes on harpy eagle in British Guiana. *Auk* 81:257–273.

Fragaszy, D.M. 1986. Comparative studies of squirrel monkeys *(Saimiri sciureus)* and titi monkeys *(Callicebus moloch)*: Performance on choice tasks in near space. *J. Comp. Psych.* 100:392–400.

Fragaszy, D.M. 1990. Early behavioral development in capuchins *(Cebus)*. *Folia Primatol.* 54:119–128.

Fragaszy, D.M., Adam-Curtis, L.E. 1998. Growth and reproduction in captive tufted capuchins *(Cebus apella)*. *Am. J. Primatol.* 44:197–203.

Fragaszy, D.M., Boinski, S. 1995. Patterns of individual diet choice and efficiency of foraging in wedge-capped capuchin monkeys *(Cebus olivaceus)*. *J. Comp. Psych.* 4:339–348.

Fragaszy, D.M., Visalberghi, E., Robinson, J.G. 1990. Variability and adaptability in the genus *Cebus*. *Folia Primatol.* 44:114–118.

Freese, C.H. 1977. Food habits of the white-faced capuchins *Cebus capuchinus* L. (Primates: Cebidae) in Santa Rosa National Park, Costa Rica. *Brenesia* 10/11:43–56.

Freese, C.H., Oppenheimer, J.R. 1981. The capuchin monkeys, genus *Cebus*. Pp. 331–390. In *Ecology and Behavior of Neotropical Monkeys. Vol. 1*. A.F. Coimbra-Filho, R.A. Mittermeier, Eds., Rio de Janeiro, Academia Brasileira de Ciências.

Fuentes, A. 1999. Re-evaluating primate monogamy. *Am. Anthropol.* 100:890–907.

Galef, B., Jr., Mittermeier, R., Bailey, R. 1976. Predation by the tayra *(Eira barbara)*. *J. Mammal.* 57:760–761.

Galetti, M., Pedroni, F. 1994. Seasonal diet of capuchin monkeys *(Cebus apella)* in a semideciduous forest in south-east Brazil. *J. Trop. Ecol.* 10:27–39.

Garcia, J.E., Braza, F. 1987. Activity rhythms and use of space of a group of *Aotus azarae*. *Primates* 28:337–342.

Garcia, J.E. and Braza, F. 1989. Densities comparisons using different analytic methods in *Aotus azarae*. *Prim. Rep.* 25:45–52.

Gaulin, S.J.C., Gaulin, C.K. 1982. Behavioral ecology of *Alouatta seniculus* in Andean cloud forest. *Int. J. Primatol.* 3:1–32.

Gebo, D.L. 1989. Locomotor and phylogenetic considerations in anthropoid evolution. *J. Hum. Evol.* 18 (3):201–233.

Gebo, D.L. 1992. Locomotor and postural behavior in *Alouatta palliata* and *Cebus capucinus*. *Am. J. Primatol.* 26 (4):277–290.

Ghiglieri, M.P. 1999. *The Dark Side of Man: Tracing the Origins of Male Violence*. Reading, Perseus Books.

Gozalo, A., Montoya, E. 1990. Reproduction of the owl monkey (*Aotus nancymai*) (Primates: Cebidae) in captivity. *Am. J. Primatol.* 21:61–68.

Green, K.M. 1978. Primate censusing in northern Colombia: a comparison of two techniques. *Primates* 19:537–550.

Hamlett, G.W.D. 1939. Reproduction in American monkeys. I. Estrous cycle, ovulation and menstruation in *Cebus*. *Anat. Rec.* 73:171–187.

Harding, R.S.O., Teleki, G., Eds. 1981. *Omnivorous primates*. New York, Columbia University Press.

Harrison, R.M. 1973. *Ovulation in* Saimiri sciureus: *Induction, Detection and Inhibition*. Ph.D. Thesis. Michigan State University, East Lansing.

Hart, D. 2000. *Primates as Prey*. Ph.D. Thesis. Washington University, St. Louis.

Harvey, P.H., Martin, R.D., Clutton-Brock, T.H. 1987. Life histories in comparative perspective. Pp. 181–196. In *Primate Societies*. B. Smuts, D. Cheney, R. Seyfarth, R. Wrangham, T. Struhsaker, Eds., Chicago, University of Chicago Press.

Heiduck, S. 1997. Food choice in masked titi monkeys (*Callicebus personatus melanochir*): selectivity or opportunism. *Int. J. Primatol.* 18:487–502.

Heltne, P.G. 1977. Census of *Aotus* in the north of Colombia. Report on *PAHO project AMRO-3171*. Washington, D.C., Pan American Health Organization.

Hernández-Camacho, J., Cooper, R.W. 1976. The non-human primates of Colombia. Pp. 35–69. In *Neotropical Primates*. R.W. Thorington, Jr., P.W. Heltne, Eds., Washington, D.C., National Academy of Sciences.

Hershkovitz, P. 1977. *Living New World Primates*. Vol. 1. Chicago, University of Chicago.

Hershkovitz, P. 1983. Two new species of night monkeys, genus *Aotus* (Cebidae, Platyrrhini): A preliminary report on *Aotus* taxonomy. *Am. J. Primatol.* 4 (3) : 209–244.

Hladik, A., Hladik, C.M. 1969. Rapports trophiques entre vegétation et primates dans la forêt de Barro-Colorado (Panama). *Terre et Vie* 1:25–117.

Hunter, J., Martin, R.D., Dixson, A.F., Rudder, B.C. 1979. Gestation and interbirth interval in the owl monkey (*Aotus trivirgatus griseimembra*). *Folia Primatol.* 31:165–175.

Izawa, K. 1980. Social behavior of the wild black-capped capuchins (*Cebus apella*). *Primates*:21:443–467.

Izawa, K. 1992. Social changes within a group of wild black-capped capuchins (Cebus apella). III. *Field Studies of New World Monkeys, La Macerena, Columbia.* 7:9–14.

Izawa, K. 1994. Group division of wild black-capped capuchins. *Field Studies of New World Monkeys, La Macerena, Columbia.* 9:5–14.

Janson, C.H. 1975. *Ecology and Population Densities of Primates in a Peruvian Rainforest.* Ph.D. Thesis. Princeton University, Princeton.

Janson, C.H. 1984. Female choice and mating system of the brown capuchin monkey (*Cebus apella*) (Primates:Cebidae). *Z. Tierpyschol.* 65:177–200.

Janson, C.H. 1986a. Capuchin counterpoint. *Nat. Hist.* 95:44–53.

Janson, C.H. 1986b. *Ecological and social consequences of food competition in brown capuchin monkeys.* Ph.D. Thesis. University of Washington, Seattle.

Janson, C.H. 1990b. Ecological consequences of individual spatial choices in foraging groups of brown capuchin monkeys, *Cebus apella. Anim. Behav.* 40:922–934.

Janson, C.H., Boinski, S. 1992. Morphological and behavioral adaptations for foraging in generalist primates: the case of the Cebines. *Am. J. Phys. Anthropol.* 88:483–498.

Janson, C.H., Terborgh, J., Emmons, L.H. 1981. Non-flying mammals as pollinating agents in the Amazonian forest. *Biotropica,* Reproductive Botany Supplement:1–6.

Jantschke, B., Welker, C; Klaiber-Schuh, 1995. A. Notes on breeding of the titi monkey *Callicebus cupreus. Folia Primatol.* 65:210–213.

Janzen, D.H. 1974. Tropical blackwater rivers, animals, and mast fruiting by Dipterocaraceae. *Biotropica* 6:69–103.

Janzen, D.H. 1983. Costa Rican natural History. Chicago, University of Chicago Press.

Kay, R.F. 1973. *Mastication, Molar Tooth Structure and Diet in Primates.* Ph.D. Thesis. Yale University, New Haven.

Kay, R.F. 1975. The functional adaptations of primate molar teeth. *Am. J. Phys. Anthropol.* 43:195–216.

Kay, R.F. 1984. On the use of anatomical features to infer foraging behavior in extinct primates. Pp. 21–53. *Adaptations for Foraging in Nonhuman Primates: Contributions to an Organismal Biology of Prosimians, Monkeys, and Apes.* P. S. Rodman, J. G. H. Cant, Eds., New York, Columbia University Press.

Kinzey, W.G. 1977. Diet and feeding behaviour of *Callicebus torquatus.* Pp. 127–151. In *Primate Ecology: Studies of Feeding and Ranging Behaviour in Lemurs, Monkeys and Apes.* T.H. Clutton-Brock, Ed., London, Academic.

Kinzey, W.G. 1978. Feeding behaviour and molar features in two species of titi monkey. Pp. 373–385. In *Recent Advances in Primatology, Vol. 1, Behaviour.* D.J. Chivers; J. Herbert, Eds., London, Academic.

Kinzey, W.G. 1981. The titi monkeys, genus *Callicebus.* Pp. 241–276. In *Ecology and Behavior of Neotropical Monkeys. Vol. 1.* A.F. Coimbra-Filho, R.A. Mittermeier, Eds., Rio de Janeiro, Academia Brasileira de Ciências.

Kinzey, W.G. 1986. Feeding, travel distance and group size in *Callicebus torquatus. Prim. Rep.* 14:11.

Kinzey, W.G. 1997a. *New World Primates: Ecology, Evolution, and Behavior.* New York, Aldine de Gruyter.

Kinzey, W.G. 1997b. New World primate studies. Pp. 743–748. In *History of Physical Anthropology: An Encyclopedia.* F. Spencer, Ed., New York, Garland.

Kinzey, W.G., Becker, 1983. Activity pattern of the masked titi monkey, *Callicebus personatus. Primates* 24:337–343.

Kinzey, W.G., Gentry A.H. 1979. Habitat utilization in two species of *Callicebus.* Pp. 89–100. In *Primate Ecology: Problem-Oriented Field Studies.* R.W. Sussman, Ed., New York, Wiley.

Kinzey, W.G., Robinson, J.G. 1983. Intergroup loud calls, range size and spacing in *Callicebus torquatus. Am. J. Phys. Anthrop.* 60:539–544.

Kinzey, W.G., Rosenberger, A.L. Reisler, P.S., Prowse, D.L., Trilling, J.S. 1977. A preliminary field investigation of the yellow handed titi monkey, *Callicebus torquatus torquatus,* in northern Peru. *Primates* 18:159–181.

Kinzey, W.G., Wright, P.C. 1982. Grooming behavior in the titi monkey, *Callicebus torquatus. Am. J. Primatol.* 3:267–275.

Klein, L.L., Klein, D.J. 1973. Observations on two types of neotropical primate inter-taxa associations. *Am. J. Phys. Anthropol.* 38:649–654.

Klein, L.L., Klein, D.J. 1975. Social and ecological contrasts between four taxa of neotropical primates. Pp. 59–85. In *Socioecology and Psychology of Primates.* R.A. Tuttle, Ed., The Hague, Mouton.

Lambert, J.E., Garber, P.A., Eds. 1998. *Special Issue: Primate Seed Dispersal. Am. J. Primatol.* 45:1–144.

Leigh, E.G., Rand, A.S., Windsor, D.M., Eds. 1982. *The Ecology of a Tropical Forest: Seasonal Rhythms and Long-Term Changes.* Washington, D.C. Smithsonian Institution Press.

Mann, F.G. 1956. Efecto del frio en mamiferos amazonicos. *Invest. Zool. Chilenas* 3:155.

Manson, J.H., Perry, S., Parish, A.R. 1997. Nonconceptive mating behavior in bonobos and capuchins. *Int. J. Primatol.* 18:767–768.

Manson, J.H., Rose, L.M., Perry, S., Gros-Louis, J. 1999. Dynamics of female-female relationships in wild *Cebus capucinus:* data from two Costa Rican sites. *Int. J. Primatol.* 20:679–706.

Martin, R.D. 1990. *Primate Origins and Evolution.* Princeton, Princeton University Press.

Mason, W.A. 1965. Territorial behavior in *Callicebus* monkeys. *Am. Zool.* 5:675.

Mason, W.A. 1966. Social organization of the South American monkey, *Callicebus moloch,* a preliminary report. *Tulane Stud. Zool.* 13:23–28.

Mason, W.A. 1968. Use of space by *Callicebus* groups. Pp. 200–216. In *Primates, Studies in Adaptation and Variability.* P. Jay, Ed., New York, Holt, Rhinehart, Winston.

Massey, A. 1987. A population survey of *Alouatta palliata, Cebus capucinus,* and *Ateles geoffroyi* at Palo Verde, Costa Rica. *Revista de Biologia Tropical* 35:345–347.

McGrew, W.C., Marchant, L.F. 1997. Using the tools at hand: manual laterality and elementary technology in *Cebus* spp. and *Pan* spp. *Int. J. Primatol.* 18:787–810.

Mendes Pontes, A.R. 1997. Habitat partitioning among primates in Maracá Island, Roraima, Northern Brazilian Amazonia. *Int. J. Primatol.* 18:131–157.

Mendoza, S.P., Lowe, E.L., Levine, S. 1978. Social organization and social behavior in two subspecies of squirrel monkey (*Saimiri sciureus*). *Folia Primatol.* 30:126–144.

Miller, L.E. 1996 The behavioral ecology of wedge-capped capuchins (*Cebus Olivaceus*). Pp. 271–288. In *Adaptive Radiations of Neotropical Primates.* M.A. Norconk, A.L. Rosenberger, P.A. Garber, Eds., New York, Plenum.

Mitchell, C.L. 1990. *The Ecological Basis for Female Social Dominance: A Behavioral Study of the Squirrel Monkey* (Saimiri sciureus) *in the Wild.* Ph.D. Thesis. Princeton University, Princeton.

Mitchell, C., Boinski, S., van Schaik, C.P. 1991. Competitive regimes and female bonding in two species of squirrel monkey (*Saimiri oerstedii* and *Saimiri sciureus*). *Behav. Ecol. Sociobiol.* 28:55–60.

Mittermeier, R.A., Coimbra-Filho, A.F. 1977. Primate conservation in Brazilian Amazonia. Pp. 117–166. In *Primate Conservation.* Prince Rainier of Monaco, G. Bourne, Eds., New York, Academic.

Mittermeier, R.A., Rylands, A.B., Coimbra-Filho, A.F. 1988. Systematics: Species and Subspecies—an update. Pp. 13–75. In *Ecology and Behavior of Neotropical Primates.* R.A. Mittermeier, A.B. Rylands, A.F. Coimbra-Filho, G.A.B. Fonseca, Eds., Washington, D.C., World Wildlife Fund.

Mittermeier, R.A., van Roosmalen, M.G.M. 1981. Preliminary observations on habitat utilization and diet in eight Suriname monkeys. *Folia Primatol.* 36:1–39.

Moore, J. 1984. Female transfer in primates. *Int. J. Primatol.* 5:537–590.

Moynihan, M. 1964. Some behavior patterns of platyrrhine monkeys. The night monkey (*Aotus trivirgatus*). *Smith. Misc. Coll.* 146:1–84.

Moynihan, M. 1966. Communication in *Callicebus. J. Zool. Soc. London* 150:77–127.

Moynihan, M. 1976. *The New World Primates.* Princeton, Princeton University Press.

Müller K.-H. 1995. Ranging in masked titi monkeys (*Callicebus personatus*) in Brazil. *Folia Primatol.* 65:224–228.

Müller K.-H. 1996. Diet and feeding ecology of masked titis (*Callicebus personatus*) in Brazil. Pp. 383–401. In *Adaptive Radiations of Neotropical Primates.* M.A. Norconk, A.L. Rosenberger, P.A. Garber, Eds., New York, Plenum.

Norconk, M.A., Rosenberger, A.L., Garber, P.A. 1996. *Adaptive Radiations of Neotropical Primates.* New York, Plenum.

Norris, J.C. 1990. *The semantics of* Cebus olivaceus *alarm calls: object designation and attribution.* Ph.D. Thesis. University of Florida, Gainsville.

O'Brien, T.G. 1988. Parasitic nursing behavior in the wedge-capped capuchin monkey (*Cebus olivaceus*). *Am. J. Primatol.* 16:341–344.

O'Brien, T.G. 1990. *Determinants and consequences of social structure in a Neotropical primate,* Cebus olivaceus. Ph.D. Thesis. University of Florida, Gainsville.

O'Brien, T.G. 1991. Female-male social interaction in wedge-capped capuchin monkeys: benefits and costs of group living. *Anim. Behav.* 41:555–567.

O'Brien, T.G. 1993. Allogrooming behaviour among adult female wedge-capped capuchin monkeys. *Anim. Behav.* 46:499–510.

O'Brien, T.G., Robinson, J.G. 1991. Allomaternal care by female wedge-capped capuchin monkeys: effects of age, rank and relatedness. *Behaviour* 119:30–50.

O'Brien, T.G., Robinson, J.G. 1993. Stabiltiy of social relationships in female wedge-capped capuchin monkeys. Pp. 197–210. In *Juvenile Primates: Development and behaviour.* M.E. Pereira, L.A. Fairbanks, Eds., Oxford, Oxford University Press.

Oppenheimer, J.R. 1968. *Behavior and Ecology of the White-faced Monkey,* Cebus capucinus, *on Barro Colorado Island, C.Z.* Ph.D. Thesis. University of Illinois, Urbana.

Oppenheimer, J.R. 1969. Changes in forehead patterns and group composition of the white-faced capuchin (*Cebus capucinus*). *Proc. 2nd Int. Congr. Primat. Vol. 1*:36–42. Basel, Karger.

Oppenheimer, J.R. 1973. Social and communicatory behavior in the *Cebus* monkey. Pp. 251–271. In *Behavioral Regulators of Behavior in Primates.* C.R. Carpenter, Ed., Lewisburg, Bucknell University Press.

Oppenheimer, J.R. 1977. Forest structure and its relation to activity of the capuchin monkey (*Cebus*). Pp. 74–84. In *Use of Non-human Primates in Biomedical Research.* M.R.N. Prasad, T.C.A. Kumar, Eds., New Delhi, Indian National Science Academy.

Oppenheimer, J.R. 1982. *Cebus capucinus:* Home range, population dynamics, and interspecific relationships. Pp. 253–270. In *The Ecology of a Tropical Forest: Seasonal Rhythms and Long-term Changes.* E.G. Leigh, A.S. Rand, D.M. Windsor, Eds., Washington, D.C., Smithsonian Institution Press.

Palacios, E., Rodriguez, A., Defler, T.R. 1997. Diet of a group of *Callicebus torquatus lugens* (Humboldt, 1812) during the annual resource bottleneck in Amazonian Colombia. *Int. J. Primatol.* 18:503–522.

Peres, C.A. 1991. Seed predation of *Cariniana micrantha* (Lecythidaceae) by brown capuchin monkeys in Central Amazonia. *Biotropica* 23:262–270.

Perry, S. 1996a. Female-female social relationships in wild white-faced capuchin monkeys, *Cebus capucinus. Am. J. Primatol.* 40:167–182.

Perry, S. 1996b. Intergroup encounters in wild white-faced capuchin monkeys (*Cebus capucinus*). *Int. J. Primatol.* 17:309–330.

Perry, S. 1997. Male-female social relationships in wild white-faced capuchin monkeys (*Cebus capucinus*). *Behaviour* 134:477–510.

Perry, S. 1998. Male-male social relationships in wild white-faced capuchin monkeys (*Cebus capucinus*). *Behaviour* 135:139–172.

Phillips, K.A. 1995. Resource patch size and flexible foraging in white-faced capuchins (*Cebus capucinus*). *Int. J. Primatol.* 16:509–519.

Podolsky, R.D. 1990. Effects of mixed-species association on resource use by *Saimiri sciureus* and *Cebus apella. Am. J. Primatol.* 21:147–158.

Prance, G.T. 1980. A note on the probable pollination of Combretum by *Cebus* monkeys. *Biotropica* 12:239.

Pyke, G.H., Pulliam, H.R., Charnov, E.L. 1977. Optimal foraging: a selective review of theory and tests. *Quart. Rev. Biol.* 52:137–153.

Rathbun, G.B., Gache, M. 1977. The status of *Aotus trivirgatus* in Argentina. *Centro Argentino de Primates and National Institutes of Health Report.* Washington, D.C.

Rathbun, G.B., Gache, M. 1980. Ecological survey of the night monkey, *Aotus trivirgatus, in* Formosa Province, Argentina. *Primates* 21:211–219.

Rettig, N. 1978. Breeding behavior of the harpy eagle *(Harpia harpyja)*. *Auk* 95:629–643.

Robinson, J.G. 1977. *Vocal regulation of spacing in the titi monkey,* Callicebus moloch. Ph.D. Thesis. Univ. of North Carolina, Chapel Hill.

Robinson, J.G. 1979a Vocal regulation of use of space by groups of titi monkeys, *Callicebus moloch. Behav. Ecol. Sociobiol.* 5:1–15.

Robinson, J.G. 1979b. An analysis of the organization of vocal communication in the titi monkey, *Calliebus moloch. Z. Tierpsychol.* 49:381–405.

Robinson, J.G. 1981a. Spatial structure in foraging groups of wedge-capped capuchin monkeys *Cebus nigrivittatus. Anim. Behav.* 29:1036–1056.

Robinson, J.G. 1981b. Vocal regulation of inter- and intra-group spacing during boundary encounters in the titi monkey *Callicebus moloch. Primates* 22:161–172.

Robinson, J.G. 1984a. Diurnal variation in foraging and diet in the wedge-capped capuchin monkey, *Cebus olivaceus. Folia Primatol.* 43:216–228.

Robinson, J.G. 1984b. Syntactic structures in the vocalizations of wedge-capped capuchin monkeys, *Cebus olivaceus. Behaviour* 90:46–79.

Robinson, J.G. 1986. Seasonal variation in use of time and space by the wedge-capped capuchin monkey *Cebus olivaceus:* Implications for foraging theory. *Smith. Contrib. to Zool. No. 431.* Washington D.C., Smithsonian Institution Press.

Robinson, J.G. 1988. Demography and group structure in wedge-capped capuchin monkeys, Cebus olivaceus. *Behaviour* 104:202–231.

Robinson, J.G., Janson, C.H. 1987. Capuchins, squirrel monkeys, and atelines: Socioecological convergence with Old World primates. Pp. 69–82. In *Primate Societies.* B.B. Smuts, D.L. Cheney, R.M. Seyfarth, R.W. Wrangham, T.T. Struhsaker, Eds., Chicago, University of Chicago Press.

Robinson, J.G., Wright, P.C., Kinzey, W.G. 1987. Monogamous cebids and their relatives: Intergroup calls and spacing. Pp. 44–53. In *Primate Societies.* B.B. Smuts, D.L. Cheney, R.M. Seyfarth, R.W. Wrangham, T.T. Struhsaker, Eds., Chicago, University of Chicago Press.

Rose, L.M. 1994 a. Benefits and costs of resident males to females in white-faced capuchins, *Cebus capuchinus. Am. J. Primatol.* 32:235–238.

Rose, L.M. 1994 b. Sex differences in diet and foraging behavior in white-faced capuchins (*Cebus capuchinus*). *Int. J. Primatol.* 15:95–114.

Rose, L.M. 1997. Vertebrate predation and food-sharing in *Cebus* and *Pan. Int. J. Primatol.* 15:727–765.

Rose, L.M. 1998. *Behavioral Ecology of White-faced Capuchins* (Cebus capucinus) *in Costa Rica.* Ph.D. Thesis. Washington University, St. Louis.

Rose, L.M. 2001. Meat and the early human diet: insights from Neotropical primate studies. pp. 141–159. In *Meat Eating and Human Evolution.* C.B. Stanford, H.T. Bunn, Eds., Oxford, Oxford University Press.

Rose, L.M., Fedigan, L.M. 1995. Vigilance in white-faced capuchins, *Cebus capucinus. Anim. Behav.* 49:63–70.

Rose, L.M., Marshall, F. 1996. Meat eating, hominid sociality, and home bases revisited. *Curr. Anthropol.* 37:307–338.

Rosenberger, A.L. 1983. Tale of tails: parallelism and prehensility. *Am. J. Phys. Anthropol.* 60:103–107.

Rosenberger, A.L., Hartwig, W.C., Takai, M., Setoguchi, T., Shigehara, N. 1991. Dental variability in *Saimiri* and the taxonomic status of *Neosaimiri fieldsi,* an early squirrel monkey from La Venta, Colombia. *Int. J. Primatol.* 12:291–301.

Rowe, N. 1996. *The Pictorial Guide to the Living Primates.* East Hampton, Pagonias Press.

Rylands, A.B. 1995. A species list for the New World primates (Platyrrhini): distribution by country, endemism, and conservation status according to the Mace-Land system. *Neotropical Primates* 3 suppl.:113–164.

Sassenrath, E.N., Mason, W.A., Fitzgerald, R.C., Kenney, M.D. 1980. Comparative endocrine correlates of reproductive states in *Callicebus* (titi) and *Saimiri* (squirrel) monkeys. *Anthropologia Contemporanea* 3:265.

Schneider, H., Rosenberger, A.L. 1996. Molecules, morphology, and platyrrhine systematics. Pp. 3–19. In *Adaptive Radiations of Neotropical Primates.* M.A. Norconk, A.L. Rosenberger, P.A. Garber, Eds., New York, Plenum.

Sleeper, B. 1997. *Primates: The Amazing World of Lemurs, Monkeys, and Apes.* San Francisco, Chronicle Books.

Smith, R.J., Jungers, W.L. 1997. Body mass in comparative primatology. *J. Hum. Evol.* 32:523–559.

Soini, P. 1972. The capture and commerce of live monkeys in the Amazonian region of Peru. *Int. Zoo. Yrbk.* 12:26–36.

Stallings, J. 1984. *Status and Conservation of Paraguayan Primates.* M.A. Thesis. University of Florida, Gainesville.

Stanford, C.B. 1999. *The Hunting Apes: Meat Eating and the Origins of Human Behavior.* Princeton, Princeton University Press.

Stark, N., Kinzey, W.G., Pawlowski, P. 1980. Soil fertility and animal distribution. *Proceedings, Symposium of Tropical Ecology, Kuala Lumpur, 1978; Tropical and Development,* pp. 101–111.

Strayer, F.F., Bovenkirk, A., Koopman, R.F. 1975. Social affiliation and dominance in captive squirrel monkeys (*Saimiri sciureus*). *J. Comp. Physiol. Psych.* 89:308–318.

Struhsaker, T.T., Leland, L. 1977. Palm-nut smashing by *Cebus a. apella* in Colombia. *Biotropica* 9:124–126.

Sussman, R.W. 1987. Morpho-physiological analysis of diets: species-specific dietary patterns in primates and human dietary adaptations. Pp. 151–179. In *The Evo-*

lution of Human Behavior: Primate Models. W.G. Kinzey, Ed., Albany, State University of New York Press.

Sussman, R.W. 1992. Smell as a signal. Pp. 157–160. In *The Cambridge Encyclopedia of Human Evolution.* R.D. Martin; D.R. Pilbeam; J.S. Jones, Eds., Cambridge, Cambridge University Press.

Sussman, R.W. 1999. The myth of man the hunter/man the killer and the evolution of human morality. Pp. 121–129. In *The Biological Basis of Human Behavior: A Critical Review.* R. W. Sussman, Ed., Upper Saddle River, Prentice Hall.

Sussman, R.W., Philips-Conroy, J. 1995. A survey on the distribution and density of the primates of Guyana. *Int. J. Primatol.* 16:761–792.

Sussman, R.W., Tattersall, I. 1976. Cycles of activity, group composition and diet of *Lemur mongoz mongoz* (Linnaeus, 1766) in Madagascar. *Folia Primatol.* 26:270–283.

Tenaza. R.R. 1975. Territory and monogamy among Kloss' gibbon (*Hylobates klossii*) in Siberut Island, Indonesia. *Folia Primatol.* 24:68–80.

Terborgh, J. 1980. Causes of tropical species diversity. *Actis XVII Congr. Internat. Ornithol.*:955–961.

Terborgh, J. 1983. *Five New World Primates: A Study in Comparative Ecology.* Princeton, Princeton University Press.

Terborgh, J. 1986. Keystone plant resources in the tropical forest. Pp. 330–344. In *Conservation Biology.* M.E. Soule, Ed., Sunderland, MA, Sinauer.

Thorington, R.W., Jr. 1968. Observations of Squirrel monkeys in a Colombian forest. Pp. 69–85. In *The Squirrel Monkey.* L.A. Rosenblum, R.W. Cooper, Eds., New York Academic Press.

Thorington, R.W., Jr., Muckenhirn, N.A., Montgomery, G.G. 1976. Movements of a wild night monkey (*Aotus trivirgatus*). Pp. 32–34. In *Neotropical Primates, Field Studies and Conservation.* R.W. Thorington, P.G. Heltne, Eds., Washington, D.C., Nat. Acad. Science.

Tilson, R.L. 1981. Family formation strategies of Kloss's gibbons. *Folia Primatol.* 35:259–287.

Van Schaik, C.P., van Noordwijk, M.A. 1989. The special role of male *Cebus* in predation avoidance and its effect on group composition. *Behav. Ecol. Sociobiol.* 24:265–276.

Visalberghi, E. 1990. Tool use in *Cebus. Folia Primatol.* 54:146–154.

Visalberghi, E. 1997. Success and understanding in cognitive tasks: a comparison between *Cebus apella* and *Pan troglodytes. Intl. J. Primatol.* 18:811–830.

Visalberghi, E., McGrew, W.C. 1997. Special Issue: *Cebus* meets *Pan. Int. J. Primatol.* 18:677–854.

Wallace, R.B., Painter, R.L.E., Taber, A.B. 1998. Primate diversity, habitat preferences, and population density estimates in Noel Kempff Mercado National Park, Santa Cruz Department, Bolivia. *Am. J. Primatol.* 46:197–211.

Waser, P.M. 1976. *Cercocebus albigena:* site attachment, avoidance and intergroup spacing. *Am. Nat.* 110:911–935.

Waser, P.M., Wiley, R.H. 1980. Mechanisms and evolution of spacing in animals. Pp. 159–233. In *Handbook of Behavioral Neurobiology. Vol. 3*. P. Marler, J.G. Vanderbergh, Eds., New York, Plenum.

Westergaard, G.C., Suomi, S.J. 1995. The production and use of digging tools by monkeys: a nonhuman primate model of hominid subsistence activity. *J. Anthropol. Res.* 51:1–8.

Wolfheim, J.H. 1983. *Primates of the World: Distribution, Abundance, and Conservation.* Seattle, University of Washington Press.

Wrangham, R., Peterson, D. 1996. *Demonic Males: Apes and the Origins of Human Violence.* New York, Houghton and Mifflin.

Wright, E.M., Jr., Fush, D.E. 1977. The reproductive cycle of the capuchin (*Cebus apella*). *Lab. Anim. Sci.* 27:651–654.

Wright, P.C. 1978. Home range, activity pattern, and agonistic encounters of a group of night monkeys (*Aotus trivirgatus*) in Peru. *Folia Primatol.* 29:43–55.

Wright, P.C. 1979. Patterns of grooming behavior in *Callicebus* and *Aotus. Am. J. Phys. Anthrop.* 50:494.

Wright, P.C. 1981. The night monkey, genus *Aotus.* Pp. 211–240. In *Ecology and Behavior of Neotropical Monkeys. Vol. 1*. A.F. Coimbra-Filho, R.A. Mittermeier, Eds., Rio de Janeiro, Academia Brasileira de Ciências.

Wright, P.C. 1982. Adaptive advantages of nocturnality in *Aotus. Am. J. Phys. Anthropol.* 57:242.

Wright, P.C. 1984. Biparental care in *Aotus trivirgatus* and *Callicebus moloch.* Pp. 59–75. In *Female Primates: Studies by Women Primatologists*. M. Small, Ed., New York, Liss.

Wright, P.C. 1985. *The Costs and Benefits of nocturnality for Aotus trivirgatus (The night monkey).* Ph.D. Thesis. City University of New York, New York.

Wright, P.C. 1986. Ecological correlates of monogamy in *Aotus* and *Callicebus.* Pp. 159–167. In *Primate Ecology and Conservation*. J. Else, P. Lee, Eds., Cambridge, Cambridge University Press.

Wright, P.C. 1989. The nocturnal primate niche in the New World. *J. Hum. Evol.* 18:635–658.

Wright, P.C. 1990. Patterns of paternal care in primates. *Int. J. Primat.* 11:89–102.

Wright, P.C. 1994. Night Watch on the Amazon. *Nat. Hist.* 103:44–51.

Wright, P.C. 1996. The neotropical primate adaptation to nocturnality. Pp. 369–382. In *Adaptive Radiations of Neotropical Primates*. M.A. Norconk; A.L. Rosenberger; P.A. Garber, Eds., New York, Plenum.

CHAPTER 4

Atelidae

INTRODUCTION

Atelidae is divided into two subfamilies: Atelinae and Pitheciinae. Four genera are included in the subfamily Atelinae: *Ateles,* the spider monkey; *Lagothrix,* the woolly monkey; *Brachyteles,* the woolly spider monkey or muriqui; and *Alouatta,* the howler monkey. All members of the subfamily have prehensile tails with an area of naked skin at the end of the tail. *Ateles* and some *Brachyteles* have lost the thumb (pollex), and the hands are elongated and used as hooks. Except for *Alouatta,* monkeys in this subfamily have an erect or orthograde posture, and their postcranial morphology is adapted for suspension below branches.

Ateles is very slender, with extremely long arms and legs giving it a spidery appearance as indicated by its common name. There currently are four species of *Ateles* recognized (Table 4-1) (but see Kinzey 1997a): *A. geoffroyi, A. fusciceps, A. belzebuth,* and *A. paniscus.* Spider monkeys have a wide geographical range, extending from southern Mexico through Central America and the Amazon as far south as northeastern Peru, eastern Bolivia, and northern Brazil (Fig. 4-1a & b).

Woolly monkeys have thick woolly fur and are sturdily built with robust limbs. They weigh approximately 7–8 kg (Table 4-1). Two species are recognized, *L. lagotricha* and *L. flavicauda.* The former species is found in the upper Amazon basin of Brazil, Peru, Equador, and the Andean headwaters of the Orinoco in Colombia and Venezuela (Ramirez 1988). *L. flavicauda* is restricted to a very small area of mountain rain forest in northern Peru and is one of the rarest of all New World species (Fig. 4-2) (Mittermeir et al. 1984, Leo Luna 1987).

Brachyteles weighs around 8–10 kg. (Lemos de Sá and Glander 1993) (Table 4-1) and is the largest endemic mammal in Brazil (Milton 1986). It is intermediate between *Ateles* and *Lagothrix* in build and pelage. It is confined to the Atlantic coastal forests of southeastern Brazil (Fig. 4-1b). At present, most primatologists recognize only one species of woolly spider monkey, *B. arachnoides.* However, the taxonomic division between northern and southern populations is still under discussion (Lemos de Sá and Glander 1993, Rylands et al. 1995, 1996, Strier and Fonseca 1996/97). *Brachyteles* and *Leontopithecus* are the most endangered

125

Table 4-1 Taxonomy, Common Names, and Weight of Atelidae

Species	Family: Atelidae Common Name	M. Weight	N	F. Weight	N
Subfamily: Atelinae					
Ateles geoffroyi	Black-handed spider monkey	7.78	25	7.29	63
A. fusciceps	Brown-headed spider monkey	8.89	6	9.16	11
A. belzebuth	Long-haired spider monkey	8.29	12	7.85	20
A. paniscus	Black spider monkey	9.11	20	8.44	42
Lagothrix lagotricha	Common woolly monkey	7.15	4	8.07	3
L. flavicauda	Yellow-tailed woolly monkey	around 10 Kg			
Brachyteles arachnoides		9.61	4	8.07	6
Alouatta seniculus	Red howler	6.31	64	4.67	46
A. belzebul	Black & red howler	7.27	26	5.52	26
A. fusca	Brown howler	6.3	4	4.35	5
A. palliata	Mantled howler	7.15	110+	5.35	177+
A. coibensis	Coiba Island howler	—	—	—	—
A. pigra	Black howler	.4		6.43	4
A. caraya	Black howler	6.4	58	4.33	117
Subfamily: Pitheciinae					
Pithecia pithecia	White-faced saki	1.94	10	1.58	4
P. monachus	Monk saki	2.61	16	2.11	10
Chiropotes satanus	Black-bearded saki	2.90	20	2.58	19
C. albinasus	White-nosed bearded saki	3.15	7	2.52	10
Cacajao calvus	Bald uakari	3.45	1	2.88	2
C. malanocephalus	Black-headed uakari	3.16	5	2.71	6

Adapted from: Smith and Jungers 1997; Original references are included therein. All data are from free-ranging animals.

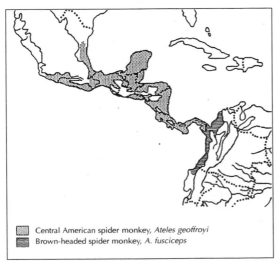

Figure 4-1a Distribution of spider monkeys in Central America. [From Emmons 1990]

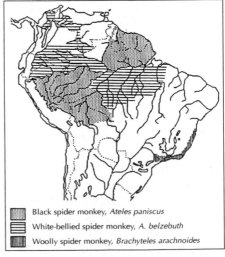

Figure 4-1b Distribution of spider monkeys and woolly spider monkeys in South America. [From Emmons 1990]

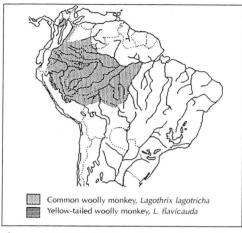

Figure 4-2 Distribution of woolly monkeys. [From Emmons 1990]

genera of neotropical primate (Mittermeier et al. 1989, Rylands et al. 1996/97).

The genus *Alouatta* (the howler monkey) is in need of revision, but Mittermeier et al. (1988) include seven species: *A. seniculus, A. belzebul, A. fusca, A. palliata, A. coibensis, A. pigra,* and *A. caraya.* Howlers weigh between 4 and >11 kg, depending upon species and sex. *Alouatta* is adapted behaviorally, and to some extent morphologically, for a highly folivorous diet. Howler monkeys are distributed from southern Mexico to northern Argentina and as far east as the coastal forests of Brazil. They have the largest geographical range of all 16 New World monkey genera (Fig. 4-3).

The subfamily Pitheciinae contains three genera: *Pithecia, Chiropotes,* and *Cacajao. Pithecia* (the saki monkey) weighs around 1.5 to 2.6 kg. Currently, five species in two species groups (*P. pithecia* and *P. monachus*) are recognized by most authors (Hershkovitz 1987a, Mittermeier et al. 1988, Kinzey 1997a). *P. pithecia* is located north of the Amazon River, whereas the four species of the *P. monachus* group are to the south of the Amazon (Fig. 4-4). Saki monkeys have characteristic long, fluffy hair, which makes them look larger than they are and a long, bushy, nonprehensile tail.

Chiropotes (the bearded saki) is slightly larger than *Pithecia,* weighing around 2.5 to 3.15 kg. It is characterized by a distinct beard, bulbous temporal swelling, and a long, thickly-haired tail. The genus contains two allopatric species: *C. satanus* of Amazonia and *C. albinasus* of Brazil south of the Amazon (Hershkovitz 1985, Fig. 4-5). The genus *Cacajao* (uakari) contains two species: *C. calvus* and *C. melanocephalus* (Hershkovitz 1987b). These monkeys are similar in weight to *Chiropotes,* around 2.5–3.5 kg. The uakari is characterized by its strange, bare face and short tail measuring about one-third of the head-to-body length. *Cacajao* is restricted

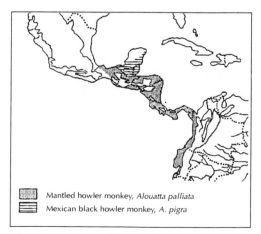

Figure 4-3a Distribution of howler monkeys in Central America. [From Emmons 1990]

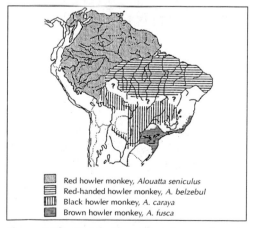

Figure 4-3b Distribution of howler monkeys in South America. [From Emmons 1990]

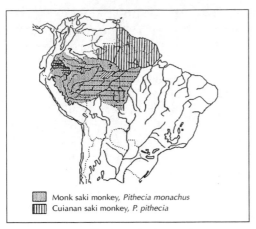

Figure 4-4 Distribution of saki monkeys. [From Emmons 1990]

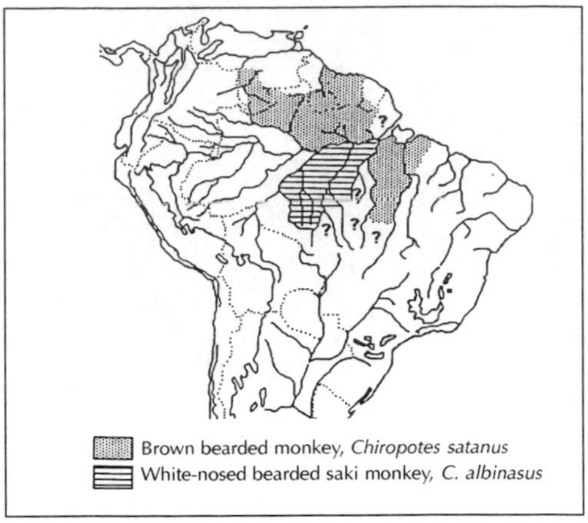

Figure 4-5 Distribution of bearded saki monkeys. [From Emmons 1990]

to Amazonia, within a limited area bounded by 4N to 7S latitude and 60W to 75W longitude (Fig. 4-6). It also may be restricted in habitat type.

Alouatta was the subject of the first systematic field study of a primate. Carpenter (1934) studied *A. palliata* on Barro Colorado Island in the early 1930's. Carpenter's study set new standards of scientific methodology for field research on primate behavior. In 1935, Carpenter conducted the first study of *Ateles,* also at BCI. Since the 1970's, many studies have been conducted of Atelines, especially spider and howler monkeys (see Kinzey 1997a,b for a detailed bibliography). In fact, between 1990–1995, approximately 700 articles

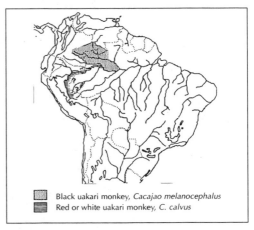

Figure 4-6 Distribution of uakari monkeys. [From Emmons 1990]

and abstracts were published on howler monkeys alone (Kinzey 1997b). Long-term studies are being conducted on spider and howler monkeys in Costa Rica and on muriquis in Brazil (see below). Members of the Pitheciinae, especially *Pithecia* and *Cacajao,* are among the most difficult to study and thus the least studied monkeys. *Pithecia* moves extremely fast and cryptically, and *Cacajao* is found mainly in flooded forests of the Amazon (Kinzey 1997b).

In this chapter, I first will compare and contrast *Ateles, Alouatta,* and *Lagothrix.* I then will discuss *Brachyteles.* Finally, I will describe the ecology and behavior of the pithecines.

ATELIDAE—
ECOLOGY AND BEHAVIOR OF *ATELES*, *ALOUATTA*, AND *LAGOTHRIX*

Habitat and Locomotion

The geographical ranges of some species of *Alouatta* and *Ateles* overlap and may have narrow hybrid zones at their geographic boundaries (Smith 1970, Rossan and Baerg 1977, Crockett 1998). Otherwise, as in the Cebidae, congeneric species are allopatric (Kinzey and Gentry 1979), and most could be considered ecological equivalents.

Ateles and *Alouatta* are widely distributed in Central and South America. *Alouatta* is mostly a high canopy forest dweller but occupies a wide variety of habitats (Crockett and Eisenberg 1987, Rodriguez-Luna et al. 1996). However, howlers are less likely to be found in edge habitats than are *Cebus* or *Saimiri* (Mittermeier and van Roosmalan 1981, Stoner 1996) and appear to occur in marginal habitats when no other areas are available (Fedigan et al. 1998) (Fig. 3-10). Howlers are found in gallery forests, evergreen and semi-deciduous forests, dry deciduous thorn forests, flooded and non-flooded rain forests, mangrove swamps, isolated forest patches, and secondary growth. In the Andes, howler monkeys are found in cloud forests up to 3200 m.

In Amazonia, *Ateles* tends to occur most frequently in mature, high forest in unflooded areas, although it also can be found in remnant or degraded forests (Hernandez-Camacho and Cooper 1976, Mittermeier and Coimbra-Filho 1977). In this region, spider monkeys may be restricted to areas with large continuous forest and cannot colonize isolated forest patches (Rylands and Keuroghlian 1988). In Surinam, Mittermeier and Van Roosmalan (1981) found *Ateles seniculus* to be the study species with the most restricted habitat.

In Santa Rosa, Costa Rica, Freese (1976) observed *Ateles geoffroyi* to have a more extensive distribution than *Alouatta* due to its wider utilization of forest types. Terborgh (1983) also noted that *Ateles paniscus* is quite opportunistic in habitat choice in Peru, using "virtually every type of vegetation at some time of year." In parts of their geographical range, spider monkeys have been observed in secondary, highland forest (Kinzey and Norconk 1990) and in dry deciduous and swamp forests (Hershkovitz 1977, van Roosmalan and Klein 1988).

Lagothrix occurs between sea level and 2500 m altitude. It lives in gallery forest, palm forest, flooded and unflooded rain forest, swamp forest, and cloud forest but also is found in liane forest and in secondary formations (Buchanan et al. 1981). Woolly monkeys are not found in secondary forest areas, are particularly vulnerable to forest disturbance (Ramirez 1988) and prefer high, non-flooded forest to low-lying forest types (Peres 1996). *L. flavicauda* occurs only in the montane cloud forest of the eastern Andes of Peru.

In sympatric populations in Surinam, over 80% of the sightings of *Ateles* and *Alouatta* were in the top three forest levels. *Ateles* was seen mainly in the upper canopy (Fig 3-12). *Alouatta* was most frequently seen in the mid-canopy. *Lagothrix* is totally arboreal and spends approximately 80% of its time in the upper canopy (Ramirez 1988).

Alouatta moves quadrupedally on the tops of branches and is slow and deliberate on terminal branches (Fleagle and Mittermeier 1980, Schön Ybarra 1984, Cant

1986) (Fig. 4-7). Fleagle and Mittermeier (1980) found that 80% of its locomotion during travel is slow quadrupedal progression on relatively large branches, 16% is climbing among small branches and twigs, and only 4% is leaping. During quadrupedal locomotion, howler monkeys grasp level or lower supports with their tails about 17% of the time, but they do not locomote by tail-arm suspension (Cant 1986).

Over 75% of *Alouatta* feeding is done using above branch postures (Cant 1986, Bergeson 1996, 1998). Twenty-two percent of feeding involves suspensory postures (Table 4-2). During feeding, howlers

Figure 4-7 Howler monkey in typical quadrupedal locomotion. [Photo by Robert W. Sussman]

also do a great amount of climbing on relatively small supports, where they use their prehensile tails extensively (Fleagle and Mittermeier 1980). In fact, 87% of tail use occurs during foraging and feeding (Bergeson 1998). Bergeson (1998) found that suspensory feeding is not more common in the tree periphery. The prehensile tail facilitates feeding in above branch positions; however, howler monkeys use their tails in suspension more often while feeding in an inverted bipedal posture (Fig. 4-8) near the trunk of the tree. Furthermore, tail use is similar when feeding on leaves, fruit, and flowers. Howlers come to the ground to cross open areas or to drink under certain circumstances and in some habitats (Neville et al. 1988).

Ateles, like *Alouatta,* prefers to run quadrupedally along the tops of large branches. Among small terminal branches, where howlers move carefully and slowly, spiders use their arms to swing with great speed and agility. This fast suspensory locomotion is a feature of positional behavior unique to hylobatids, spider, and woolly spider monkeys and may be an adaptation in these primates to exploit widely dispersed and ephemeral food patches (Cant 1986, Strier 1992a). The arms and hands of spider monkeys are adapted for this agile, suspensory mode of locomotion. The arms are long in relation to body length, and the hands are somewhat like suspensory hooks.

Swinging by the arms below branches is referred to as *brachiation;* however, spider monkeys do not brachiate in the true sense of the term. They use their tails as an additional limb while progressing through the branches and do not propel themselves solely with their arms. Spider monkeys also use their tails while pos-

**Table 4-2 Proportion of Time Spent in Different Feeding Postures
by *Alouatta palliata* & *Ateles geoffroyi***

Posture	*Alouatta* (Mendel 1976)	*Alouatta* (Bergeson 1996)	*Ateles* (Cant 1986)	*Ateles* (Bergeson 1996)
Stand	3	20	3	28
Sit	75	57	45	26
Various Suspensory	22	13	31	33
Inverted Bipedal	—	9	21	13
	100%	99%	100%	100%

turing and in a behavior referred to as bridging: a female bridges a gap in the canopy by holding branches and then allowing juveniles to cross over her body (Fig. 4-9).

Fleagle and Mittermeier (1980) found *Ateles paniscus* in Surinam to divide its travel fairly evenly between bimanual locomotion (38.6%), climbing (31.1%), and quadrupedal walking and running (25.4%). Leaping (4.2%) and bipedalism (0.7%) accounted for a small proportion of its travel. Using different categories, Cant (1986) observed *A. geoffroyi* in Guatamala to use quadrupedalism 52% of the time, tail-arm suspension 25%, and postures involving appreciable tail but not arm suspension 23% of the time. Leaping was only seen in 1% of the observations. Thus, the tail was used in a major way approximately 50% of the time. Small supports also were used 50% of the time. During feeding, over 50% of the time was spent in various suspensory postures including inverted bipedalism (Table 4-2).

Figure 4-8 A howler monkey in an inverted bipedal posture. [From Rowe 1996]

In Costa Rica, Bergeson (1996, 1998) found that, during foraging and feeding, *A. geoffroyi* used its tail 91% of the time, and the animals were supported by the tail alone mainly during these activities (Fig. 4-10). Spider monkeys also used different positional behaviors in different locations of the canopy. These postures did not conform to previous predictions. It is generally assumed that suspension is used more while feeding in the periphery of trees. However, Bergeson (1996, 1998) found that inverted bipedal suspensory postures were

Figure 4-9 Spider monkey bridging a gap in the canopy for a youngster. [From M. Kavanagh 1983]

used more frequently close to the trunk, sitting was more common on medium supports in the middle of the canopy, and quadrupedal standing was used most in the terminal branches. He also observed high tension prehensile tail use to be more common when spider monkeys fed on leaves than on fruit, although suspension near the trunk also allowed access to vine stems and fruits. These findings were similar to those on howler monkeys though, overall, spiders used their tails more than howlers (70% vs. 59% of all posture and locomotion).

Figure 4-10 Spider monkey hanging by its tail. [From Sleeper 1997, *Primates: The Amazing World of Lemurs, Monkeys, and Apes.* Chronicle Books, San Francisco (Photos by Art Wolfe)]

Figure 4-11 *Lagothrix* [From Sleeper 1997, *Primates: The Amazing World of Lemurs, Monkeys, and Apes.* Chronicle Books, San Francisco (Photos by Art Wolfe)]

Lagothrix is a robustly built animal, which in many ways resembles howler monkeys (Fig. 4-11). It is a quadrupedal walker and runner and frequently uses its prehensile tail (Ramirez 1988). Suspensory locomotion using hand-over-hand movements or assistance of the tail occurs rarely (about 8% of the time). The tail is used frequently for suspensory feeding postures, however. Woolly monkeys rarely leap, and they cross gaps by dropping to lower branches (Durham 1975). They are usually slow but can move rapidly if need be (Fooden 1963, Moynihan 1976). *Lagothrix* does not move as quickly as *Ateles* but is quicker and more agile than *Alouatta* (Ramirez 1988). Though quantitative data are not available, in many ways woolly monkeys seem intermediate in locomotor behavior between howlers and spiders.

In captive studies, Turnquist et al. (1999) found that brachiation in *Lagothrix* and *Ateles* differs in use of the prehensile tail, stride length, stride frequency, and length of hand holds, and that *Lagothrix* brachiation and morphology is less gibbon-like than that of *Ateles*. It is, however, difficult to specify how the locomotor substrate preferences of *Lagothrix* differ from those of *Ateles* and *Alouatta* until more comparative data are available from field studies.

Diet

Atelines subsist mainly on plant material and utilize little or no animal protein. *Alouatta* is one of the few New World monkeys that consumes a large proportion of leaves. Depending on the season, between 30–65% of its diet is mainly young, but also some mature, leaves (Table 4-3). Howlers prefer leaves low in fiber content (Oftedal 1991). The morphology of the intestinal tract (Chivers and Hladik 1984, Milton 1984a, Martin et al. 1985), molars (Kay and Hylander 1978), salvary glands (Milton 1987a), and the gut histology (Hladik 1967) of the howler monkey are adapted for a largely folivorous diet. However, these mor-

Table 4-3 Percentage of Dietary Items Eaten by Howler Monkeys During One Year at Five Study Sites

Species	Leaves	(Immature Leaves)	Fruit	Flowers	Other	Source
A. palliata	64	(44)	12	18	6	Glander 1975
A. palliata	49	(39)	51	<1	—	Estrada 1984
A. palliata	48	(>34)	42	10	—	Milton 1977
A. palliata	48	(45)	42	5	—	Gaulin & Gaulin 1982
A. fusca	71	(24)	19	9	6	Mendes 1989

phological features are not as highly specialized as those seen in the Colobinae or Indriidae. Milton (1978, 1984a, 1998) prefers to refer to *Alouatta* as a "behavioral folivore" rather than an "anatomical folivore." However, the hindgut is somewhat enlarged, food passage rate is extremely slow, and over 30% of their energy may derive from fermentation end products (Milton 1984a, 1987a, 1998).

Because the leaves eaten are relatively easy to find but often difficult to digest, howlers eat very small amounts of a great variety of species but concentrate on a few species for bulk (similar in many ways to the diet of *Propithecus* discussed in Volume 1). Thus, a small number of plant species (12–15) accounts for a large proportion (up to 80%) of the diet. Howlers are very selective in the leafy portion of their diet, usually choosing species that are not abundant in the forest and often selecting very few individual trees of particular species (e.g., Hladik and Hladik 1969, Smith 1977, Glander 1978, Milton 1980, Chapman 1988a, Chiarello 1994, Silver et al. 1998, Estrada et al. 1999).

The remainder of the howler diet is made up mainly of fruit, flowers, and buds (between about 40 and 70%). Many of the fruits eaten by howlers are immature (Terborgh 1983, Crockett and Eisenberg 1987). The fruit portion of the diet is less diverse than the leaf portion. In fact, it is quite monotonous, with very few species accounting for a great percentage of the fruits eaten (e.g., Milton 1980, Estrada 1984, Chapman 1988a). In most forests, figs (*Ficus* ssp.) are an important component of the diet, sometimes accounting for up to 40% of time spent feeding. Figs are patchily distributed in the forest but are usually available throughout the year.

The seeds of fruits eaten by howlers are not destroyed and are often more viable than controls. Furthermore, the slow food passage rate results in seeds being "dropped" away from the parent plant. These factors indicate that howlers may be instrumental in dispersing many of the fruit trees that they feed upon (Hladik and Hladik 1969, Howe 1980, Estrada and Coates-Estrada 1984a, Estrada et al. 1984, Chapman 1989a, Galetti et al. 1994). In fact, Howe (1980) found that 70% of the seeds removed from a commonly used fruit tree in Panama were taken by howlers, including approximately 60% of those likely to survive immediate mortality. Furthermore, it appears that some insects are ingested with ingestion of figs and other fruit. Howlers may be aiding the successful dispersal of these plants by "cleaning" them of insect parasites while gaining protein and other nutritional benefits not found in plant foods (Bravo and Zunino 1998).

The relatively indigestible diet (leaves and immature fruit) necessitates balancing nutrients by feeding on a mix of food types each day (Hladik and Hladik

1969, Smith 1977, Milton 1980, Gaulin and Gaulin 1982). However, in a four-year study in Costa Rica, Chapman (1987) found that, although howlers ate a mixture of leaves, fruits and flowers in most months, they fed almost exclusively on flowers in one month and on leaves in two months of the study. He also found that the diet was not consistent from year to year. Since howlers are found in a wide variety of habitats, it is not surprising that they can be quite flexible in their diets. This dietary flexibility obviously is one factor enabling them to survive in various habitats.

Protein content appears to be an important factor in food choices of howler monkeys. They require approximately 15% of their daily diet in dry weight to be protein. Howlers also often come to the ground for water, salt, or dirt (Terborgh 1983, Gilbert and Stouffer 1989, Izawa and Lozano 1990), or search for particular sources of water (Glander 1978, Neville et al. 1988). This type of behavior has been observed in other leaf-eaters (see Volumes 1 and 3), but its significance is still poorly understood (Izawa et al. 1990, Oates 1994). The resources ingested may serve as antacids, to help absorb toxins, or to supply mineral supplements (Kay and Davies 1994). In any case, these behaviors seem to be part of the complex foraging strategy of a folivore.

In contrast to *Alouatta, Ateles* eats few leaves (Fig. 4-12, Table 4-4). Approximately 80% of the its diet consists of fruits, of which almost all are ripe (Hladik and Hladik 1969, Klein and Klein 1977, Milton 1981, van Roosmalen 1985, Symington 1988a, Chapman 1988a, Kinzey and Norconk 1990, Campbell ms.). The remainder is made up of young leaves and buds, flowers, and dead or decaying wood, which is often obtained from the same sources over many months. Although some figs are eaten, these fruits are much less important to spider monkeys than to howlers. At some sites, spider monkeys eat palm fruits throughout the year and, depending on the season, these fruits account for 20–60% of the diet (Klein and Klein 1975, Campbell 1994, ms., Nunes 1998).

The distribution of food resources is one of the determinants of *Ateles* social structure (see below). Most *Ateles* foods occur at low densities and are widely distributed, patchy, and ephemeral (Chapman 1988b, 1990, Symington 1988a, Silva-Lopes et al. 1987, Campbell 1994, ms.). The number of individuals able to feed together is dependent upon food patch size and density. Although on some days spider monkeys may visit a large number of plants for fruit, the annual diet is not extremely diverse and a few plant species make up a large proportion of the diet (Hladik and Hladik 1969, Cant 1977, Klein and Klein 1977, White 1986, Chapman 1988, Campbell ms., Nunes 1998). Two to three plant species often account for over half of the yearly diet.

The majority of fruits eaten by spider monkeys have a single seed or several large seeds to which the pulp adheres tightly (Fig. 4-13). Seeds are often swallowed whole and a major volume of the feces is undamaged seeds. These seeds are defecated intact and are viable after defecation. Thus, spiders are most likely important seed dispersal agents, especially for plants with relatively large seeds (Hladik and Hladik 1969, Klein and Klein 1975, 1977, Muskin

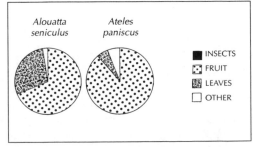

Figure 4-12 General comparison of food items eaten by howler and spider monkeys. [Adapted from Fleagle 1999]

up date with new stude

Table 4-4 Percentage of Dietary Items Eaten by Spider Monkeys During One Year at Four Study Sites

Species	Leaves	Fruit	(Ripe Fruit)	Other	Source
A. belzebuth	7	83	(82)	10	Klein & Klein 1977
A. geoffroyi	20	80	(—)	—	Hladik & Hladik 1969
A. paniscus	8	83	(80)	7	van Roosmalen 1980
A. geoffroyi	13	71	(—)	16	Chapman & Chapman 1990

and Fischgrund 1981, Howe 1983, Fleming et al. 1985, van Roosmalen 1987, Chapman 1989a, Kinzey and Norconk 1990). In Surinam, Mittermeier and van Roosmalen (1981) found that *Ateles* was a dispersal agent for over 80% of the fruit species that it fed upon.

Like *Ateles, Lagothrix* is essentially frugivorous, with fruits accounting for 70–80% of the annual diet (Soini 1986, Ramirez 1988, Nishimura 1990, Peres 1994). Seeds, leaves, flowers, bark, twigs and some insects and occasional vertebrates also are included in the diet. Because of the extremely worn incisors and canines of

Figure 4-13 Typical fruit eaten by spider monkeys in Surinam during the month of May. [From van Roosmalen & Klein 1988]

most mature museum specimens he examined, Fooden (1963) speculated that woolly monkeys ate hard shelled fruits. Others have theorized that their dental structure is secondarily adapted for leaf-eating (Kay 1973, Eaglan 1984, Rosenberger and Strier 1989). In fact, during seasons when fruit is scarce, both seeds and leaves can become important. In some months, seeds account for 25–35% of the diet and young leaves close to 50% (Soini 1986, Peres 1994). In a field site in Brazil, woolly monkeys selected primarily large food patches, regardless of feeding party size (Peres 1996).

Lagothrix feeds on seeds from one of the same plant families (Lecythidaceae) eaten by *Chiropotes* (see below) but these two genera are allopatric, and *Lagothrix* eats seeds only seasonally. Among the atelines, *Lagothrix* and *Ateles* have similar diets, but they have not yet been studied in sympatry (Peres 1994, Kinzey 1997a). It would appear that the reliance of *Lagothrix* on leaves and seeds during some seasons would lead to food niche separation between these two genera.

Cycles of Activity

Primates that depend mainly on plant materials for food can eat large quantities at one sitting but must have concomitant long periods of rest for digestion (Clutton-Brock and Harvey 1977). Both *Ateles* and *Alouatta* fit this pattern. In *Ateles,* long rest periods follow periods of intensive feeding when the monkeys rapidly ingest large quantities of food (about 10% of the animal's weight). Travel time is positively correlated with fruit availability and negatively with the amount of leaves and nectar in the diet (van Roosmalen and Klein 1988). There may be three to five periods of alternating activity and rest, and rest becomes more frequent and longer during the midday (Richard 1970, Klein and Klein 1977). Ramirez (1988) observed *Lagothrix* to remain active throughout the day, but most travel and feeding occurred in the first hours of the morning and last two hours of the day. The animals mainly rested in midday.

The pattern is similar in *Alouatta,* which eats three to four meals each day, separated by resting periods of two or more hours (Gaulin and Gaulin 1982). Peaks of feeding occur in

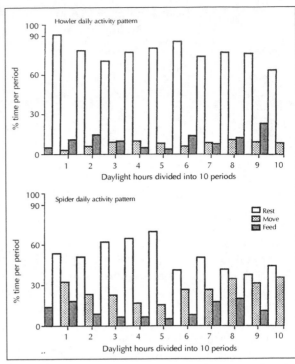

Figure 4-14 Comparison of the activity cycles of howler and spider monkeys at Barro Colorado, Panama. [From Richard 1970]

the early morning and late afternoon, and resting peaks at midday. Howlers rest up to 75–80% of the day (Smith 1977, Neville et al. 1988, Estrada et al. 1999) and rest more than spider monkeys throughout the day (Fig. 4-14) (Richard 1970, Klein and Klein 1977, Gaulin and Gaulin 1982, Crocket 1987).

Predation

Howlers appear to be quite prone to predation. Peres (1990a) observed a harpy eagle kill an adult male *A. seniculus* and, in Peru, Terborgh (1983) and Eason (1989) observed unsuccessful attacks on howlers by these eagles. Sherman (1991) saw a harpy perched next to a recently killed howler. Carpenter (1934) observed a possible attack by an ocelot on a young howler, and Peetz et al. (1992) observed a jaguar (Fig. 4-15) killing a howler (see also, Cuarón 1997). Chapman (1986) reports an unsuccessful attack of a howler by a boa constrictor. As

Figure 4-15 The jaguar, a potential predator for most New World monkeys. [Photo by Robert W. Sussman]

described above, howlers are slow, and often come to the ground for water and may be vulnerable at these times.

In the Andes, *Lagothrix,* has been observed to be hunted by eagles (Lehman 1959), and in Colombia, two species of eagles are known as "Aguilas Churuqueres" (woolly monkey hawks) because of their reputation as *Lagothrix* predators (Hernandez-Camacho and Cooper 1976). Jaguars may also hunt *Lagothrix* (Ramirez 1988). The woolly monkey is approximately the same size and weight as the spider monkey (Table 4-1). There is little information on natural predation on *Ateles,* but Emmons (1987) reports remains of spider monkeys in the feces of jaguars and possibly puma. Alarm calls are given by spider monkeys at large eagles (Janson and van Schaik 1993). Generally, however, these large monkeys do not show specific adaptations for predator avoidance and even during rest periods, they sprawl conspicuously about in the trees.

Humans hunt all of the species included in this section (Fig. 4-16), though the amount of hunting pressure depends upon the species and the area. They all are hunted for food, but the meat of *Ateles* and *Lagothrix* is the most prized (Marsh et al. 1987, Peres 1990b). Correspondingly, these two species are becoming very rare in many areas of their range. In addition to their use as food, these monkeys are hunted for various types of bait, for pets, for curios (e.g., stuffed monkeys, necklaces, etc.), and to a lesser extent for research. *Alouatta* is hunted in some regions for medicinal purposes where drinking from its specialized hyoid bone is thought to cure goiters or stuttering, or to ease labor pains. In Peru, a medication made from the hair of howler monkeys is thought to relieve coughing (Mittermeier and

Figure 4-16 Humans hunt both spider and howler monkeys: **a.** A hunter bringing home a recently shot spider monkey. [From Mittermeier and Coimbra-Filho 1977] **b.** Howler monkey hyoid bones are used as medicines. [From Mittermeier 1987]

Coimbra-Filho 1977). The density of these species in various regions is directly related to hunting and other human pressures (Redford and Robinson 1987, Mittermeier 1987, Redford 1992, Sussman and Phillips-Conroy 1995, Peres 1996).

SOCIAL STRUCTURE AND ORGANIZATION

Ateles and *Lagothrix*

The social organization of *Ateles*, first described by Raymond Carpenter in 1935, is complex and unique for New World monkeys. The basic social structure is "fission-fusion" (see Volume 1-Chapter 1). It is characterized by the existence of closed bisexual social groups which fragment into smaller, widely dispersed, foraging subgroups of varying size and composition. Social groups contain approximately 15–40+ members (Table 4-5) (Klein and Klein 1975, 1977, van Roosmalen 1980, Robinson and Janson 1987, Chapman 1988a, Symington 1988b). *Ateles* is rarely seen in mixed-species associations (Carpenter 1935, Richard 1970, Mittermeier and van Roosmalen 1981).

Adjacent groups maintain separate home ranges, although varying amounts of range overlap are common, from none (van Roosmalen 1980) to 10–30% overlap (Klein and Klein 1975, Symington 1988b). Intergroup relations have been characterized as agonistic, particularly among males, and most of this agonism occurs near home range boundaries (Klein 1972, 1974, Symington 1987a,b). However, females also are known to visit adjacent groups and participate in friendly intergroup interactions. These visits can last from several hours to an entire day, with some overnight stays (van Roosmalen and Klein 1988). There is also evidence that females migrate between groups, whereas males do not (van Roosmalen and Klein 1988, Symington 1988b, 1990).

The larger group rarely, if ever, aggregates in its entirety. Rather, small temporary subgroups are formed from the larger unit. Subgroups range from 1–35, with a modal size of 2–5 individuals (Klein and Klein 1975, 1977, Cant 1977, van Roosmalen 1980, van Roosmalen and Klein 1988, White 1986, Ahumada 1989, Symington 1988b, 1990, Chapman 1989b, 1990a,b). The Kleins (1975, 1977) were the first to do a detailed study of spider monkey (*A. belzebuth*) social organization in Colombia. They observed that the median size of subgroups was 3.5 independently locomoting animals. The modal subgroup size was two animals (21% of the sightings), and subgroups of four animals comprised 16% of the sightings. Isolated animals and groups of eight or more each made up 15% of the total. Although precise numbers differ from study to study, the patterns are quite similar (see fig. 4-17, Chapman et al. 1995:65).

Age and sexual composition of subgroups of spider monkeys are variable and consist of all possible permutations. In the Kleins' study, bisexual subgroups were the most common, accounting for 51% of the sample. These groups often contained from 1–5 males and, in some instances, males outnumbered females. Subgroups containing only females accounted for 45% of the observed subgroups and ranged in size from 2–11 animals. Entirely male subgroups accounted for 4%, and consisted of from 2 to 4 males. Subgroup stability was assumed to be similar in all three types, lasting from 15 minutes to over a day. Individual animals also moved alone and often remained separated from other animals for one to three days. Solitary females were sighted most frequently, accounting for 66.7% of the isolated individuals; females with infants accounted for 10.7%; and solitary males for 22.7% of the cases.

Table 4-5 Group Size, Home and Day Range Size and Population Density for Some Ateline Populations

Species & Site	Average Group Size (N)	Home Range (ha)*	Day Range (meters)	Population Density (#/km)	Source
Ateles belzebuth, Colombia	18	260–310	500–4000	15–18	Klein & Klein 1975
A. paniscus, Surinam	18	220	500–5000	8	van Roosmalen 1980
A. paniscus, Peru	38 (2)	192	465–4070 x = 1977	25–30	Symington 1988b
A. geoffroyi	42	170 (community home range)	x = 1297	<28	Chapman et al. 1989; Chapman & Chapman 1990
Lagothrix lagotricha					
Colombia	23–43	>400	@ 1000	12	Nishimura & Izawa 1975
Colombia	24	760	2880	5.5	Defler 1996
Colombia	17	169	1633	—	Stevenson et al. 1994
Peru	12	>300	—	5	Ramirez 1988
Brazil	39–55	>860	—	19	Perez 1994
Brachyteles arachnoides, FMC	22–65 (1)	168– @ 300	141–3403	3.4–5.8	Strier 1987c, 1991 b, pers. comm.
Alouatta palliata					
Mexico	5–16 x = 9.1 (17)	60	11–503 x = 123	23	Estrada 1984
Costa Rica (BCI)	2–39	10	207–1261	90	Crockett & Eisenberg 1987
Panama	2–45 x = 8–23	31	104–792 x = 443	16–90	Crockett & Eisenberg 1987 [From Milton 1980, Collias & Southwick 1952]
Costa Rica (Santa Rosa)	x = 16.3 (34)			7.9	Fedigan et al. 1998
A. pigra, Guatamala	4–7	125	40–700 x = 250	5, 13	Schlichte 1978
A. seniculus					
Venezuela	4–16	4–25	20–840 x = @ 350–550	c. 35–118	Crockett & Eisenberg 1987
Colombia	9	22	706	ca. 15	Gaulin & Gaulin 1982
Peru	6	10–20	—	30	Terborgh 1983
Pitheciinae					
Pithecia hirsuta, Peru	4.5	—	—	37.5	Happel 1982
Chiropotes albinasus	25	250–350	2500–5000	7–8	Ayres 1981
Cacajao	25–50	500–550	1500–5000	2.5–4.7	Ayres 1986, 1989

139

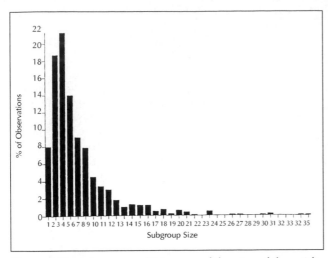

Figure 4-17 A frequency histogram of the size of the spider monkey subgroups seen in Santa Rosa National Park, Costa Rica (*n* = 1018) [From Chapman 1990b]

Juveniles and infants were not observed outside of a subgroup.

Although generally similar, the sexual composition of subgroups varies from site to site. At Santa Rosa, for example, Chapman found that the most common subgroups were those with adult females with or without infants (48%). Solitary females, with or without dependent infants, accounted for 33% of the sightings. Mixed sex groups made up 16%, and adult males accounted for only 2% of the subgroups sited (Chapman 1990b, Chapman et al. 1995).

The Kleins were able to individually identify most of the spider monkeys at their study site. They noted that any particular animal at times could be solitary or a member of a subgroup of any size or sexual composition. Subgroup membership changed constantly and was usually unstable over a period of days as individuals moved in and out of associations or remained alone for a period of time. Subgroups could be separated for as much as half a mile and would sleep a quarter to a half a mile apart.

Symington (1987b, 1990) examined associations between dyads, noting the amount of time specific individuals spent together in the same subgroup. She found that certain males had much higher levels of association than did either female-female or male-female dyads. The highest frequency of grooming occurred between males, and females groomed each other least frequently. This pattern of affiliations has been found in other primate species in which males are philopatric and remain in close proximity to male relatives throughout their life (see below, and Volumes 1 and 3). Fedigan and Baxter (1984) found a similar pattern among *Ateles,* but in their study males were most affiliative both with other males and with adult females.

Klein and Klein (1975) found that subgroup size and stability corresponded to the distribution, abundance and variety of ripe fruit available. When large fruit bearing trees were in season, large, relatively stable subgroups were more frequent. On the other hand, during months when small, widely dispersed resources were utilized maximal group fission occurred. For example, in September, when widely dispersed palm fruits were utilized, the median subgroups size was 2.2 and isolated animals were observed frequently. Groups of eight or more made up only 6% of the sightings. This contrasts with a mean subgroup size of 5.2, and subgroups of 8 or more sighted 43% of the time in October when a large fruit tree species, *Brosimum,* was available. When a wide variety of fruit trees with differing patterns of dispersal were in fruit, spider monkey subgroups were more variable in size and less stable. A correspondence between fruit patch size, density and distribution, amount of time spent traveling, and subgroup size has been verified by Chapman (1990a,b, Chapman et al. 1995) and Symington (1988a, 1990) (Fig.4-18).

Spider monkeys use food calls to manipulate foraging subgroups and in this way may decrease feeding competition between individuals (Chapman and Leve-brve 1990). Furthermore, subgroups typically forage in small, localized areas, following roughly a circular path and returning to one of a number of regularly used

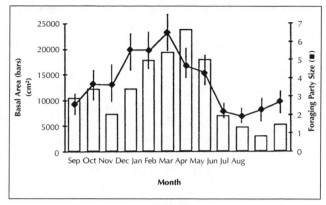

Figure 4-18 Average monthly foraging party size (± SE) in relation to the basal area of trees and lianas bearing fleshy mammal-dispersed fruits for September 1984 through August 1985. [From Symington 1988a]

sleeping sites in the evening (Chapman 1989b). Chapman et al. (1989a) characterize spider monkeys as multiple central place foragers since they reduce travel costs by sleeping in trees closest to the feeding area being used and then change to a new sleeping site once local resources are exhausted. Thus, the fission-fusion social structure of *Ateles* allows the adjustment of subgroup size to seasonal fluctuations in the size of resource patches.

Within subgroups of *Ateles*, females may associate with one or several males. Reproduction occurs throughout most of the year (Carpenter 1935, Klein 1971, Symington 1987b). Aggression between males is infrequent, and estrous females actively choose their mating partners. Females initiate sexual activity and have been observed to mate with a number of different males on the same day (Robinson and Janson 1987). Females display menstrual cycles of about 24 days on average (Hernandez Lopes et al. 1998), and the gestation period is 7.5 months (Eisenberg 1973). Births are single. The interbirth interval averages 35 months (range = 25–42 months) (Symington 1988b, van Roosmalen and Klein 1988, Chapman and Chapman 1990). In the wild, infants move from the mother's belly to her back at around 4–6 months. Spider monkey infants are almost totally dependent upon their mothers for 10 months. After this, they gradually become more independent. Even after young are moving independently, they are watched closely by adult females of the group, who also form bridges in the canopy for their young to cross. Carpenter (1935) describes one instance of a female spider monkey allowing five young to cross over her back. By 24–36 months, juveniles are no longer carried by their mothers, though they remain close to her up to 50 months of age (van Roosmalen 1980). Spider monkeys are considered subadults between 50–65 months of age (Eisenberg 1976, van Roosmalen and Klein 1988) but they do not reproduce in the wild until they reach 7–8 years of age (Symington 1987b, Chapman and Chapman 1990).

Lagothrix social structure and organization is similar to that of *Ateles*. Reports of group size are quite variable, ranging in size from 4–60+ (see Ramirez 1988, Stevenson et al. 1994, Defler 1996, Peres 1996). Group size appears to be related to habitat. Although groups have been described as multimale and cohesive (Izawa 1976, Nishimura 1990), Ramirez found that her groups split into subgroups, usually of

2–6 individuals who traveled and fed together, similar to those of *Ateles*. Defler (1996) studied a group that commonly traveled in two subgroups separated by 100–200 m but kept in vocal contact, he states that groups practice fission-fusion according to food conditions. Stevenson (1998) reports that in her study population, like *Ateles,* woolly monkeys did not form cohesive subgroups, except for mothers and infants. Proximity between group members varied and depended upon age/sex class, activity, and individual identity.

Little is known about reproduction or infant development in natural populations of woolly monkeys. However, mating is reported to be promiscuous within the group (Nishimura et al. 1992, Stevenson 1998). The gestation period has been reported to be approximately 225 days (Napier and Napier 1967, Williams 1974, Mack and Kafka 1978). Young females disperse from their natal group, as in other atelines (Nishimura 1988).

Howler Monkeys

Howler monkeys generally live in cohesive multi-male groups. *A. palliata* groups average 8–21 animals, whereas other species have smaller groups of 5–10 individuals (Crockett and Eisenberg 1987, Neville et al. 1988, Clarke and Zucker 1994, Fedigan et al. 1998; Table 4-5). Groups normally contain 1–4 adult males and have a sex ratio of approximately 1 male to 2–4 females. Recently formed groups are smaller than established ones (Crockett and Eisenberg 1987), and study sites with high population density have larger groups with more females and lower male:female ratios than do low density sites (Fedigan et al. 1998, Crockett 1996). The home ranges overlap extensively, and in some groups, no part of the home range is used exclusively (Carpenter 1965, Baldwin and Baldwin 1972, Smith 1977, Glander 1975, Milton 1980, Sekulic 1982a,b).

Howlers may avoid contact between groups throughout the day with choruses of loud howling (Fig. 4-19). The hyoid bone and larynx are adapted for eliciting these loud vocalizations. Intergroup interactions are rare, usually peaceful, and seem to function to maintain group integrity and immediate control of a resource rather than absolute space. In fact, two groups may intermittently share a food tree during a single feeding bout, with one group resting nearby, waiting its turn, while the other is feeding (Glander 1975). Thus, howlers are not territorial (Neville et al. 1988, but see Crockett and Eisenberg 1987). This pattern of interaction between groups is reminiscent of that seen between groups of *Eulemur fulvus* in southwestern Madagascar (see Volume 1, Chapter 5).

In howler monkeys, both male and female juveniles emigrate from their natal group. This results in groups consist-

Figure 4-19 Howler monkeys exchanging loud calls between groups. [From Rowe 1996, *The Pictorial Guide to Living Primates,* Pogonias Press, East Hampton, NY]

ing of unrelated adults and their most recent offspring (Clarke et al. 1998). Overt social interaction is often difficult to observe within howler groups. Extremely little allogrooming occurs in *A. palliata* and *A. pigra,* but it is common in *A. caraya, A. seniculus,* and *A. fusca* (Neville et al. 1988, Sáchez-Villergra et al. 1998). In most early studies, intergroup aggression was rarely observed (Altmann 1959, Bernstein 1964, Richard 1970, Neville 1972, Smith 1977, Jones 1980). Smith (1977) noted that adult *A. palliata* at B.C.I. spent less than one percent of their time in even the slightest response to one another, and Crockett (1984) observed only two serious fights in over 1500 h of observation. However, long-term field studies of individually identified mantled howler monkeys (*A. palliata*) in Costa Rica (e.g., Glander 1975, 1980, 1992, Clarke and Glander 1984, Clarke et al. 1986, 1994) and red howlers (*A. seniculus*) in Venezuela (e.g., Rudran 1979, Crockett 1984, Crockett and Eisenberg 1987, Eisenberg 1991, Crockett and Pope 1993) have revealed that dominance interactions are extremely important to howler social organization.

Glander (1975, 1992, Glander et al. 1991) captures all of the monkeys in his groups using a tranquilizer gun, and each individual is marked. In this way, he has been able to trace the life histories of individuals for over thirty years. In his detailed study of mantled howler social behavior in Costa Rica, Glander observed frequent aggressive behavior within groups. For example, he recorded approximately 400 dominance interactions in a period of 172 days of observation (Glander 1975), and resident alpha males were violently attacked by three extra group males (Glander 1992). Scars and wounds, seemingly from bites, have often been seen on howlers (Fig. 4-20) (Carpenter 1934, Chivers 1969, Baldwin and Baldwin 1972, Otis et al. 1981, Crockett 1984) but rarely were attacks witnessed (see however Young 1981, Glander 1992). Glander believes that fights are often missed because they are of short duration and totally silent.

Glander (1975, 1980) has used the criteria of (1) access to estrous females, (2) access to resting and sleeping locations, and (3) access to food to rank each adult in a linear hierarchy (see also Gaulin and Gaulin 1982, Jones 1982, Clarke and Glander 1984, Zucker and Clarke 1998). Males were dominant over females, and between 1970 and 1991, tenure of dominance among males averaged about 46 months (range 16–30 mo, n = 7) (Glander 1992). Rank among females is related to age; young adult females reach alpha position just before or just after producing their first infant. The tenure of rank for female alpha position has averaged 21 months with a range of 4–52 mo (n = 11), and all females move down one rank when a new animal takes the alpha position (Glander 1980,

Figure 4-20 Scars on howler monkeys are often seen, but actual fights are rarely observed because fights are quick and quiet. [From Crockett and Eisenberg 1987]

1992, Jones 1983a, see also Neville et al. 1988). Adult females engage in agonistic and affiliative relationships with other, unrelated adults of the group. However, the rates of interaction are highly variable and are sensitive to and influenced by female status, reproductive condition, and changing male membership in the group (Zucker and Clarke 1998). For example, when environmental or other conditions cause high levels of instability within groups, maintaining high rank correlates with a high level of agonism (Zucker and Clarke 1998).

In multimale groups, more than one male copulates with an estrus female, often on the same day (Smith 1977), but alpha males mainly have access to females in the middle of their receptive periods (Glander 1980, Jones 1985, Crockett and Eisenberg 1987, Crockett and Pope 1993). In red howler monkeys, Crockett and Eisenberg (1987) hypothesize that most groups may be functionally unimale, in that only the alpha male copulates during peak estrus, and paternity exclusion analysis in one study of this species indicated that only one male sires the group's infants (Pope 1990). This does not appear to be the case in mantled howlers, in which a relatively high proportion of offspring may be sired by extra-group males (Glander pers. comm.)

In red howlers, male-male competition is severe and males have died of injuries during fights (Clarke 1983, Crockett and Sekulic 1984, Izawa and Lozano 1994). Males often invade and take over groups, sometimes forming temporary coalitions, and this is sometimes associated with infant deaths or disappearances (Rudran 1979, Sekulic 1981, Clarke 1983, Crockett and Sekulic 1984, Eisenberg 1979, Izawa and Lozano 1994, Clarke et al. 1994). This pattern is very similar to that reported in Hanuman langurs of India and will be discussed further in Volume 3.

In the mantled howler monkeys studied by Glander (pers. comm.), secondary migration has never been observed among males and is extremely rare among females. There is some indication that some populations and species of howlers may live in typical multimale groups (Carpenter 1934, Smith 1977, Jones 1985, Izawa and Lozano 1994). The social behavior of howler monkeys appears to be as variable among populations of the same species as among different species. Social structure and organization in different populations of howlers appears to vary with intragroup relatedness, which in turns varies with environmental factors that affect group size and migration patterns (see Clarke et al. 1998).

As stated above, dispersal is normal among both natal male and female howler monkeys. The rate of immigration and emigration seems to be a dynamic pattern related to the ratio of adult males and females in the group. The critical ratio seems to be about one male to four females (Scott et al. 1978, Young 1981, Crockett 1984, Crockett and Pope 1993, Glander pers. comm.) At least in *A. palliata,* the number of males per howler group is more strictly limited and less variable than the number of females, especially in sites with high population density (Fedigan et al. 1998).

Males have a protective and policing role within the group (Carpenter 1965, Smith 1977, Gaulin and Gaulin 1982, Milton 1980, Glander pers. comm) often settling fights between females (Glander 1975). Emigration is associated with aggression towards juveniles by like-sexed adults, suggesting it is not voluntary and is likely related to sexual competition (Crockett and Pope 1988, Rumiz 1990, Clarke et al. 1994). It also may be related to population density, with low rates of emigration and relative stability of male tenure in groups at low population densities. The establishment of new groups also is dependent upon available habitat (Eisenberg 1979).

Crockett and Eisenberg (1987) suggest that the main difference in group size between species is the typical number of adult females, with adult males tracking the number of females. They suggest that the number of females may be limited by female reproductive competition. In *A. seniculus,* group size may remain small because adult female membership seems to be limited to 4 or less due to female aggression, which promotes emigration and prevents immigration (Crockett 1996). The ultimate factors leading to these differences remains a question, since inter-specific differences between mantled and red howler in such factors as foraging ecology, habitats occupied, or predation pressures, if they exist, are not conspicuous (Crockett and Eisenberg 1987). Furthermore, among mantled howlers, Fedigan et al. (1998) found that group size and sex ratio were correlated with population density at various study sites.

At high density sites, mantled howler groups were larger and contained relatively fewer adult males. They suggest that in this species the number of male "positions" within groups may be strictly limited because of higher levels of competition between males. If this is the case, in high density habitats there may be few opportunities for males to form new groups and more difficult for them to enter established ones. In regenerating forests with low density of howler population, males may have increased dispersal opportunities and there may be some relaxation of factors causing male mortality. There is evidence for this at the recently established national park in Santa Rosa, Costa Rica (Fedigan et al. 1998).

Thus, population density and other demographic factors appear to affect a number of aspects of howler social behavior. Such factors as group size, migration patterns, and intragroup relatedness, in turn, are related to variations in social behavior between populations (Clarke et al. 1998). As stated by Clarke et al. (1998:467):

> *social behaviors of howlers, including interaction with infants, do not appear to be species-typical, but are expected to vary with intra-group relatedness, which in turn varies along a continuum of environmental factors that affect group size and migration patterns.*

Although howlers have been the subject of a great deal of research, much remains to be done to determine the relationships that exist between social structure and ecology in these monkeys.

Generally, there is no seasonality in howler breeding or births, though births in some populations occur in clusters (Glander 1980, Clarke and Glander 1984, Crockett and Eisenberg 1987, Crockett and Rudran 1987, Neville et al. 1988, Fedigan et al. 1998). Glander (1980) collected statistics on reproductive cycles and development in *A. palliata.* The female estrous cycle is between 11 and 24 days, with a mean of 16 days (N=23). The female is receptive for 2–4 days during each cycle. Gestation lasts for 180 to 194 days with a mean of 186 (N=4). These data are similar to those reported for other *Alouatta* species (Neville et al. 1988). The mean time for 16 complete interbirth intervals in seven females was 22.5 months (Glander 1980), though shorter intervals of 16–17 months have been reported in other populations (Milton 1982, Neville et al. 1988, Crockett and Pope 1993). The infant is carried ventrally by the mother until about 3 weeks and then on her back. It is still carried during difficult crossings up to 6 months of age. After this time, the infant moves independently (Fig. 4-21). Infants are weaned at 10–14 months of age (Crockett and Pope 1993).

Sexual maturity is reached at 4 years for females and 5 years for males (Crockett and Pope 1993). First births have been reported at between 4–7 years of age (median = 5 yrs). Males first become fathers at 6–8 years (median = 7 yrs) (Pope 1990). As stated above, juveniles normally are forced to emigrate (Glander 1980, 1992, Clarke and Glander 1984, Zucker and Clarke 1998). Full weight is reached in the female (4–5 kg) at 5–6 years and in the male (5–6 kg) by 7–8 years (Crockett and Pope 1993). In Glander's (1980) group, a 16 year old female and a male estimated to be 21 years old were still reproductively active.

Figure 4-21 Young howler monkeys do not begin to become independent of their mothers until around 6 months of age. [Photo by R.W. Sussman]

Ranging Behavior

To date, there are few data available on the home and day range of *Lagothrix*. Estimates of home range are quite variable, ranging from 5 to 19 km² (Table 4-5) (Soini 1986, Ramirez 1988, Nishimura and Izawa 1975, Nishimura 1990). Peres (1996) estimated the home range of one large group to be 12–13.5 km². These are the largest home ranges reported for strictly arboreal monkeys. However, given the large size of the animals and of groups of *Lagothrix*, this is not surprising (Peres 1996). All observers indicate that home range boundaries of woolly monkeys overlap, retain little if any areas of exclusive use, and that they do not defend home ranges against conspecifics (Ramirez 1988, Nishimura 1990, Peres 1996). Day ranges are between 100–3000 m (Soini 1986, Defler 1987, Ramirez 1988). As stated earlier, some groups are cohesive and others divide into subgroups of various types during travel.

Ateles is quite variable in its ranging pattern, both in the direction and length of travel and, as we have seen, in size of foraging party. Some groups remain together throughout the day (Durham 1975, Coehlo et al. 1976), other groups split into subgroups and reform at night using the same roosting trees (Carpenter 1935, Coehlo et al. 1976), and still others remain dispersed and even sleep 400–800 meters apart (Klein and Klein 1975). Day ranges vary from 465 to 4070 m (avg. = 1977 m), with males traveling more and spending less time feeding than females (Symington 1988b). Day ranges of groups and subgroups are directly dependent upon the density and dispersion of fruit sources (Table 4-5) (Richard 1970, Klein and Klein 1977, Terborgh 1983, Symington 1988a).

Spider monkeys move short distances for three or four days, following the same arboreal pathways, and then suddenly switch to a different route. As described above, they are multiple central place foragers in that they choose one of a number of central places for sleeping sites each night (Chapman 1989b) (Fig. 4-22). Thus, subgroups reduce travel costs by selecting sleeping sites close to current feeding areas.

Group home ranges overlap 10–30% and relations between groups are usually antagonistic, especially between adult males (Klein and Klein 1975, Symington 1988b, Chapman 1990b). Home range size is reported to be around 60 ha in Costa Rica (Fedigan et al. 1988) and 190 ha in Peru (Symington 1988b). Adult males use core areas that are larger than those of adult females (90 ha vs. 50 ha in Costa Rica, for example), and females with infants have the smallest core areas. The core areas of individuals overlap extensively and male core areas tend to overlap those of several females. However, core areas of all adult females in the group over-

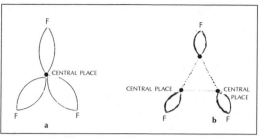

Figure 4-22 Diagrammatic representation of the central place foraging strategy (**a**) and the multiple central place foraging strategy (**b**). The curved lines represent the length of a foraging trip (made one or more times) to a feeding site (F), and the dashed lines represent the travel distance between central places in a MCPF strategy. [From Chapman et al. 1989]

lap those of neighboring females, with whom they often travel (Fedigan et al. 1988). Adult males tend to band together and are frequently sighted near group boundaries, whereas females with infants often travel alone or in small groups and avoid these boundaries (Chapman 1990b). In general, the social system and ranging pattern of spider monkeys is extremely similar to that of chimpanzees (Symington 1990, Chapman et al. 1995, Volume 3).

Milton (1980) gives the most detailed discussion of ranging behavior of *Alouatta*. As folivores, howlers subsist on resources that are densely and evenly distributed but that also provide little energy per item ingested and are difficult to digest. Together these factors enable and necessitate howlers to minimize energy expenditure both in general activity and in movement and travel. Thus, howlers have small home and day ranges in relation to body size (Crockett and Eisenberg 1987; Table 4-5). *Alouatta* groups do not return to the same sleeping tree on successive nights but sleep in convenient trees near evening feeding sites. Alternating between feeding on fruit and leaves necessitates travel between feeding trees each day.

Milton (1980) found travel to be directly followed by feeding 90% of the time. In her study at BCI, the mean distance traveled was 443 meters, and most daily travel was between 300 and 600 meters. Milton's study groups used one or two pivotal trees each day. These trees were usually primary fruit resources from which the group focused its daily activity. The group would leave and return to the pivotal tree, balancing its diet with leaves and searching for nearby ripening fruit recourses. When switching between these resources, the group was cohesive, and group members traveled in direct and single line fashion to a new pivotal tree. The alpha male usually led the group in travel, and while traveling, the group traversed at least one and sometimes many fig trees.

Other observers have not seen this pattern of resource utilization. Earlier studies describe howlers as using very small areas for a limited period of time, usually rarely returning to a tree in the same day, and then making one long continuous movement to a new part of their home range (Carpenter 1935, Richard 1970, Smith 1977). The home range is usually traversed in 1 to 2 weeks (Baldwin and Baldwin 1972, Richard 1970, Gaulin and Gaulin 1982). These different patterns of range use may be dependent upon the distribution of resources. There is considerable variation in home range size, both inter- and intraspecifically. As summarized by Crockett and Eisenberg (1987:57):

> *Energetic constraints may make very long day-travel impossible for a howler, while the size of the supplying area required by a troop on an annual basis may vary enormously depending upon density and distribution of food sources as well as on the presence of food competitors.*

In any case, the normal amount of travel per day by howler groups is very small. Travel is further minimized by intergroup spacing mechanisms. Home ranges of howler groups overlap extensively and sometimes groups do not have any areas of exclusive use within their ranges (Carpenter 1935, Smith 1977, Glander 1978, Milton 1980, Neville et al. 1988). Home range size is inversely related to howler population density (Crockett and Eisenberg 1987). Spacing between groups is usually maintained by dawn choruses and by loud calls given by the adult male before and after travel to a new site. When groups do come face to face, they usually ignore or avoid each other, or enter into a ritualized vocal battle and then one or both move off in another direction. Thus, howlers avoid excessive movement by (1) moving directly to new feeding sites, (2) not having preferred sleeping sites to which they return each night, and (3) using loud calls to maintain spacing between groups.

THE ECOLOGY AND BEHAVIOR OF *BRACHYTELES*

Figure 4-23 *Brachyteles* [From Mittermeier 1993]

Brachyteles (Fig. 4-23), weighing around 7 to 10 kg, is the largest endemic mammal in Brazil (Milton 1986, Lemos de Sá and Glander 1993). The Tupi Indian name for this impressive monkey is muriqui (Strier 1992b). When suspended from their long arms or tail, muriquis measure about 5 feet. Populations in northern Brazil show sexual dimorphism in canine length. Furthermore, some individuals in the north retain thumbs (Lemos de Sá and Glander 1993). However, populations south of 22°00' latitude are sexually monomorphic in body size, canine size, and in pelage color. Adult males have large testes and females have a pendulous clitoris (Nishimura 1988). As in other atelines, the tail is fully prehensile.

Muriquis are found only in the Atlantic coastal forests of southeastern Brazil, an area with the largest human concentration in the country (Lemos de Sá and Strier 1992, Lemos de Sá et al. 1993). They are one of the most endangered species of Neotropical monkey. Only 19 populations with a total of around 1000 individuals are known to exist and most in small, isolated forest patches (Strier and Fonseca 1996/97).

Brachyteles is the subject of few intensive field studies that have been published. Katie Milton conducted a 10-month study at Fazenda Barreiro Rico (FBR), and an ongoing 18 year study is being directed by Karen Strier at Fazenda Montes Claros (FMC). Lemos de Sá (1991) completed a 12-month study at a third site. Results of a fourth long-term study have recently been published (Moraes et al. 1998). Other short-term studies and surveys are listed in Nishimura et al. (1988), Kinzey (1997a) and Strier and Fonseca (1996/97).

Habitat and Locomotion

Brachyteles exists both in the evergreen forests along the eastern coastal slopes, where annual rainfall exceeds 2000 mm, and to the west of these slopes, in drier semideciduous forests. These latter forests have a pronounced dry season which lasts up to six months (Nishimura et al. 1988). The muriqui is found in primary forest habitats as well as in tall secondary forest, and even in severely disturbed remnant forests (Milton 1984b, 1987b, Fonseca 1985, Lemos de Sá and Strier 1992). Strier (1992b) suggests that muriquis may be found at higher densities in mixed habitats containing both primary and secondary vegetation. These habitats offer a greater variety of potential foods for the eclectic muriqui (Pinto et al. 1993). Muriquis spend most of their time in the mid- and upper canopy (Nishimura et al. 1988).

Muriquis mainly use suspensory locomotion and climbing, and can move very quickly through the canopy (Young et al. 1983, cited in Nishimura et al. 1988). In this large primate, as in *Ateles,* rapid suspensory locomotion may be critical for moving between dispersed patches of high quality foods like fruit and nectar (Strier 1987a, Rosenberger and Strier 1989). Most muriquis possess only vestiges of a thumb, and their other fingers are long and curved to hook over the tops of branches, though some individuals in southern Brazil still retain a thumb (Lemos de Sá and Glander 1993). They normally follow each other on well-tested branches when moving rapidly (Strier 1992b). Quadrupedal walking and running is used only on large, mainly horizontal supports. Muriquis also employ leaping on a regular basis. During feeding, they sit, stand, and use suspensory postures. Most feeding takes place on small, terminal branches and involves below branch suspension. The prehensile tail is used in many locomotor and postural contexts (Nishimura et al. 1988, Fig. 4-24).

Diet

Muriquis, like howlers, have a highly folivorous diet, with leaves accounting for over 50% of their annual diet and reaching 80–90% in drier months (Milton 1984b, Strier 1991a). The annual diet at FMC consisted of 51% leaves, 32% fruit and seeds, 11% flowers and floral nectar, and 6% other plant material (Strier 1991a). When available, fruit makes up over half of the diet. However, leaves are eaten even when other preferred foods are abundant. Leaves probably are eaten for bulk and protein and not simply because of their relative abundance. Immature leaves and ripe fruit are preferred. Muriquis are probably important dispersers for many of the fruit species they eat (Strier 1992b). During periods of fruit scarcity and flower

Figure 4-24 A muriqui using its tail during feeding [From Mittermeier 1993]

abundance, floral nectar becomes a valuable resource and the muriquis might serve as pollinators for some of these plants (Torres de Assumpção 1981, Milton 1984b, Ferrari and Strier 1992). Muriquis are able to include more fruit in their diets than sympatric howler monkeys because, with their rapid locomotion, they can find it more easily (Strier 1992a). They are also dominant to sympatric howler and capuchin monkeys, which often wait for muriquis to finish eating before entering a fruiting tree (Strier 1992b).

At FMC, muriquis ate 63 species of plant from 57 genera during a one-year study period, and at both this site and FBR, they were highly selective and chose a number of rare plant species (Milton 1984b, Strier 1991a). Muriquis are able to tolerate high levels of tannins, presumably due to the relatively rapid rate of food passage through the digestive tract (Strier 1993a). Strier (1991a) believes that, although large body size may allow muriquis to subsist on leaves when more preferred foods are scarce, it may also preclude them from specializing on fruit even when it is abundant. Besides large body size, the dentition, jaw morphology, and digestive system of the muriquis show adaptations for folivory (Hill 1962, Zingeser 1973, Gaulin 1979, Rosenberger and Strier 1989). Muriquis obtain most of their water from the plants they consume, although in the dry season they drink from tree cavities and standing water (Strier 1992b).

Cycles of Activity

The activity pattern of *Brachyteles* varies from site to site and is dependent upon seasonality, habitat, group size, and food quality and distribution (Strier 1987a). For example, muriquis spent more time resting and feeding and less time traveling at FBR than at FMC. Strier (1987a) speculates that the greater frugivory and large group size of muriquis of FMC is responsible for this difference in activity patterns.

The muriquis at FMC shifted their activity times between seasons, resting during the hot mid-afternoon in summer and remaining inactive until midday during winter. However, the actual amount of time they spent feeding (19%) and traveling (29%) remained constant throughout the year (Strier 1987a). Although, generally, the activity budgets of males and females were similar, lactating females spent a greater proportion of their time feeding than other adults (Strier 1987a).

Muriqui groups usually sleep at night in the mid-canopy. The whole group generally sleeps in neighboring trees, although sometimes it may settle in a single tree.

There are no regularly used sleeping sites, but animals settle near late afternoon feeding sites. Long calls often are exchanged prior to settling for the night and serve to reduce distance between group members (Nishimura et al. 1988).

Predation

Jaguars, small carnivores, feral dogs, harpy eagles and other avian predators may present a threat to younger muriquis (Nishimura et al. 1988, Olmos 1994, Galetti 1996, Printes et al. 1996). Printes et al. (1996) report two incidents in which 13 month old infants were suspected to have been preyed upon by tayra (*Eira barbara*) and an avian predator. Alarm calls are given to potential predators. Historically, humans have hunted muriquis for food. Although hunting is still a major problem, habitat destruction is currently the primary cause of muriqui population decline (Milton 1986, Mittermeier et al. 1989, Strier 1992b).

Social Structure and Organization

Brachyteles has a multimale-multifemale social structure and a polygynous mating system. Groups range in size from 13 to 65 individuals (Nishimura et al. 1988, Strier 1992b, 1997a, pers. comm., Table 4-5). Two types of social organization have been described. At FBR, the muriquis lived in fluid, fission-fusion groups similar to those of spider monkeys. Milton (1984b) observed small groups of 3–5 females, their young offspring, and 1–2 subadults to occupy discrete portions of the forest, whereas adult and subadult males moved throughout the study area. Males moved alone or in groups of up to eight individuals and joined associations with one or more females for periods of a few minutes to over a week. The only permanent associations at FBR were between mother and offspring. Similarly, small subgroups were observed at another site, Parque Estadval de Carlos Botelho (Moraes et al. 1998).

At FMC, Strier (see for example 1992b, 1999a,b) has studied one group of muriquis for over 17 years. This group maintained a cohesive social organization, with group members traveling and feeding together for the first 6 years of the study. Since 1988, it began to split into smaller temporary subgroups on occasion (Strier et al. 1993). Over the years, in this protected forest, the group has grown from 22 to 65 individuals and has contained between 6–13 adult males and 8–21 adult females. The sex ratio has also changed significantly (Strier 1994, 1999a). Lemos de Sá (1988) found a cohesive social organization in a fourth muriquis study site.

As is common in other atelines, muriqui males are philopatric (Strier 1990a) and subadult females disperse at 5–6.5 years of age (Strier 1987b, 1991b, 1996a, 1999a). At FMC, the group members normally remain close to one another and they spend more time than expected closer to individuals of their own sex. Furthermore, muriqui males spend more time in close association than do any other primate species studied to date (Strier 1990a). They also exhibit extremely low rates of aggression (Milton 1985a,b, Mendes 1987, Strier 1986, 1990a, 1992b). Few if any agonistic encounters occur over access to resources or sexual partners. There are no noticeable dominance hierarchies, and females are codominant to males. Muriquis do not mutual or allogroom, but they do embrace one another (Fig. 4-25). Embraces probably relieve tension and help reinforce social bonds (Strier 1992b).

Male relationships are permanent and affiliative, and are based on a patrilineal kinship system. Strier (1994) refers to this as a brotherhood. Females, on the other hand, transfer between groups (Strier 1990a, 1993b), a characteristic common among many Neotropical monkeys (Strier 1994, 1999b). This period of transfer is stressful, since transferring muriqui females often are chased by resident females before emigrating and remain peripheral to their new groups for several months (Strier 1993b), though they rapidly integrate into their new group (Printes and Strier in prep.). Males begin to develop strong male-male relationships by the time they are subadults, the same age at which females begin to migrate (Strier 1993b). Generally, adult males maintain proximity to other group members more than do females, and adult females are more often solitary.

In recent years at FMC, as the study group has grown larger, it has a greater tendency to temporarily split into smaller feeding subgroups (Strier 1991b, 1992b, Strier et al. 1993). Currently, it is not clear whether the group is moving toward the fluid associations seen at FBR and in *Ateles,* or whether

Figure 4-25 Muriquis embracing [From Strier 1992b]

it is in the process of dividing into two independent cohesive groups (see Strier et al. 1993). Strier (1992b) points out that the muriqui, which modifies its grouping associations in response to patchy food resources and yet remains within calling proximity, may represent an intermediate social organization on a continuum between cohesive and fission-fusion social systems. In habitats where large patches of preferred fruit are scarce, muriquis may form small, fluid associations similar to those observed by Milton. In sites more rich in large food patches, like FMC, cohesive groups would be expected. However, increase in group size may lead to a greater tendency for fragmentation (Strier 1987a,b, 1989). Moraes et al. (1998) tested some of these hypotheses at two sites, Parcue Estacual de Carlose Botelho, São Paulo (PECB) and Estação Biológica de Caratinga, Minas Gerais (EBC). Contrary to expectations, at PECB, where food patches were significantly larger than those at ECB, feeding parties were smaller. Moraes et al. (1998) speculate that higher population densities and sympatric primates at EBC may make large associations more advantageous to these muriquis than to those living at lower population densities at PECB.

Muriquis are polygamous and both sexes mate with multiple partners (Milton 1985a,b, Strier 1986, 1991b, 1997b). Although Strier (1994, 1997c) observed differences between individual success in mating, this was not related to male-male competition or hierarchical interactions; rather, female choice appeared to be the most significant component. Females actively initiate sexual inspections and copulations with particular males, and easily avoid unwanted attention from others. Mothers avoid mating with sexually active sons (Strier 1997b). In a 60-month period, all sexually active males and females within the focal study group were observed to copulate, and 13% of the 527 observed copulations were performed by extra-group males. Fourteen of seventeen group females participated in these extra-group copulations. It was not evident why certain males were more successful in mating than others. Strier (1997b) believes that familiarity and established social bonds are important factors in muriqui mate choice.

Females do not cycle throughout the year, and cycling among group females is asynchronic (Strier and Ziegler 1994). The average ovulatory cycle lasts 21 ± days and gestation length is roughly 7 months (Strier and Ziegler 1997). Births occur throughout the year but there is a peak during the dry season (May–September) (Strier 1991b, 1996a, 1999a). During the first year, infants are fully dependent upon their mothers (Strier 1991b, 1993b). They begin to move onto mothers' backs at 6 months and, at this time, may be left alone for short periods as she feeds. At around one year, infants begin to travel and feed on their own. Weaning occurs between 18 and 24 months. Strier (1993b, 1996a) considers individuals to be subadults at 5–7 years when they are still smaller than adults but have well developed genitalia. Females migrate at this age. One known female first gave birth at 7.5 years of age. Mothers with surviving infants give birth at approximately 3 year intervals (N=34), whereas those who lost unweaned infants have shorter interbirth intervals (14–28 months, N=3) (Strier 1999a).

Ranging Behavior

Muriquis have relatively large home ranges, from 70–300 ha, and home ranges increase with group size. The group of 7 individuals at FBR had the smallest home range (Milton 1984b), and the home ranges of the FMC study group increased from 168 to 184 ha as the group increased from 26 to 34 members during the first few years of the study (Strier et al. 1993). At FMC, there was 46% overlap of the study group range with that of an adjacent group (Strier 1987c). Adjacent groups exchange long calls and often avoid one another by moving away from each other. Aggressive intergroup encounters occur in areas of overlap, usually over a particular large fruit patch, and both males and females participate (Strier 1986, 1992b,c). These encounters are usually brief and involve vocal exchanges, chases, and touching. However, sometimes the two groups feed in adjacent trees, exchange "neigh" calls, but do not threaten one another (Strier 1992bc). Muriquis do not defend territories (Strier 1990b).

Day range length appears to vary with group size and with food distribution and availability. The small group at FBR had an average day range of 630 ± 128 m (range 350–1400 m) (Milton 1984a), whereas at FMC day ranges averaged 1283 ± 642 m (range 141–3403 m) (Strier 1987c). The larger group at FMC depended more on fruit and had a relatively greater number of large fruit patches available than did that at FBR (Strier 1989, 1991a). At FMC, day ranges were longer during the wet months, when more fruit was available, than during dry months. Because of their large size, muriquis must cover relatively long distances to maintain a frugivorous diet. As stated above, their mode of suspensory locomotion enables them to do this.

Muriquis are as large, or larger, than howler monkeys and, given their body size, one might predict they should be more folivorous (Gaulin 1979). Strier (1987c:589) argues that:

> energetic constraints of body size and diet may be relaxed in muriquis
> because their mode of locomotion enables them to monitor a larger
> food supply than is possible for quadrupedal primates.

Locomotor adaptations may be as essential to understanding species differences in primate ranging behavior as are traditional group size and resource variables.

PITHECIINAE—THE ECOLOGY AND BEHAVIOR OF *CHIROPOTES* AND *PITHECIA*

Habitat and Locomotion

Chiropotes and *Pithecia* are restricted essentially to Amazonia. They are found mainly in primary forest. *Chiropotes* is the most restricted in habitat choice. It only is found in unflooded primary rain forest and high mountain savannah forest and is rarely found outside of areas with high canopy forest (Ayres 1989, Sussman and Phillips-Conroy 1995, Norconk et al. 1996, Kinzey 1997a). *Pithecia* is the least restricted of the pithecines in habitat choice. It inhabits both highland and lowland forests, seasonally flooded forests, secondary forests, and disturbed habitats (Johns 1986, Robinson et al. 1987, Kinzey 1992, Peres 1993; Walker 1996).

Chiropotes (Fig. 4-26) is dependent upon the upper portions of the canopy. In Surinam, it was more restricted in its vertical ranging than other canopy forms (Fig. 3-6). It feeds, travels, and rests mainly in the small branches in the crowns of tall trees (Walker 1993a,b). The bearded saki is essentially a quadrupedal walking or running animal (80% of observed bouts) (Fleagle and Mittermeier 1980, Fleagle and Meldrum 1988; Walker 1996). When in a hurry, it bounds or gallops. Leaping or jumping accounts for around 18% of locomotor bouts, and in certain situations, *Chiropotes* can be an adept leaper. *Chiropotes* leaps from a pronograde position and lands in the terminal branches of a neighboring tree (Walker 1993a). Suspensory locomotion is very rare, but hindlimb suspensory postures are common, especially during feeding and play. The tail is not prehensile but is often used to help support the animal as it hangs by its feet during feeding (Walker

Figure 4-26 *Chiropotes* [From van Roosmalen et al. 1981]

Figure 4-27 *Pithecia* [Photo by Terry Gleason]

1996). The tail is prehensile in the infant until it is about two months old (van Roosmalen et al. 1981).

Pithecia pithecia (Fig. 4-27) is usually seen lower in the canopy than *Chiropotes*, spending most of its time in the understory (Fig. 3-12). It has been observed to come to the ground in search of specific food items and can spend up to several hours a day there (Gleason 1998). Like *Chiropotes, P. pithecia* is an above-branch quadruped, but bipedal hopping and leaping is a peculiar and characteristic

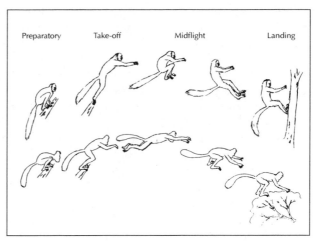

Figure 4-28 Leap phases in *Pithecia* (top) and *Chiropotes* (bottom). [From Walker 1998]

locomotor pattern in this genus. In fact, quadrupedal jumping and leaping are the most frequently used modes of travel (Fleagle and Mittermeier 1980, Walker 1993a, 1996). Unlike *Chiropotes, P. pithecia* usually leaps from larger vertical supports (Fig. 4-28) and often maintains a vertical body orientation when resting, feeding, and leaping (Walker 1994, 1996). In fact, Walker (1996, 1998) considers *P. pithecia* to be a vertical clinger and leaper much like the indriids of Madagascar. Bounding, galloping and bipedal hopping are used to cross from branch to branch and sometimes to move on horizontal branches. When in a hurry, *P. pithecia* can cover distances rapidly. It often moves in quick spurts and then freezes in dense foliage. Because of the rapid locomotion of *Pithecia* and its leaping abilities, saki monkeys have a number of colorful vernacular names. In Guyana, they are known as "flying jack" or "breezy monkey," and in Colombia as "flying monkey" (*mico volador*) (Buchanan et al. 1981).

In southern Amazonia, *Pithecia* is larger and generally not sympatric with *Chiropotes*. These species show some differences in habitat preference and locomotor pattern (Peres 1993). For example, *P. albicans* rarely descends to the understory but is found higher, in the forest canopy and subcanopy. It also rarely uses bipedal hopping and vertical clinging (Johns 1986, Peres 1993). Some of the habitat choices and locomotor behaviors of *P. pithecia* may be related to ecological divergence from its potential pithecine competitor, *Chiropotes* (Peres 1993).

Diet

Unlike similar sized *Cebus* and *Saimiri*, *Pithecia* and *Chiropotes* subsist mainly on plant material, and insects do not make up a major component of the yearly diet. They are both frugivores and specialized seed predators. Unlike atelines who often swallow seeds whole and pass them in their feces unharmed, these genera destroy the seeds. They can bite into fruits with hard covers (pericarps) and thus obtain seeds that are softer than those eaten by other primates (Kinzey 1997a). *Pithecia*, however, cannot eat fruits as hard as those eaten by *Chiropotes* or *Cacajao* and may compensate by consuming seeds higher in toxic tannins and lipids (Kinzey and Norconk 1993, Norconk and Kinzey 1994, Norconk et al 1998).

Besides fruit and seeds, *Pithecia* regularly includes leaves and insects in its diet. In a 16-month study in Venezuela, *P. pithecia* was observed to feed on fruit 85–93% of the time, ingesting seeds in over 95% of these samples. The diet was supplemented by young leaves (1–13% of monthly samples); insects, especially ants (1–6% of samples); and flowers (Norconk and Kinzey 1990, Kinzey and Norconk 1993). The amount of time eating fruit was related to seasonal availability (see below). Feeding data from other, shorter studies of *P. pithecia, P. albicans,* and *P. hirsuta* are similar, though fruit consumption is somewhat lower and leaf eating slightly higher in some studies (Buchanan et al. 1981, Johns 1986, Soini 1986, Setz 1988, Peres 1993).

Chiropotes feeds mainly on unripe fruit (often the same fruit species eaten by other monkeys when they ripen) and on seeds (of species that other primates eat only for the mesocarp) (van Roosmalen et al. 1981, Kinzey and Norconk 1990, Kinzey 1997a). Special adaptations of the anterior teeth and jaws permit it to feed on very hard fruit (Fig. 4-29) (Kinzey 1992, Anapol and Lee 1994, Norconk et al 1998). Interestingly, the molar morphology is adapted for chewing soft foods (Rosenberger and Kinzey 1976, Martin et al. 1994). In a 9-month study in Venezuela, *Chiropotes* ate seeds 27–96% of the time in any given month; flowers were eaten in 4 months, making up 8% of the diet in one month. Unlike in *Pithecia,* leaves account for a small proportion of the *Chiropotes* diet, making up more than 1% of the diet in only 5 months (Peetz in prep., cited in Kinzey 1997a). At the same site, insects, mainly soft caterpillars, were eaten by *Chiropotes* every month, accounting for up to 24% of the diet in some months when fruit was scarce (see Norconk 1996).

The fruit eaten by *Chiropotes* is very hard; however, the seeds are softer than those eaten by *Pithecia* or even by *Ateles* (Kinzey and Norconk 1990, Kinzey 1992). As mentioned above, insects eaten by *Chiropotes* also are soft (Peetz in prep., Ayres and Nessimian 1982). *Chiropotes* has stereotyped and very efficient techniques of removing seeds from several species of the Brazil nut family Lecythidaceae and fruits from the plant family Sapotaceae (Mittermeier and van Roosmalen 1981, van Roosmalen et al. 1981, Norconk 1996, Gleason pers. comm.). Although *Chiropotes* and *Pithecia* are both seed predators, they eat different types of seeds, supplement their diets with different items, and feed in different levels of the forest. Norconk (1996) found evidence that the ability to feed on seeds may remove these species from seasonal effects of low rainfall. At her site in Venezuela, the "dry season" could not be considered a period of scarcity for sakis. Generally, both *Chiropotes satanas* and *Pithecia pithecia* ingest many dry season resources (winged seeds, legumes, nuts, and immature fruit). Seed ingestion declined in the wet season with the ripening of fleshy fruits.

In comparing the diets of these two species (Norconk 1996) found that: (1) *Chiropotes* tended

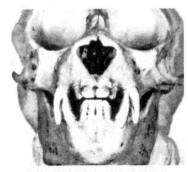
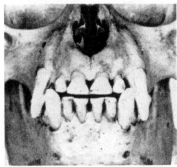

Figure 4-29 Saki monkeys have dental adaptations enabling them to eat hard fruit and seeds. Notice the differences between the seed eater *Pithecia* (top) and the fruit eater *Ateles* (bottom). [From Kinzey 1992]

to maximize the use of resources by ingesting younger seeds but more mature meso-carp of the same plants. *Pithecia,* on the other hand, was more selective, usually ingesting fruit at only one stage of maturity. They do, however, also have several key resources (e.g., *Licania discolor:* Chrysobalanaceae), which they eat at several stages of ripening (Gleason pers. comm.). (2) *Chiropotes* increased the number of species it ate during the dry season and narrowed its diet in the wet season with the maturation of its keystone resource, *Pradosia caracasana* (Sapotaceae), whereas *Pithecia* maintained a nearly constant diversity of fruit species in its diet by adjust-ing to changes in fruit availability.

The use of seeds as a major component of the diet is not restricted to pithecines. Some colobines and Malagasy prosimians also are seed specialists (See volumes 1 and 3). However, because most animals are unable to utilize these hard and/or toxic resources, they are usually fairly abundant. Seeds often provide high concentra-tions of valuable nutrients such as protein and lipids. However, in order to exploit seeds, these species need morphological adaptations of the dentition to pene-trate hard coverings and either gut tract adaptations for detoxifying chemically protected seeds, or behavioral mechanisms to reduce their affect. Dental adapta-tions and perhaps hindgut enlargement in the pithecines and forgut adaptations in the colobines provide these anatomical specializations (Norconk 1996).

Cycles of Activity

Pithecia and *Chiropotes* move from dawn to dusk although they have shorter days than most Neotropical monkeys (10 vs. 12 hours). This may be due to their ability to feed on high quality seeds and thus reduce the amount of time foraging (Kinzey 1997a).

Predation

Few data are available on natural predation of these species. Gleason and Nor-conk (in prep) describe the community of predators that are potential threats to *Pithecia pithecia* and the sakis' behavioral reactions to them. These primates are vulnerable to large raptors (e.g., *Spizeatus ornatus, Harpya harpyja*), large and small cats (e.g., *Panthera onca, Felis wiedii*), mustelids (*Eira barbara*), and large snakes (e.g., *Boa constrictor*). When threatened by a terrestrial predator, *Pithecia* will mob the threat if it is small or flee quickly if it is large. Large birds elicit the most fre-quent alarm response from this species. The reaction ranges from small bird-like warning "peeps" that may or may not be answered by other group members, to loud whistles and growls that are always echoed by other group members. When loud calls are given, the sakis usually will descend from the canopy and hide in the dense undergrowth, sometimes remaining immobile for more than one hour.

Humans sometimes kill *Chiropotes* and *Pithecia* for their long, thickly furred tails. The tails are used as dusters.

Social Structure and Organization

Pithecia was originally thought to live in family groups (Buchanan et al. 1981, Robin-son et al. 1987, Rosenberger et al. 1997), but recent studies indicate that this may not be true. In Peru, *P. hirsuta* has been reported to live in groups of 2–9 individu-als with 2–5 adults (1–3 adult males and 1–2 adult females). These groups were extremely stable over 2–6 years (Soini 1986). One group of *P. pithecia* currently under study in Venezuela consists of 3 adult females and 2 adult males and at one time consisted of 3 adult females, 3 adult males, and 3 juveniles (Gleason and Norconk 1995, Gleason 1998). Single individuals also are sighted frequently, but these animals are difficult to see and sightings may often underestimate the number of monkeys present (Norconk pers. comm.). Small groups may come together to form larger aggregations from time to time (Kinzey 1997a). Detailed research on the social organization of saki monkeys has not yet been published.

Sexual dichromatism is present shortly after birth, and adult coloration (Fig. 4-30) is attained by the 3rd month (Bode 1953). Newborn infants cling to their mothers' chests, but by the end of the first month, they are carried dorsally. At three to five months, the young saki begins to travel and feed independently of its mother, and by 7 months, it is quite independent (Hanif 1967, Buchanan et al. 1981, Soini 1986, Savage et al. 1992, Brush and Norconk 1999). Weaning begins at around 8 months and is complete at around one year (Soini 1986). Infants are carried and cared for by the mothers and possibly other adult and subadult females. Mothers often share food with infants for up to two years. Most populations studied have a well-defined birth season (Soini 1986, Robinson et al. 1987, Kinzey 1997a). In *P. pithecia,* females can give birth at 37 months (Dugmore 1986), and the gestation period is between 163–176 days (Hick 1968). The oestrous cycle is 16–17 days (Savage et al. 1992, Shideler et al. 1994).

Chiropotes (the bearded saki) lives in multi-male groups of between 8 and 30 or more animals, and groups have been reported to merge or break into subgroups during foraging (van Roosmalen et al. 1981, Ayres 1989, Norconk and Kinzey 1994). Groups contain adult and subadult individuals and are multimale with an adult sex ratio close to 1:1. The large group travels as a cohesive unit, and although the group frequently splits into subgroups while traveling, individuals are never more than a few hundred meters from one another (Ayres 1989, Norconk and Kinzey 1994). Although *Pithecia* is rarely seen in mixed species groups, *Chiropotes* was seen with other species (mainly *Saimiri* and *Cebus*) in 11 of 35 sightings in Surinam (van Roosmalen et al. 1981) and occasionally travels with *Cebus* in Venezuela (Gleason pers. comm.).

As with *Pithecia, Chiropotes* has a definite birth season (van Roosmalen et al. 1981, Kinzey 1997a). By two months of age, the infant is carried ventrally but begins to ride on the mother's back and is groomed by other group members. At 3 months of age, the infant rides dorsally most of the time and may move short distances from the mother. By the sixth month, it locomotes independently for short distances but is carried by the mother during long-distant travel. Between 10–13 months of age, the young bearded saki becomes fully independent, though it continues to take some food from the mother at this time (Peetz in prep, cited in Kinzey 1997a). Gestation lasts between 4.5 to

Figure 4-30 Saki monkeys display sexual dichromatism. [Photo by R.W. Sussman]

5.5 months (Hick 1968, van Roosmalen et al. 1981, Kinzey 1997a). Single births are the rule in both *Chiropotes* and *Pithecia*.

Ranging Behavior

Little is known about the ranging behavior of *Pithecia* or *Chiropotes*. *P. pithecia* may have small home ranges (4–40 ha) (Buchanan 1978, Soini 1986). Soini (1986) found the home ranges of two groups of *P. hirsuta* to overlap 70%. When contiguous groups came into contact, they vigorously displayed at one another, though occasional aggregations of groups did form. Sympatric groups of *P. pithecia* in Venezuela engage in frequent chases and occasionally more extreme aggressive behavior. These groups never coalesce (Gleason 1998). Day ranges for *P. pithecia* may be less than 1000 m (Kinzey 1997a), but longer day paths have been observed (Gleason pers. comm). Home ranges of *Chiropotes* are relatively large (200–550 ha) (van Roosmalen et al. 1981, Ayres 1989, Kinzey 1997a). Average day ranges are 1000–4500 m, with larger distances traveled during the dry season (Ayres 1981, Kinzey 1997a). *Chiropotes* moves rapidly between food trees and then feeds intensively. Data on home and day ranges and population density are given in Table 4-5.

THE ECOLOGY AND BEHAVIOR OF *CACAJAO*

Cacajao (uakari) is one of the rarest, most unusual, and strangest looking of the South American monkeys (Fig. 4-31). Different populations are black, white, or red. Uakaris all have bare faces with bulbous foreheads and they can raise their long hair, in a behavior called pilo-erection, to make themselves look twice their actual size. This latter ability is probably used to intimidate predators or in social displays. Uakari is the largest pithecine, weighing around 3–3.5 kg, and has the highest degree of sexual dimorphism (males are 23% larger than females) (Ford and Davis 1992). It also is the only Neotropical monkey that has a short tail. Uakaris are among the most endangered and least studied of the South American primates (Robinson et al. 1987, Barnett and Brandon-Jones 1997).

Habitat and Locomotion

Cacajao occurs in the western Amazon basin, in northern Brazil, eastern Peru, eastern Colombia, and northwestern Venezuela (Ayres 1989, Walker 1993b). It is restricted to a narrow range of Amazonia near the equator, in areas distinguished by high temperatures, heavy precipitation, and little seasonal variation in climate. Uakaris are found mainly in flooded forests, although they also occur in high *terra ferma* forests (high ground forests that are never flooded), as well (Ayres 1986, 1989, Walker 1996). Uakari ecology is

Figure 4-31 *Cacajao* [Photo by R.W. Sussman]

strongly influenced by riverine forest habitats found in the Amazon (Barnett and Brandon-Jones 1997) and may migrate seasonally from flooded areas to dry land during the dry season in some areas (Da Cunha and Barnett 1989, Heymann 1990, Boubli 1993, 1999).

Cacajao is quadrupedal and often leaps between gaps in the canopy. Approximately one quarter of its travel time is spent leaping. Walker (1996) describes its most typical locomotion as quadrupedal, pronograde clambering. It is the only species of pithecine that frequently uses bipedal suspension in posture and locomotion (Walker 1993a, 1996). Uakaris often collect fruit in terminal branches and then carry it to larger supports to eat (Ayres 1986). They shinny up angled large branches by pushing with their hind limbs (Fontaine 1981, Walker 1993a). The functional significance of the shortened tail is unknown but may be related to peculiar aspects of the vine-filled, flooded forests in which this monkey is found, and to its extensive use of the ground (Fig. 4-32) (Walker 1993a). The only other tail-less

Figure 4-32 Uakaris are the only New World monkeys with a short tail. [From Rowe 1996, *The Pictorial Guide to Living Primates*, Pogonias Press, East Hampton, NY]

arboreal mammal in the Neotropics is the sloth, which frequently crosses gaps on the ground. Ayres (1986) estimated that *Cacajao* spent 20–40% of its foraging time on the ground during the dry season. Most of its time, however, is spent in the middle to upper canopy, usually higher than *Chiropotes*.

Diet

Cacajao, like other pithecines, is highly frugivorous and a seed predator. Over 90% of its annual diet is fruit, most of which (67%) is immature seeds (Fig. 4-33) (Ayres 1989, see also Defler 1989, Boubli 1999). Small quantities of insects and arthropods (5%) and flowers (6%) are eaten. In the dry season, when fruit sources are scarce, *C. melanocephalus* has been seen raiding eggs of river turtles on white sand beaches (Barnett and Blandon-Jones 1997). Uakaris ate over 100 species of fruit from at least 24 plant families in a 1.5-year study (Ayres 1989). Like many frugivorous primates, a few

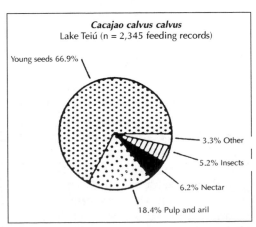

Figure 4-33 Proportion of time uakaris spent feeding on different food items at Ayres study site. [From Ayres 1989]

species of plant make up a large proportion of the diet. Most of their diet (around 50%) is attained from three highly representative plant families, Hippocrateaceae, Lecythidaceae, and Annonaceae. For *Cacajao*, five species account for almost 50% of the annual diet.

Fruits eaten generally contain large seeds and have a hard husk (Ayres 1989, Lehman and Robertson 1994, Boubli 1999). They also usually have yellow pulp or a red aril and seem to be relatively rich in lipids, proteins, and carotenoids, and have a high energy content (Ayres 1989). In some areas of the Brazilian Amazon characterized by very poor soils and dominated by plant species that produce dry fruits protected by hard husks, uakaris are able to thrive because of their adaptations for sclerocarpic feeding (i.e., eating hard-husked fruit) (Boubli 1999). In these forests, other frugivores are rare except for other seed predators such as parrots and macaws. In seasonally inundated forests, the uakaris make use of the ground during dry periods, eating seeds from newly emerged plants. Potential ground feeding competitors appear to be missing from these areas because of the annual rise in waters (Ayres 1989).

Social Structure and Organization

Group size has been reported to be between 15 and 50 or more, and may even reach 100 individuals (Mittermeier and Coimbra-Filho 1977, Fontaine 1981, Ayres 1989). Whether the larger groups are aggregations of more than one group is unknown. Mixed species groups of *Cacajao* and *Cebus* and/or *Saimiri* have been reported (Mittermeier and Coimbra-Filho 1977). The main group studied by Ayres (1989) contained 45–50 individuals, and three other nearby groups had at least 25–30 individuals. Ayres' study group was multimale and had a sex ratio of 1:1. Its home range was 500–550 ha, but the group spent over 90% of its time in 250–300 ha. It moved from 1,500 m to as much as 5000 m in a day. The *Cacajao* group often split into a number of smaller subgroups of 12–15 or fewer individuals. These subgroups frequently dispersed over the home range, 1–2 km apart. Splitting was more common during dry periods when mature fruit was not abundant.

Probably because of their pattern of spatial dispersion, *Cacajao* has a very rich repertoire of intragroup communication, including a number of vocal, visual and tactile signals. For example, uakaris have more facial expressions than any other Neotropical primate, and their red faces display secondary sexual characteristics (Fig. 4-34). Even though they have short tails, tail-wagging is used as a communicative signal (Fontaine 1981, Walker 1993a). The density of *Cacajao* has been estimated at 20 individuals per square km in forests with high plant species diversity, but much lower in less diverse habitats (Ayres 1989).

Infant development has been observed under semi-natural conditions in Monkey Jungle, Miami, Florida (Fontaine 1981). The infant is carried ventrally for about 3 months and then moves to the back of the mother. At 12 months, it locomotes independently but still may sleep on the mother's back. Suckling and sleeping in contact with the mother is prolonged and may last until the infant is two years old. One female born at Monkey Jungle in Florida gave birth to her first infant at 42 months of age. Two males reached adulthood at 5 and 6 years, whereas a third showed adult sexual characteristics and reached adult weight at 33 months. Births in Monkey Jungle and in zoos of the northern hemisphere are seasonal, normally occurring between May and October. Gestation length is unknown. Much remains to be learned about this species.

THEORETICAL INSERT

Dispersal and Cooperation Between Non-Kin

One might think that howler social organization is an excellent model for the selective advantage of (1) characteristics associated with dominance and (2) kin selection, where dominant animals are able to better ensure the survival of their offspring and relatives and thus pass on certain genetic traits (Wilson 1975). However, the situation is more complex than this. First, as stated above, the tenure of dominance in both males and females is short; in fact, less than the time it takes for offspring to reach maturity. Second, Glander (1980, 1992) found an inverse correlation between the dominance rank of a female and survival of her offspring. In the first 20 years of his study, alpha females lost all but one of their infants compared to an average of 28% mortality for the second through fifth ranked females. [In fact, it is not unusual to find negative effects to high rank (Sauther 1992, Packer et al. 1995, Morell 1996, Strier 1997a).] Finally, both

Figure 4-34 The faces of uakaris display secondary sexual characteristics, and these monkeys often use facial expressions in communication. [Photo by R.W. Sussman]

males and females constantly leave the natal group, disrupting opportunities for kin to interact. Dispersal of both sexes is rare in polygynous primate groups.

Changing of group membership is a normal phenomenon among howlers (Carpenter 1965, Neville 1972, Smith 1977, Scott et al. 1978, Gaulin and Gaulin 1982, Crockett 1984, Clarke and Glander 1984, Glander 1992, Crockett and Pope 1993), though there is variation among different species and populations (Crockett and Eisenberg 1987). For example, in Glander's (1992) population of mantled howlers, 96% of the females and 79% of the males emigrated from their natal group while they were juveniles. These individuals lived as extra-group animals for up to one (females) to three or more (males) years. Females then attempted to assume the alpha position in an established group and remained transient until they were successful. Thus, among females, transient dispersal is common until obtaining membership in a group. Glander observed secondary dispersal only once in 20 years. Males also remain solitary until successful at defeating a group's alpha male and assuming his position. If there is more than one male in the group, just as in females, a hierarchy is established which is inversely related to age (Glander, 1980 1992, Jones 1983). In mantled howlers, there have been no instances of secondary dispersal among these older males.

Among red howlers (*A. seniculus*), in contrast to mantled howlers, 79% of the females and 98% of males emigrated from their natal group (Crockett and Pope

1993). Of females reaching adulthood, approximately 20% bred in their natal group. The number of females remaining in their natal group is related to the number of breeding females in that group, with few or none remaining in groups with as many as 3–4 adult females. Out of 65 groups censused (Crockett 1984), none had more than 4 adult females and 90% had only 2–3. Unlike mantled howlers, emigrating females do not join established groups. Instead they join a solitary male and form a new group. This may be a means by which red howlers colonize successional habitats (Crockett 1984, Eisenberg 1991). These females usually disperse far from their natal group (up to distances equivalent to 5 home range diameters), and there is a high mortality among juvenile red howler females until they reach a reproductive position in a group.

Red howler males leave their natal group at a relatively late age (60 months vs. 22 months for mantled howler males) and do not disperse as far as females (Crockett and Pope 1993, Izawa and Lozano 1994). Thus, juvenile mortality rates are much lower for males than for females. Approximately half of the males join established groups while the rest establish new groups. Unlike mantled howlers, red howler males move more than once in their lifetimes and may incur repeated injuries in fights with other males over breeding status. In the Venezuela population, breeding male tenure averaged 5–7.5 years, and males moved approximately three home range diameters during their lives. Maximum reproductive life span is estimated to be 20 years (Crockett and Pope 1993).

In some cases, two males may attempt to immigrate together, and some of these pairs may be related (Crockett and Eisenberg 1987). However, in red and mantled howlers, most groups are probably composed of unrelated animals, and neighboring groups are distantly related because of the high rate of gene flow (Crockett and Eisenberg 1987, Glander 1992). Members of howler groups often cooperate with nonkin indicating that, in howlers as in many primate species, kinship is not an essential component for cooperation (Crockett and Eisenberg 1987, Strier 1994, 1996b).

BIBLIOGRAPHY

Ahumedo, J.A. 1989. Behavior and social structure of free ranging spider monkeys (*Ateles belzebuth*). *La Macarena Field Studies of New World Monkeys, La Macarena, Colombia* 2:7–31.

Altmann, S.A. 1959. Field observations on the howling monkey society. *J. Mammal.* 40:317–330

Anapol, F., Lee, S. 1994. Morphological adaptation to diet in platyrrhine primates. *Am. J. Phys. Anthropol.* 94:239–261.

Ayres, J.M. 1981. Observaçiônes sobre a ecologia e o comportamento dos cuxius (*Chiropotes albinasus e Chiropotes satanas.* Cebidae, Primates). Instituto Nacional de Pesquisas da Amazonia (INPA), Manaus, Brazil.

Ayres, J.M. 1986. *Uakaris and Amazonian Flooded Forest.* Ph.D. Thesis. University of Cambridge, Cambridge.

Ayres, J.M. 1989. Comparative feeding ecology of the uakari and bearded saki, *Cacajao* and *Chiropotes. J. Hum. Evol.* 18:697–716.

Ayres, J.M., Nessimian, J.L. 1982. Evidence for insectivory in *Chiropotes satanas. Primates* 23:458–459.

Baldwin, J.D., Baldwin, J.I. 1972. The ecology and behavior of squirrel monkeys (*Saimiri oerstedi*) in a natural forest in western Panama. *Folia Primatol.* 18:161–184.

Barnett, A.A., Brandon-Jones, D.B. 1997. The ecology, biogeography and conservation of the uakari, *Cacajao* (Pitheciinae). *Folia Primatol.* 68:223–235.

Bergeson, D.J. 1996. *The Positional Behavior and Prehensile Tail use of* Alouatta palliata, Ateles geoffroyi, *and* Cebus capucinus. Ph.D. Thesis. Washington University, St. Louis.

Bergeson, D.J. 1998. Patterns of suspensory feeding in *Alouatta palliata, Ateles geoffroyi,* and *Cebus capucinus* Pp. 45–60. In *Primate Locomotion: Recent Advances.* E. Strasser, J. Fleagle, A. Rosenberger, H. McHery, Eds., New York, Plenum.

Bernstein, I.S. 1964. A field study of the activities of howler monkeys. *Anim. Behav.* 12:92–97.

Bode, N. 1953. Sakis, Junior. *Zoonooz.* 26:5.

Boubli, J.P. 1993. Southern expansion of the geographic distribution of *Cacajao melanocephalus melanocephalus. Int. J. Primatol.* 14:933–937.

Boubli, J.P. 1999. Feeding ecology of one group of Humboldt's black uakari (*Cacajao melanocephalus melanocephalus*) in a forest on white-sand soils of Pico da Neblina National Park, Brazil. *Am. J. Primatol.* 49:37–38.

Bravo, S.P., Zunino, G.E. 1998. Effects of black howler monkey (*Alouatta caraya*) seed ingestion on insect larvae. *Am. J. Primatol.* 45:411–415.

Brush, J.A., Norconk, M.A. 1999. Early behavioral development in wild white-faced saki monkey (*Pithecia pithecia*). *Am. J. Phys. Anthropol.* Suppl. 28:99.

Buchanan, D.B. 1978. *Communication and Ecology of Pithecine Monkeys with Special Reference to* Pithecia pithecia. Ph.D. Thesis. Wayne State University, Detroit.

Buchanan, D.B., Mittermeier, R.A., Roosmalen, M.G.M. van. 1981. The saki monkeys, genus *Pithecia.* Pp. 391–418. In *Ecology and Behavior of Neotropical Monkeys. Vol. 1.* A.F. Coimbra-Filho, R.A. Mittermeier, Eds., Rio de Janeiro, Academia Brasileira de Ciências.

Campbell, A.F. 1994. Patterns of home range use by *Ateles geoffroyi* and *Cebus capucinus* at Le Selva Biological Station, Costa Rica. *Am. J. Primatol.* 33:199–200.

Campbell, A.F. ms. Ecology of *Ateles geoffroyi* and *Cebus capucinus* at Le Selva Biological Station, Costa Rica.

Cant, J.G.H. 1977. *Ecology, Locomotion and Social Organization of Spider Monkeys* (Ateles geoffroy). Ph.D. Thesis. University of California, Davis.

Cant, J.G.H. 1986. Locomotion and feeding postures of spider and howling monkeys: Field study and evolutionary interpretation. *Folia Primatol.* 46:1–4.

Carpenter, C.R. 1934. A field study of the behavior and social relations of howling monkeys. *Comp. Psych. Monographs* 10:1–168.

Carpenter, C.R. 1935. Behavior of red spider monkeys (*Ateles geoffroyi*) in Panama. *J. Mammal* 16:171–180.

Carpenter, C.R. 1965. The howler of Barro Colorado Island. Pp. 250–291. In *Primate Behavior: Field Studies of Monkeys and Apes.* I. DeVore, Ed., New York, Holt, Rinehart and Winston.

Chapman, C.A. 1986. Boa constrictor predation and group response in white faced cebus monkeys. *Biotropica* 18:171–172.

Chapman, C.A. 1987. Flexibility in diets of three species of Costa Rican Primates. *Folia Primatol.* 49:90–105.

Chapman, C.A. 1988a. Patterns of foraging and range use by three species of neotropical primates. *Primates* 29:177–194.

Chapman, C.A. 1988b. Patch use and patch depletion by the spider and howling monkeys of Santa Rosa National Park, Costa Rica. *Behaviour* 105:99–116.

Chapman, C.A. 1989a. Primate seed dispersal: the fate of dispersed seeds. *Biotropica* 21:148–154.

Chapman, C.A. 1989b. Spider monkey sleeping sites: use and availability. *Am. J. Primatol.* 18:53–60.

Chapman, C.A. 1990a. Ecological constraints on group size in three species of neotropical primates. *Folia Primatol.* 73:1–9.

Chapman, C.A. 1990b. Association patterns of spider monkeys: the influence of ecology and sex on social organization. *Behav. Ecol. Sociobiol.* 26:409–414.

Chapman, C.A., Chapman, L.J. 1990. Reproductive biology of captive and free-ranging spider monkeys. *Zoo Biol.* 9:1–9.

Chapman, C.A., Chapman, L.J., McLaughlin, R.L. 1989. Multiple central place foraging by spider monkeys: travel consequences of using many sleeping sites. *Oecologia* 79:506–511.

Chapman, C.A., Lefebvre, L. 1990. Manipulating foraging group size: spider monkey food calls at fruiting trees. *Anim. Behav.* 39:891–896.

Chapman, C.A., Wrangham, R.W., Chapman, L.J. 1995. Ecological constraints on group size: an analysis of spider monkey and chimpanzee subgroups. *Behav. Ecol. Sociobiol.* 36:59–70.

Chiarello, A.G. 1994. Diet of the brown howler monkey *Alouatta fusca* in a semi-deciduous forest fragment of southeastern Brazil. *Primates* 35:25–34.

Chivers, D.J. 1969. On the daily behavior and spacing of howling monkey groups. *Folia Primatol.* 10:48–102.

Chivers, D.J., Hladik, C.M. 1984. Diet and gut morphology in primates. Pp. 213–230. In *Food Acquisition and Processing in Primates.* D.J. Chivers, B.A. Wood, A. Bilsborough, Eds., New York, Plenum.

Clarke, M.R. 1983. Infant-killing and infant disappearance following male takeovers in a group of free-ranging howling monkeys (*Alouatta palliata*) in Costa Rica. *Am. J. Primatol.* 5:241–247.

Clarke, M.R., Glander, K.E. 1984. Female reproductive success in a group of free-ranging howling monkeys (*Alouatta palliata*) in Costa Rica. Pp. 111–126. In *Female Primates: Studies by Women Primatologists.* M.F. Small, Ed., New York. Alan R. Liss.

Clarke, M.R., Glander, K.E., Zucker, E.L. 1998. Infant-nonmother interactions of free-ranging mantled howlers (*Alouatta palliata*) in Costa Rica. *Int. J. Primatol.* 19:451–472.

Clarke, M.R., Zucker, E.L. 1994. Survey of the howling monkey population at La Pacifica: A seven-year follow-up. *Int. J. Primatol.* 15:61–74.

Clarke, M.R., Zucker, E.L., Glander, K.E. 1994. Group takeover by a natal male howling monkey (*Alouatta palliata*) and associated disappearance and injuries of immatures. *Primates* 35:435–442.

Clarke, M.R., Zucker, E.L., Scott, N.J. 1986. Population trends of the mantled howler groups of La Pacifica, Guanacaste, Costa Rica. *Am. J. Primatol.* 11:79–88.

Clutton-Brock, T.H., Harvey, P.H. 1977. Species differences in feeding and ranging behaviour in primates. Pp. 557–584. In *Primate Ecology: Studies of Feeding and Ranging Behaviour in Lemurs, Monkeys and Apes.* T.H. Clutton-Brock, Ed., London, Academic Press.

Coehlo, A.M., Jr., Coehlo, L., Bramblett, C., Bramblett, S., Quick, L. 1976. Ecology, population characteristics, and sympatric association in primates: a socio-bioenergetic analysis of howler and spider monkeys in Tikal, Guatemala. *Yrbk. Phys. Anthropol.* 46:253–264.

Collias, N., Southwick, C. 1952. A field study of population density and social organization in howling monkeys. *Proc. Am. Phil. Soc.* 96:143–156.

Crockett, C.M. 1984. Emigration by female red howler monkeys and the case for female competition. Pp. 159–173. In *Female Primates: Studies by Women Primatologists.* M.F. Small, Ed., New York. Alan R. Liss.

Crockett, C.M. 1987. Diet, dimorphism, and demography: Perspectives from howlers to hominids. Pp. 115–135. In *The Evolution of Human Behavior: Primate Models.* W.G. Kinzey, Ed., Albany, SUNY Press.

Crockett, C.M. 1996. The relation between red howler monkey (*Allouatta seniculut*) troop size and population growth in two habitats. Pp. 489–510. In *Adaptive Radiations of Neotropical Primates.* M.A. Norconk, A.L. Rosenberger, P.A. Garber, Eds., New York, Plenum.

Crockett, C.M. 1998. Conservation biology of the genus *Alouatta*. *Int. J. Primatol.* 19:549–578.

Crockett, C.M., Eisenberg, J.F. 1987. Howlers: variation in group size and demography. Pp. 54–68. In *Primate Societies.* B.B. Smuts, D.L. Cheney, R.M. Seyfarth, R.W. Wrangham, T.T. Struhsaker, Eds., Chicago, University of Chicago Press.

Crockett, C.M., Pope, T. 1988 Inferring patterns of aggression from red howler monkey injuries. *Am. J. Primatol.* 15:289–308.

Crockett, C.M., Pope, T. 1993. Consequences of sex differences in dispersal for juvenile red howler monkeys. Pp. 104–118. In *Juvenile Primates Life History, Development, and Behavior.* M.E. Pereira, L.A. Fairbanks, Eds., New York, Oxford University Press.

Crockett, C.M., Rudran, R. 1987a. Red howler monkey birth data. I: Seasonal variation. *Am. J. Primatol.* 713:347–368.

Crockett, C.M., Rudran, R. 1987b. Red howler monkey birth data. II: Interannual, habitat, and sex comparisons. *Am. J. Primatol.* 13:369–384.

Crockett, C.M., Sekulic, R. 1984. Infanticide in red howler monkeys (*Alouatta seniculus*). Pp. 173–191. In *Infanticide: Comparative and Evolutionary Perspectives.* G. Hausfater, S.B. Hrdy, Eds., New York, Aldine.

Cuarón, A.D. 1997. Conspecific aggression and predation: costs for a solitary mantled howler monkey. *Folia Primatol.* 68:100–105.

Cunha da, A.C., Barnett, A. 1989. *Project Uakari. First Report; The Preliminary Survey; Part One—Zoology.* Unpublished report to WWF-Netherlands and Royal Geographical Society, London.

Defler, T.R. 1987. Ranging and the use of space in a group of woolly monkeys (*Lagothrix lagotricha*) in the NW Amazon of Colombia. *Int. J. Primatol.* 8:420.

Defler, T.R. 1989. Ranging and the use of space in a group of woolly monkeys (*Lagothrix lagotricha*) in Mono Lanudo, Churuco, Colombian Amazon. *Trianea (Act. Cient. Teen., Inderena)* 3:183–205.

Defler, T.R. 1996. Aspects of the ranging pattern in a group of wild woolly monkeys (*Lagothrix lagotricha*). *Am. J. Primatol.* 38:289–302.

Dugmore, S.J. 1986. Behavioral observations on a pair of captive white-faced saki monkeys (*Pithecia pithecia*). *Folia Primatol.* 46:83–90.

Durham, N.M. 1975. Some ecological, distributional and group behavioral patterns of Atelinae in southern Peru: with comments of interspecific relations. Pp. 87–101. In *Socioecology and Psychology of Primates.* R.A. Tuttle, Ed., The Hague, Mouton.

Eaglen, R.H. 1984. Incisor size and diet revisited: the view from a platyrrhine perspective. *Am. J. Phys. Anthropol.* 65:263–275.

Eason, P. 1989. Harpy eagle attempts predation on adult howler monkey. *Condor* 91:469–470.

Eisenberg, J.F. 1973. Reproduction in two species of spider monkeys, *Ateles fusciceps* and *Ateles geoffroyi. J. Mammal.* 54:955–957.

Eisenberg, J.F. 1976. Communication mechanisms and social integration in the black spider monkey, *Ateles fusciceps robustus,* and related species. S*mith. Contrib. Zool.* 213:1–108.

Eisenberg, J.F. 1979. Habitat, economy, and society: some correlations and hypothesis for the neotropical primates. Pp. 215–262. In *Primate Ecology and Human Origins.* I.S. Bernstein, E.O. Smith, Eds., New York, Garland.

Eisenberg, J.F. 1991. Mammalian social organization and the case of *Alouatta.* Pp. 127–138. In *Man and Beast Revisited.* J.G. Robinson, L. Tiger, Eds., Washington, D.C., Smithsonian Institution Press.

Emmons, L.E. 1987. Comparative feeding ecology of felids in Neotropical rain forest. *Behav. Ecol. Sociobiol.* 20:271–283.

Emmons, L.E. 1990. *Neotropical Rainforest Mammals.* Chicago, University of Chicago Press.

Estrada, A. 1984. Resource use by howler monkeys (*Alouatta palliata*) in the rain forest of Los Tuxtlas, Vera Cruz, Mexico. *Int. J. Primatol.* 5:105–131.

Estrada, A., Coates-Estrada, R. 1984. Fruit-eating and seed dispersal by howling monkeys (*Alouatta palliata*) in the tropical rain forest of Los Tuxtlas, Mexico. *Am. J. Primatol.* 6:77–91.

Estrada, A., Coates-Estrada, R., Vazquez-Yanes, C. 1984. Observation on fruiting and dispersers of *Cecropia obtusifolia* at Los Tuxtlas, Mexico. *Biotropica* 16:315–318.

Estrada, A., Juan-Solano, S., Otiz-Martinez, T., Coates-Estrada, R. 1999. Feeding and general activity patterns of a howler monkey (*Alouatta palliata*) troop living in a forest fragment at Los Tuxtlas, Mexico. *Am. J. Primatol.* 48:167–183.

Fedigan, L.M., Baxter, M.F. 1984. Sex differences and social organization of free-ranging spider monkeys (*Ateles geoffroyi*). *Primates* 25:279–294.

Fedigan, L.M., Fedigan, L., Chapman, C., Glander, K.E. 1988. Spider monkey home ranges: A comparison of radio telemetry and direct observation. *Am. J. Primatol.* 16:19–29.

Fedigan, L.M., Rose, L.M., Avila, R.M. 1998. Growth of mantled howler groups in a regenerating Costa Rican dry forest. *Int. J. Primatol.* 19:405–432.

Ferrari, S.F., Strier, K.B. 1992. Exploitation of *Mabea fistulifera* nectar by marmosets (*Callithrix flaviceps*) and muriquis (*Brachyteles arachnoides*) in south-east *Brazil. J. Trop. Ecol.* 8:225–239.

Fleagle, J.G. 1999. *Primate Adaptation and Evolution.* New York, Academic Press.

Fleagle, J.G., Meldrum, D.J. 1988. Locomotor behavior and skeletal morphology of two sympatric pithecine monkeys, *Pithecia pithecia* and *Chiropotes satanas. Am. J. Primatol.* 16:227–249.

Fleagle, J.G., Mittermeier, R.A. 1980. Locomotor behavior, body size, and comparative ecology of seven Surinam monkeys. *Am. J. Phys. Anthropol.* 52:301–314.

Fleming, T.H., Williams, C.F., Bonacorso, F.J. Herbst, L.H. 1985. Phenology, seed dispersal, and colonization in *Muntingia calabura*, a neotropical pioneer tree. *Am. J. Bot.* 72:383–391.

Fonseca, G.B.A. da. 1985. Observations on the ecology of the muriqui (*Brachyteles arachnoides* E. Geoffroy 1806): implications for its conservation. *Prim. Conserv.* 5:48–52.

Fontaine, R. 1981. The Uakaris, Genus *Cacajao.* Pp. 443–493. In *Ecology and Behavior of Neotropical Monkeys. Vol. 1.* A.F. Coimbra-Filho; R.A. Mittermeier, Eds., Rio de Janeiro, Academia Brasileira de Ciências.

Fooden, J. 1963. A revision of the woolly monkeys (genus *Lagothrix*). *J. Mammal.* 44:213–247.

Ford, S.M., Davis, L.C. 1992. Systematics and body size: implications for feeding adaptations in New World monkeys. *Am. J. Phys. Anthropol.* 88:416–468.

Freese, C.H. 1976. Censusing *Allouatta palliata*, *Ateles geoffroyi* and *Cebus capucinus* in the Costa Rican dry forest. Pp. 4–9. In *Neotropical Primates; Field Studies and Conservation.* R.W. Thorington, Jr., P.G. Heltne, Eds., Washington, D.C., National Academy Sciences

Galetti, M. 1996. Comportamentos antipredatórios de quatro espécies de primatas no sudeste do Brasil. *Rev. Brasil. Biol.* 56:203–209.

Galetti, M., Pedroni, F., Morellato, L.P.C. 1994. Diet of the brown howler monkey (*Alouatta fusca*) in a forest fragment in Brazil. *Mammalia* 58:111–118.

Gaulin, S.J.C. 1979. A Jarmon/Bell model of primate feeding niches. *Hum. Ecol.* 7:1–17.

Gaulin, S.J.C., Gaulin, C.K. 1982. Behavioral ecology of *Alouatta seniculus* in Andean cloud forest. *Int. J. Primatol.* 3:1–52.

Gilbert, K.A., Stouffer, P.C. 1989. Use of a ground water source by mantled howler monkeys (*Alouatta palliata*). *Biotropica* 21:380.

Glander, K.E. 1975. *Habitat and Resource Utilization: An Ecological View of Social Organization in Mantled Howling Monkeys.* Ph.D. Thesis. University of Chicago, Chicago.

Glander, K.E. 1978. Howling monkey feeding behavior and plant secondary compounds: a study of strategies. Pp. 561–573. In *Ecology of Arboreal Folivores*. G.G. Montgomery, Ed., Washington, D.C., Smithsonian Institution Press.

Glander, K.E. 1980. Reproduction and population growth in free-ranging mantled howler monkeys. *Am. J. Phys. Anthropol.* 53:25–36.

Glander, K.E. 1992. Dispersal patterns in Costa Rican mantled howling monkeys. *Int. J. Primatol.* 13:415–436.

Glander, K.E., Fedigan, L.M., Fedigan, L., Chapman, C. 1991. Field methods for capture and measurement of three monkey species in Costa Rica. *Folia Primatol.* 57:70–82.

Gleason, T. 1998. The ecology of olfactory communication in Venezuelan white-faced sakis (*Pithecia pithecia*). *Am. J. Primatol.* 45:183.

Gleason, T., Norconk, M.A. 1995. Intragroup spacing and agonistic interactions in white-faced sakis. *Am. J. Primatol.* 36:125.

Hanif, M. 1967. Notes on breeding the white-headed saki monkey, *Pithecia pithecia,* at Georgetown Zoo. Int. Zoo Yrbk. 7:81–82.

Happel, R.E. 1982. Ecology of *Pithecia hirsuta* in Peru. *J. Hum. Evol.* 11:581–590.

Hernández-Camacho, J., Cooper, R.W. 1976. The nonhuman primates of Colombia. Pp. 35–69. In *Neotropical Primates; Field Studies and Conservation*. R.W. Thorington, Jr., P.G. Heltne, Eds., Washington, D.C., National Acad. Sciences.

Hernández-López, L., Mayagoitia, L., Esquivellacroix, C., Rojas-Maya, S., Mondragón-Ceballos, R. 1998. The menstrual cycle of the spider monkey (*Ateles geoffroyi*). *Am. J. Primatol.* 44:183–195.

Hershkovitz, P. 1977. *Living New World Primates. Vol. 1.* Chicago, University of Chicago Press.

Hershkovitz, P. 1985. A preliminary taxonomic review of the South American bearded saki monkeys, genus *Chiropotes* (Cebidae, Platyrrhini), with the description of a new subspecies. *Fieldiana, (Zool.),* n.s. 27:1–46.

Hershkovitz, P. 1987a. The taxonomy of South American sakis, genus *Pithecia* (Cebidae, Platyrrhini): A preliminary report and critical review of the description of a new species and a new subspecies. *Am. J. Primatol.* 12:387–468.

Hershkovitz, P. 1987b. Uacaries, New World Monkeys of the genus *Cacajao* (Cebidae, Platyrrhini): a preliminary taxonomic review with the description of a new subspecies. *Fieldiana (Zool.)* n.s. 27, 1363:1–46.

Heymann, E. 1990. Further field notes on red uacaris, *Cacajao calvus rubicundus,* from the Quebrada Blanco, Amazonian Peru. *Prim. Conserv.* 11:7–8.

Hick, U. 1968. The collection of saki monkeys at Cologne Zoo. *Int. Zoo Yrbk.* 8:192–194.

Hill, W.C.O. 1962. *Primates, Comparative Anatomy and Taxonomy, V. Cebidae, Part B.* Edinburgh, Edinburgh University Press.

Hladik, C.M. 1967. Surface relative du tractus digestif de quelques primates, morphologie des villosities intestinales et correlations avec le regime alimentaire. *Mammalia* 31:120–147.

Hladik, A., Hladik, C.M. 1969. Rapports trophiques entre végétation et primates dans la forÎt de Barro-Colorado (Panama). *Terre Vie* 1:25–117.

Howe, H.F. 1980. Monkey dispersal and waste of a neo-tropical fruit. *Ecology* 61:944–959.

Howe, H.F. 1983. Annual variation in a neotropical seed-dispersal system. Pp. 211–227. In *Tropical Rain Forest: Ecology and Management.* S.L. Sutton, T.C. Whitmore, A.C. Chadwick, Eds., London, Blackwell.

Izawa, K. 1976. Group sizes and compositions of monkeys in the upper Amazon basin. *Primates* 17:367–399.

Izawa, K., Kimura, K., Ohnishi, Y. 1990. Chemical properties of soils eaten by red howler monkeys *(Alouatta seniculus),* II. Colombia. *Field Studies of New World Monkeys, La Macarena, Columbia* 4:47–56.

Izawa, K., Lozano, H.M. 1990. Frequency of soil-eating by a group of wild howler monkeys *(Alouatta seniculus)* in La Macarena, Colombia. *Field Studies of New World Monkeys, La Macarena, Columbia* 4:47–56.

Izawa, K., Lozano, H.M. 1994. Social changes within a group of red howler monkeys, V. *Field Studies of New World Monkeys, La Macarena, Columbia* 9:33–39.

Janson, D.H., van Schaik, C.P. 1993. Ecological risk aversion in juvenile primates: Slow and steady wins the race. Pp. 57–76. In *Juvenile Primates; Life History, Development, and Behavior.* M.E. Pereira, L.A. Fairbanks, Eds., New York, Oxford University Press.

Johns, A.D. 1986. Notes on the ecology and current status of the buffy saki, *Pithecia albicans. Prim. Conserv.* 7:26–29.

Jones, C.B. 1980. The function of status in the mantled howler monkey, *Alouatta palliata* Gray: intraspecific competition for group membership in a folivorous neotropical primate. *Primates* 20:389–405.

Jones, C.B. 1982. A field manipulation of spatial relations among male mantled howler monkeys. *Primates* 23:130–134.

Jones, C.B. 1983. Social organization of captive black howler monkeys *(Alouatta caraya):* "Social competition" and the use of non-damaging behavior. *Primates* 24:25–39.

Jones, C.B. 1985. Reproductive patterns in mantled howler monkeys: Estrus, mate choice and copulation. *Primates* 26:130–142.

Kavanagh, M. 1983. *A Complete Guide to Monkeys, Apes and other Primates.* New York, Viking.

Kay, R.F. 1973. *Mastication, Molar Tooth Structure and Diet in Primates.* Ph.D. Thesis. Yale University, New Haven.

Kay, R.F., Hylander, W.L. 1978. The dental structure of mammalian folivores with special reference to primates and phalangeroidea (Marsupalia). Pp. 173–191. In *Ecology of Arboreal Folivores.* G.G. Montgomery, Ed., Washington, D.C., Smithsonian Institution.

Kay, R.N.B., Davies, A.G. 1994. Digestive physiology. Pp. 229–249. In *Colobine Monkeys: Their Ecology, Behaviour and Evolution.* A. G. Davies, J.F. Oates, Eds., Cambridge, Cambridge University Press.

Kinzey, W.G. 1992. Dietary and dental adaptations in the Pithecinae. *Am. J. Phys. Anthropol.* 88:499–514.

Kinzey, W.G. 1997a. *New World Primates: Ecology, Evolution, and Behavior.* New York, Aldine de Gruyter.

Kinzey, W.G. 1997b. New World primate studies. Pp. 743–748. In *History of Physical Anthropology: An Encyclopedia.* F. Spencer, Ed., New York, Garland.

Kinzey, W.G., Gentry A.H. 1979. Habitat utilization in two species of *Callicebus.* Pp. 89–100. In *Primate Ecology: Problem-Oriented Field Studies.* R.W. Sussman, Ed., New York, Wiley.

Kinzey, W.G., Norconk, M.A. 1990. Hardness as a basis of fruit choice in two sympatric primates. *Am. J. Phys. Anthropol.* 81:5–15.

Kinzey, W.G., Norconk, M.A. 1993. Physical and chemical properties of fruit and seeds eaten by *Pithecia* and *Chiropotes* in Surinam and Venezuela. *Int. J. Primatol.* 14:207–227.

Klein, L.L. 1971. Observations on copulation and seasonal reproduction of two species of spider monkeys, *Ateles belzebuth* and *Ateles goeffroyi. Folia Primatol.* 15:233–248.

Klein, L.L. 1972. *The Ecology and Social Organization of the Spider Monkey* (Ateles belzebuth). Ph.D. Thesis. University of California, Berkeley.

Klein, L.L. 1974. Agonistic behavior in neotropical primates. Pp. 77–122. In *Primate Aggression, Terrhorluliy und Xenophobiu. A Comparative Perspective.* R. Holloway, Ed., New York, Academic Press.

Klein, L.L., Klein, D.J. 1975. Social and ecological contrasts between four taxa of neotropical primates. Pp. 59–85. In *Socioecology and Psychology of Primates.* R.A. Tuttle, Ed., The Hague, Mouton.

Klein, L.L., Klein, D.J. 1977. Feeding behaviour of the Colombian spider monkey (*Ateles belzebuth*). Pp. 153–181. In *Primate Ecology: Studies of Feeding and Ranging Behaviour in Lemurs, Monkeys and Apes.* T.H. Clutton-Brock, Ed., London, Academic Press.

Lehman, F. 1959. Contribuciones al estudio de la faunne de Colombia. XIV. Nuevas observaciones sobre *Oroaetus isidori* (Des Murs). *Novedades Colombianas: Contribuciones Cientificas des Museo Der Historia Natural der la Universidad del Cauca, Popayan-Colombia* 1:169–195.

Lehman, S.M., Robertson, K.L. 1994. Preliminary survey of *Cacajao melanocephalus melanocephalus* in southern Venezuela. *Int. J. Primatol.* 33:223.

Lemos de Sá, R.M. 1988. *Situação de uma populaçãode mono-carveiro,* Brachyteles arachnoides, *em fragmento da mata Atlântica (M.G.), e implicação para sua conservação.* M.A. Thesis. Universidade de Brasilia, Brasilia.

Lemos de Sá, R.M. 1991. A população de *Brachyteles arachnoides* (Primates, Cebidae) da Fazenda Esmeralda, Rio Casca, Minas Gerais. Pp. 235–238. In *A Primatologia no Brasil–3.* A.B. Rylands; A.T. Bernardes, Eds., Belo Horizonte, Fundação Biodiversitas and Sociedade Brasileira de Primatologia.

Lemos de Sá, R.M., Glander, K. 1993. Capture techniques and morphometrics for the woolly spider, muriqui (*Brachyteles arachnoides* E. Geoffroyi 1806). *Am. J. Primatol.* 29:145–153.

Lemos de Sá, R.M., Pope, T.r., Strushaker, T.t., Glander, K.E. 1993. Sexual dimorphism in canine length of woolly spider monkeys (*Brachyteles arachnoides*, E. Geoffroy 1806). *Int. J. Primatol.* 14:755–763.

Lemos de Sá, R.M., Strier, K.B. 1992. A preliminary comparison of forest structure and use by two isolated groups of woolly spider monkeys, *Brachyteles arachnoides. Biotropica* 24:455–459.

Leo Luna, M. 1987. Primate conservation in Peru: A case study of the yellow-tailed woolly monkey. *Prim. Conserv.* 8:122–123.

Mack, D.S., Kafka, H. 1978. Breeding and rearing of woolly monkeys at the National Zoological Park, Washington. *Int. Zoo Yrbk.* 18:117–122.

Marsh, C.W., Johns, A.D., Ayres, J.M. 1987. Effects of habitat disturbance on rain forest primates. Pp. 83–107. In *Primate Conservation in the Tropical Rain Forest.* C.W. Marsh, R.A. Mittermeier, Eds., New York, Alan R. Liss.

Martin, L.B., Kinzey, W.G., Maas, M.C. 1994. Enamel thickness in pithecine primates. *Am. J. Phys. Anthropol.* Suppl. 9:138.

Martin, R.D., Chivers, D.J., MacLarnon, A.M., Hladik, C.M. 1985. Gastrointestinal allometry in primates and other mammals. Pp. 61–89. In *Size and Scaling in Primate Biology.* W.L. Jungers, Ed., New York, Plenum.

Mendel, F.C. 1976. Postural and locomotor behavior of *Alouatta palliata* on various substrates. *Folia Primatol.* 26:36–53.

Mendes, F.D.C. 1987. Social behavior in the muriqui: The problem of dominance relationships. *Int. J. Primatol.* 8:422.

Mendes, F.D.C. 1989. Estudo ecológico de *Alouatta fusca* (Primates: Cebidae) na Estação Biológica de Caratiniga, MG. *Rev. Nordestina Biol.* 6:71–104.

Milton, K. 1977. *The Foraging Strategy of the Howler Monkey in the Tropical Forest of Barro Colorado Island, Panama.* Ph.D. Thesis. New York University, New York.

Milton, K. 1978. Behavioral adaptations to leaf-eating by the mantled howler monkey (*Alouatta palliata*). Pp. 535–549. In *Ecology of Arboreal Folivores.* G.G. Montgomery, Ed., Washington, D.C., Smithsonian Institution Press.

Milton, K. 1980. *The Foraging Strategy of Howler Monkeys: A Study in Primate Economics.* New York, Columbia University Press.

Milton, K. 1981. Food choice and digestive strategies of two sympatric primate species. *Am. Nat.* 117:496–505.

Milton, K. 1982. Dietary quality and population regulation in a howler monkey population. Pp. 273–289. In *The Ecology of a Tropical Forest.* E.G. Leigh, A.S. Rand, D.M. Windsor, Eds., Washington D.C., Smithsonian Institution Press.

Milton, K. 1984a. The role of food-processing factors in primate food choice. Pp. 249–279. In *Adaptations for Foraging in Nonhuman Primates: Contributions to an Organismal Biology of Prosimians, Monkeys and Apes.* P.S. Rodman, J.G.H. Cant, Eds., New York, Columbia University Press.

Milton, K. 1984b. Habitat, diet, and activity patterns of free-ranging woolly spider monkeys (*Brachyteles arachnoides* E. Geoffrey 1806). *Int. J. Primatol.* 5:491–514.

Milton, K. 1985a. Multi-male mating and absence of canine dimorphism in woolly spider monkeys (*Brachyteles arachnoides*). *Am. J. Phys. Anthropol.* 68:519–523.

Milton, K. 1985b. Mating patterns of woolly spider monkeys, *Brachyteles arachnoides:* Implications for female choice. *Behav. Ecol. Sociobiol.* 17:53–59.

Milton, K. 1986. Ecological background and conservation priorities for woolly spider monkeys (*Brachyteles arachnoides*). Pp. 241–250. In *Primates: The Road to Self-Sustaining Populations.* K. Benirschke, Ed., New York, Springer-Verlag.

Milton, K. 1987a. Physiological characteristics of the genus *Alouatta. Int. J. Primatol.* 8:428.

Milton, K. 1987b. Behavior and ecology of the woolly spider monkey, *Brachyteles arachnoides. Int. J. Primatol.* 8:422.

Milton, K. 1998. Physiological ecology of Howlers *(Alouatta)*: energetics and digestive considerations and comparison with the Colobinae. *Int. J. Primatol.* 19:513–548.

Mittermeier, R.A. 1987. Effects of hunting on rain forest primates. Pp. 109–146 In *Primate Conservation in the Tropical Rain Forest.* C.W. Marsh, R.A. Mittermeier, Ed., New York, Alan R. Liss.

Mittermeier, R.A. 1993. S.O.S. muriqui: o maior macaco das Américas em perigo. *Rev. Geográfica. Univers.* 221:102–107.

Mittermeier, R.A., Coimbra-Filho, A.F. 1977. Primate conservation in Brazilian Amazonia. Pp. 117–166. In *Primate Conservation.* H.S.H. Prince Ranier III of Monaco, G.H. Bourne, Eds., New York, Academic Press.

Mittermeier, R.A., Kinzey, W.G., Mast, R.B. 1989. Neotropical primate conservation. *J. Hum. Evol.* 18:597–610.

Mittermeier, R.A., Macedo-Ruiz, H. de, Leo Luna, M., Young, A., Constable, I.D., Ponce del Prado, C., Luscombe, B.A. 1984. Conservation education campaign for the Peruvian yellow-tailed woolly monkey to be launched in Peru. *Prim. Conserv.* 4:19–22.

Mittermeier, R.A., Roosmalen, M.G.M. van. 1981. Preliminary observations on habitat utilization and diet in eight Suriname monkeys. *Folia Primatol.* 36:1–39.

Mittermeier, R.A., Rylands, A.B., Coimbra-Filho, A.F. 1988. Systematics: species and subspecies—an update. Pp. 13–75. In *The Ecology and Behavior of Neotropical Primates, Vol. 2.* R.A. Mittermeier, A.B. Rylands, Coimbra-Filho, A.F., G.A.B. da Fonseca, Eds., Washington D.C., World Wildlife Fund.

Mittermeier, R.A., Valle, C.M.C., Alves, M.C., Santos, I.B., Machado Pinto, C.A., Strier, K.B., Young, A.L., Veado, E.M., Constable, I.D., Paccagnella, S.G., Lemos de Sa, R.M. 1987. Current distribution of the muriqui in the Atlantic Coastal Forest Region of eastern Brazil. *Prim. Conserv.* 8:143–149.

Moraes, P.L.R. de, Carvalho, O. de, Jr., Strier, K.B. 1998. Population variation in patch and party size in muriqui (*Brachyteles arachnoides*). *Int. J. Primatol.* 19:325–337.

Morell, V. 1999. Life at the top: animals pay the high price of dominance. Pp. 345–346. In *The Biological Basis of Human Behavior: A Critical Review.* R.W. Sussman, Ed., Upper Saddle River, Prentice Hall.

Moynihan, M. 1976. *The New World Primates.* Princeton, Princeton University Press.

Muskin, A., Fischgrund, A.J. 1981. Seed dispersal of *Stemmadenia* (Apocynaceae) and sexually dimorphic feeding strategies by *Ateles* in Tikal, Guatemala. *Biotropica, Suppl. Reproductive Botany* 13:78–80.

Napier, J.R., Napier, P.H. 1967. *A Handbook of Living Primates.* London, Academic Press.

Neville, M.K. 1972. Social relations within troops of red howler monkeys (*Alouatta seniculus*). *Folia Primatol.* 18:47–77.

Neville, M.K., Glander, K.E., Braza, F., Rylands, A.B. 1988. The howling monkeys, genus *Alouatta.* Pp. 349–453. *Ecology and Behavior of Neotropical Primates, Vol. 2.* R.A. Mittermeier, A.B. Rylands, A.F. Coimbra-Filho, G.A.B. da Fonseca, Eds., Washington D.C., World Wildlife Fund.

Nishimura, A. 1988. Mating behavior of woolly monkeys (*Lagothrix lagotricha*) at La Macarena, Colombia. *Field Studies of New World Monkeys, La Macarena, Colombia* 1:19–27.

Nishimura, A. 1990. A sociological and behavioral study of woolly monkeys, *Lagothrix lagotricha,* in the Upper Amazon. *Science and Engineering Reviews of Doshisha University* 31:87–121.

Nishimura, A., Izawa, K. 1975. The group characteristics of woolly monkeys (*Lagothrix lagotricha*) in the upper Amazonian basin. Pp. 351–357. In *Contemporary Primatology.* S. Kondo, M. Kawai, A. Ehara, Eds., Basel, S. Karger.

Nishimura, A., Wilches, A.V., Estrada, C. 1992. Mating behaviors of woolly monkeys (*Lagothrix lagotricha*) at La Macarena, Colombia (III): reproductive parameters viewed from a long-term study. *Field Studies of New World Monkeys, La Macarena, Colombia* 7:1–7.

Norconk, M.A. 1996. Seasonal variation in the diets of white-faced and bearded sakis (*Pithecia pithecia* and *Chiropotes satanus*) in Guri Lake, Venezuela. Pp. 403–423. In *Adaptive Radiations of Neotropical Primates.* M.A. Norconk, A.L. Rosenberger, P.A. Garber, Eds., New York, Plenum.

Norconk, M.A., Grafton, B.W., Conklin-Brittain, N.L. 1998. Seed dispersal by neotropical seed predators. *Am. J. Primatol.* 45:103–126.

Norconk, M.A., Kinzey, W.G. 1990. Preliminary data on feeding ecology of *Pithecia pithecia* in Bolivar State, Venezuela. *Am. J. Primatol.* 20:215.

Norconk, M.A., Kinzey, W.G. 1994. Challenge of neotropical frugivory: foraging patterns of spider monkeys and bearded sakis. *Am. J. Primatol.* 34:171–183.

Norconk, M.A., Sussman, R.W., Phillips-Conroy, J. 1996. Primates of Guayana Shield forests: Venezuela and the Guianas. Pp. 69–83. In *Adaptive Radiations of Neotropical Primates.* M.A. Norconk, A.L. Rosenberger, P.A. Garber, Eds., New York, Plenum.

Nunes, A. 1998. Diet and feeding ecology of *Ateles belzebuth belzebuth* at Maraca Ecological Station, Roraima, Brazil. *Folia Primatol.* 69:61–76.

Oates, J.F. 1994. The natural history of African colobines. Pp. 75–127. In *Colobine Monkeys: Their Ecology, Behavious and Evolution.* A. G. Davies, J.F. Oates, Eds., Cambridge, Cambridge University Press.

Oftedal, O.T. 1991. The nutritional consequences of foraging in primates: the relationship of nutrient intakes to nutrient requirements. *Phil. Trans. R. Soc. London* 334B:161–170.

Olmos, F. 1994. Jaguar predation on muriqui *Brachyteles arachnoides. Neotrop. Prim.* 2:16.

Otis, J.S., Froehlich, J.W., Thorington, R.W., Jr. 1981. Seasonal and age-related differential mortality by sex in the mantled howler monkey, *Alouatta palliata*. *Int. J. Primatol.* 2:197–205.

Packer, C., Collins, D.A., Sindlimwo, A., Goodall, J. 1995. Reproductive constraints on aggressive competition in female baboons. *Nature* 373:60–63.

Peetz, A. in prep. *Habitatnutzung, Nahrungökologie und Soziale Organisation Beim Rotrückensaki* (Chiropotes satanas chiropotes) *im Estado Bolivar, Venezuela.* Ph.D. Thesis. Universität Bielefeld, Germany.

Peetz, A., Norconk, M.A., Kinzey, W.G. 1992. Predation by jaguar on howler monkeys (*Alouatta seniculus*) in Venezuela. *Am. J. Primatol.* 28:223–228.

Peres, C.A. 1990a. A harpy eagle successfully captures an adult male red howler monkey. *Wilson Bulletin* 102:560–561.

Peres, C.A. 1990b. Effects of hunting on western Amazonian primate communities. *Bio. Conserv.* 54:47–59.

Peres, C.A. 1993. Notes on the ecology of buffy saki monkeys (*Pithecia albicans,* Gray 1860): A canopy seed-predator. *Am. J. Primatol.* 31:129–140.

Peres, C.A. 1994. Diet and feeding ecology of gray woolly monkeys (*Lagothrix lagotricha cana*) in central Amazonia: Comparisons with other atelines. *Int. J. Primatol.* 15:333–372.

Peres, C.A. 1996. Use of space, spatial group structure, and foraging group size of gray woolly monkeys (*Lagothrix lagotricha cana*) at Urucu, Brazil: a review of Atelinae. Pp. 467–488. In *Adaptive Radiations of Neotropical Primates.* M.A. Norconk, A.L. Rosenberger, P.A. Garber, Eds., New York, Plenum.

Pinto, L.P.S., Costa, C.M.R., Strier, K.B., da Fonseca, G.A.B. 1993. Habitat, density and group size of primates in a Brazilian tropical forest. *Int. J. Primatol.* 61:135–143.

Pope, T.R. 1990. The reproductive consequences of male cooperation in the red howler monkey: Paternity exclusion in multi-male and single-male troops using genetic markers. *Behav. Ecol. Sociobiol* 27:439–446.

Printes, R.C., Costa, C.G., Strier, K.B. 1996. Possible predation on two infant muriquis, *Brachyteles arachnoides,* at the Estagco Biolsgica de Caratinga, Minas Gerais, Brazil. *Neotrop. Primates* 85–86.

Ramirez, M. 1988. The woolly monkey, genus *Lagothrix*. Pp. 539–575 In *Ecology and Behavior of Neotropical Primates, Vol 2.* R.A. Mittermeier, A.B. Rylands, A. Coimbra-Filho, G.A.B. da Fonseca, Eds., Washington, D.C., World Wildlife Fund.

Redford, K.H. 1992. The empty forest. *Bioscience* 42:412–422.

Redford, K.H., Robinson, J.G. 1987. The game of choice; patterns of indian and colonist hunting in the neotropics. *Am. Anthropol.* 89:650–667.

Richard, A.F. 1970. A comparative study of the activity patterns and behavior of *Alouatta villosa* and *Ateles geoffroyi. Folia Primatol.* 12:241–263.

Robinson, J.G., Janson, C.H. 1987. Capuchins, squirrel monkeys, and atelines: socioecological convergence with Old World primates. Pp. 69–82. In *Primate Societies.* B.B. Smuts, D.L. Cheney, R.M. Seyfarth, R.W. Wrangham, T.T. Struhsaker, Eds., Chicago, University of Chicago Press.

Robinson, J.G., Wright, P.C., Kinzey, W.G. 1987. Monogamous cebids and their relatives: intergroup calls and spacing. Pp. 44–53, In *Primate Societies.* B.B. Smuts,

D.L. Cheney, R.M. Seyfarth, R.W. Wrangham, T.T. Struhsaker, Eds., Chicago, University of Chicago Press.

Rodríguez-Luna, E., Cortis-Ortiz, L., Miller, P., Ellis, S. 1996. *Population and Habitat Viability Assessment for the Mantled Howler Monkey* (Alouatta palliata mexicana). Apple Valley, Minnesota, IUCN/SSC Conservation Breeding Specialist Group.

Roosmalen, M.G.M. van. 1980. *Habitat Preferences, Diet, Feeding Strategy and Social Organization of the Black Howler Monkey* (Ateles paniscus paniscus L.). Ph.D. Thesis. Agricultural University of Wageningen, Wageningen.

Roosmalen, M.G.M. van. 1985. Habitat preferences, diet, feeding strategy and social organization of the black spider monkey (*Ateles paniscus paniscus* Linnaeus 1758) in Surinam. *Acta Amazonica* 15 (3/4 *Suppl.*):1–238.

Roosmalen, M.G.M. van. 1987. Diet, feeding behaviour and social organization of the Guianan black spider monkey (*Ateles paniscus paniscus*). *Int. J. Primatol.* 8:421.

Roosmalen, M.G.M. van, Klein, L.L. 1988. The spider monkeys: Genus *Ateles*. Pp. 455–537. In *The Ecology and Behavior of Neotropical Primates, Vol. 2.* R.A. Mittermeier, A.B. Rylands, Coimbra-Filho, A.F., G.A.B. da Fonseca, Eds., Washington D.C., World Wildlife Fund.

Roosmalen, M.G.M., Mittermeier, R.A., Milton, K. 1981. The bearded sakis, genus *Chiropotes*. Pp. 419–441. In *Ecology and Behavior of Neotropical Monkeys. Vol. 1.* A.F. Coimbra-Filho, R.A. Mittermeier, Eds., Rio de Janeiro, Academia Brasileira de Ciências.

Rosenberger, A.L., Kinzey, W.G. 1976. Functional patterns of molar occlusion in platyrrhine primates. *Am. J. Phys. Anthropol.* 45:281–298.

Rosenberger, A.L., Strier, K.B. 1989. Adaptive radiation of the ateline primates. *J. Hum. Evol.* 18:717–750.

Rossan, R.N., Baerg, D.C. 1977. Laboratory and feral hybridization of *Ateles geoffroyi panamensis* Kellog and Goldman 1944 and *A. fusciceps robustus* Allen 1914 in Panama. *Primates* 18:235–237.

Rowe, N. 1996. *The Pictorial Guide to the Living Primates.* East Hampton, Pagonias Press.

Rudran, R. 1979. The demography and social mobility of a red howler (*Alouatta seniculus*) population in Venezuela. Pp. 107–126 In *Vertebrate Ecology in the Northern Neotropics.* J. Eisenberg, Ed., Washington, D.C., Smithsonian Institution Press.

Rumiz, D.I. 1990. *Alouatta caraya:* Population density and demography in northern Argentina. *Am. J. Primatol.* 21: 279–294.

Rylands, A.B., Keuroghlian, A. 1988. Primate populations in continuous forest and forest fragments in central Amazonia. *Acta Amazônica* 18:291–307.

Rylands, A.B., Fonseca, G.A.B. Da, Leite, L.Y.R., Mittermeier, R.A. 1996. Pp. 21–51. In *Adaptive Radiations of Neotropical Primates.* M.A. Norconk, A.L. Rosenberger, P.A. Garber, Eds., New York, Plenum.

Rylands, A.B., Mittermeier, R.A., Rodriguez-Luna, E. 1995. A species list for the New World primates (Platyrrhini): distribution by country, endemism, and conservation status according to the Mace-Lande system. *Neotrop. Prim. 3* Suppl.: 113–164.

Sanchez-Villagra, M.R., Pope, T.R., Salas, V. 1998. Relations of intergroup variation in allogrooming to group social structure and ectoparasite loads in red howlers (*Alouatta seniculus*). *Int. J. Primatol.* 19:473–491.

Sauther, M.L. 1992. *The Effect of Reproductive State, Social Rank and Group Size on Resource Use Among Free-Ranging Ringtailed Lemurs* (Lemur catta) *of Madagasar.* Ph.D. Thesis. Washington University, St. Louis.

Savage, A., Shideler, S.E., Moorman, E.A., Ortuno, A., Whittier, C.A., Casey, K.K., McKinney, J. 1992. The reproductive biology of the white-faced saki (*Pithecia pithecia*) in captivity. *Abstracts of the XIVth Congress of the International Primatological Society, Strasbourg*:59–60.

Schön Ybarra, M.A. 1984. Locomotion and postures of red howlers in a deciduous forest-savanna interface. *Am. J. Phys. Anthropol.* 63:65–76.

Schlichte, H.-J. 1978. A preliminary report on the habitat utilization of a group of howler monkeys (*Alouatta villosa pigra*) in the National Park of Tikal, Guatemala. Pp. 551–559. In *The Ecology of Arboreal Folivores.* G.G. Montgomery, Ed., Washington D.C., Smithsonian Institution Press.

Scott, N.J., Malmgren, L.A., Glander, K.E. 1978. Grouping behavior and sex ratio in mantled howler monkeys. Pp. 183–185. In *Recent Advances in Primatology, Vol. 1.* D.J. Chivers, J. Herbert, Eds., New York, Academic Press.

Sekulic, R. 1981. *The Significance of Howling in the Red Howler Monkey* (Alouatta seniculus). Ph.D. Thesis. University of Maryland, College Park.

Sekulic, R. 1982a. Behavior and ranging patterns of a solitary female red howler (*Alouatta seniculus*). *Folia Primatol.* 38:217–232.

Sekulic, R. 1982b. The function of howling in red howler monkeys (*Alouatta seniculus*). *Behavior.* 81:38–54.

Sherman, P.T. 1991. Harpy eagle predation on a red howler monkey. *Folia Primatol.* 56:53–56.

Shideler, S.E., Savage, A., Ortoño, A.M., Moorman, E.A., Lasley, B.L. 1994. Monitoring female reproductive function by measurement of fecal estrogen and progesterone metabolites in the white-faced saki (*Pithecia pithecia*). *Am. J. Primatol.* 32:95–108.

Silva-Lopes, G., Jimenez-Huerta, J., Benitez-Rodriguez, J. 1987. Monkey populations in disturbed areas: A study on *Ateles* and *Alouatta* at Sierra de Santa Martha, Veracruz, Mexico. *Am. J. Primatol.* 12:355–356.

Silver, S.C., Ostro, L.E.T., Yeager, C.P., Horwich, R. 1998. Feeding ecology of the black howler monkey (*Alouatta pigra*) in northern Belize. *Am. J. Primatol.* 45:263–279.

Sleeper, B. 1997. *Primates: The Amazing World of Lemurs, Monkeys, and Apes.* San Francisco, Chronicle Books.

Smith, C.C. 1977. Feeding behaviour and social organization in howling monkeys. Pp. 97–126. In *Primate Ecology: Studies of Feeding and Ranging Behaviour in Lemurs, Monkeys and Apes.* T.H. Clutton-Brock, Ed., London, Academic Press.

Smith, J.D. 1970. The systematic status of the black howler monkey, *Alouatta pigra* Lawrence. *J. Mammal.* 51:358–369.

Smith, R.J., Jungers, W.L. 1997. Body mass in comparative primatology. *J. Hum. Evol.* 32:523–559.

Soini, P. 1986. A synecological study of a primate community in the Pacaya-Samiria National Reserve, Peru. *Prim. Conserv.* 7:63–71.

Stevenson, P.R. 1998. Proximal spacing between individuals in a group of woolly monkeys (*Lagothrix logotricha*) in Tinigua National Park, Colombia. *Int. J. Primatol.* 19:299–311.

Stevenson, P.R., Quiñones, M.J., Ahumada, J.A. 1994. Ecological strategies of woolly monkeys (*Lagothrix logotricha*) at Tinigua National Park, Colombia. *Am. J. Primatol.* 32:123–140.

Stoner, K.E. 1996. Habitat selection and seasonal patterns of activity and foraging of mantled howling monkeys (*Alouatta palliata*) in northeastern Costa Rica. *Int. J. Primatol.* 17:1–30.

Strier, K.B. 1986. *The Behavior and Ecology of the Woolly Spider Monkey, or Muriqui* (Brachyteles arachnoides) *E. Geoffroy 1806.* Ph.D. Thesis. Harvard University, Cambridge.

Strier, K.B. 1987a. Activity budgets of woolly spider monkeys, or muriquis (*Brachyteles arachnoides*). *Am. J. Primatol.* 13:385–396.

Strier, K.B. 1987b. Demographic patterns of one group of free-ranging woolly spider monkeys. *Prim. Conserv.* 8:73–74.

Strier, K.B. 1987c. Ranging behavior of woolly spider monkeys, or muriquis, *Brachyteles arachnoides. Int. J. Primatol.* 8:575–591.

Strier, K.B. 1989. Effects of patch size on feeding associations in muriquis (*Brachyteles arachnoides*). *Folia Primatol.* 52:70–77.

Strier, K.B. 1990a. New World primates, new frontiers: Insights from the woolly spider monkey, or muriqui (*Brachyteles arachnoides*). *Int. J. Primatol.* 11:7–19.

Strier, K.B. 1990b. Demography, ecology and conservation: An example from Southeastern Brazil. *Am. J. Phys. Anthropol.* 81:302–303.

Strier, K.B. 1991a. Diet in one group of woolly spider monkeys, or muriquis (*Brachyteles arachnoides*). *Am. J. Primatol.* 23:113–126.

Strier, K.B. 1991b. Demography and conservation of an endangered primate, *Brachyteles arachnoides. Conserv. Biol.* 5:214–218.

Strier, K.B. 1992a. Atelinae adaptations: behavioral strategies and ecological constraints. *Am. J. Phys. Anthropol.* 88:515–524.

Strier, K.B. 1992b. *Faces in the Forest, the Endangered Muriqui Monkeys of Brazil.* New York, Oxford University Press.

Strier, K.B. 1992c. Causes and consequences of nonaggression in the woolly spider monkey, or muriqui (*Brachyteles arachnoides*). Pp. 100–116. In *Aggression and Peacefulness in Humans and Other Primates.* J. Silverberg, J. Patrick Gray, Eds., New York, Oxford University Press.

Strier, K.B. 1993a. Menu for a monkey. *Nat. Hist.* 103:34–43.

Strier, K.B. 1993b. Growing up in a patrifocal society: sex differences in the spatial relations of immature muriquis. Pp. 138–147. In *Juvenile Primates.* M.E. Pereira, L.A. Fairbanks, Eds., New York, Oxford University Press.

Strier, K.B. 1994. Brotherhoods among atelins: kinship, affiliation, and competition. *Behaviour* 130:151–167.

Strier, K.B. 1996a. Reproductive ecology of female muriqui *(Brachyteles arachnoides)*. Pp. 511–532 In *Adaptive Radiations of Neotropical Primates.* M.A. Norconk, A.L. Rosenberger, P.A. Garber, Eds., New York, Plenum.

Strier, K.B. 1996b. Male reproduction strategies in New World monkeys. *Hum. Nat.* 7:105–123.

Strier, K.B. 1997a. Behavioral ecology and conservation biology of primates and other animals. *Adv. Stud. Behav.* 26:101–158.

Strier, K.B. 1997b. Mate preferences of wild muriqui monkeys *(Brachyteles arachnoides)*: reproductive and social correlates. *Folia Primatol.* 68:120–133.

Strier, K.B. 1997c. Subtle cues of social relations in male muriqui monkeys *(Brachyteles arachnoides)*. Pp.109–118. In *New World Primates: Ecology, Evolution, and Behavior.* W.G. Kinzey, Ed., New York, Aldine de Gruyter.

Strier, K.B. 1999a. Predicting primate responses to "stochastic" demographic events. *Primates* 40:131–142.

Strier, K.B. 1999b. Why is female kin bonding so rare? Comparative sociality of neotropical primates. Pp. 300–319. In *Comparative Primate Socioecology.* P.C. Lee, Ed., Cambridge, Cambridge University Press.

Strier, K.B., Fonseca, G.A.B. da. 1996/1997. The endangered muriqui in Brazil's Atlantic forest. *Prim. Conserv.* 17:131–137.

Strier, K.B., Mendes, F.D., Rimoli, J., Rimoli, A. 1993. Demography and social structure in one group of muriquis *(Brachyteles arachnoides)*. *Int. J. Primatol.* 14:513–526.

Strier, K.B., Ziegler, T.E. 1994. Insights into ovarian function in wild muriqui monkeys *(Brachyteles arachnoides)*. *Am. J. Primatol.* 32:31–40.

Strier, K.B., Ziegler, T.E. 1997. Behavioral and endocrine characteristics for the reproductive cycle in wild muriqui monkeys *(Brachyteles arachnoides)*. *Am. J. Primatol.* 42:299–310.

Sussman, R.W., Philips-Conroy, J. 1995. A survey on the distribution and density of the primates of Guyana. *Int. J. Primatol.* 16:761–792.

Symington, M.M. 1987a. Sex ratio and maternal rank in wild spider monkeys: When daughters disperse. *Behav. Ecol. Sociobiol.* 20:421–425.

Symington, M.M. 1987b. *Ecological and Social Correlates of Party Size in the Black Spider Monkey,* Ateles paniscus chamek. Ph.D. Thesis. Princeton Unversity, Princeton.

Symington, M.M. 1988a. Food competition and foraging party size in the black spider monkey *(Ateles paniscus chamek)*. *Behavior* 105:117–134.

Symington, M.M. 1988b. Demography, ranging patterns, and activity budgets of black spider monkeys *(Ateles paniscus chamek)* in the Manu National Park, Peru. *Am. J. Primatol.* 15:45–57.

Symington, M.M. 1990. Fission-fusion social organization in *Ateles* and *Pan.* *Int. J. Primatol.* 11:47–60.

Terborgh, J. 1983. *Five New World Primates: A Study in Comparative Ecology.* Princeton, Princeton University Press.

Torres de Assumpção, C. 1981. *Cebus apella* and *Brachyteles arachnoides* (Cebidae) as potential pollinators of *Mabea fistulifera* (Euphorbiaceae). *J. Mammal.* 62:386–388.

Turnquist, J.E., Schmitt, D., Rose, M.D., Cant, J.G.H. 1999. Pendular motion in the brachiation of captive *Lagothrix* and *Ateles. Am. J. Primatol.* 48:263–281.

Walker, S.E. 1993a. Qualitative and quantitative differences in leaping behavior between *Pithecia pithcia* and *Chiropotes satanas. Am. J. Phys. Anthropol.* Suppl. 16:202–203.

Walker, S.E. 1993b. *Positional Adaptations and Ecology of the Pitheciini.* Ph.D. Thesis. City University of New York, New York.

Walker, S.E. 1994. Habitat use by *Pithecia pithecia* and *Chiropotes satanas. Am. J. Phys. Anthropol.* Suppl. 18: 203.

Walker, S.E. 1996. The evolution of positional behavior in the saki-uakaris (*Pithecia, Chiropotes,* and *Cacajao*). Pp. 335–367. In *Adaptive Radiations of Neotropical Primates.* M.A. Norconk, A.L. Rosenberger, P.A. Garber, Eds., New York, Plenum.

Walker, S.E. 1998. Fine-grained differences within positional categories: a case study of *Pithecia* and *Chiropotes.* Pp. 31–43. In *Primate Locomotion: Recent Advances.* E. Strasser, J. Fleagle, A. Rosenberger, H. McHery, Eds., New York, Plenum.

White, F. 1986. Census and preliminary observations on ecology of the black-faced spider monkey (*Ateles paniscus chamek*) in Manu National Park, Peru. *Am. J. Primatol.* 11:125–132.

Williams, L. 1974. *Monkeys and the Social Instinct: An inter-living study from The Woolly Monkey Sanctuary.* Looe (Cornwall), Great Britain, Monkey Sanctuary Publications.

Wilson, E.O. 1975. *Sociobiology: The New Synthesis.* Cambridge, Belknap Press.

Young, O.P. 1981. Copulation-interrupting behavior between females within a howler monkey troop. *Primates* 22:135–136.

Zengeser, M.R. 1973. Dentition of *Brachyteles arachnoides* with reference to alouattine and atelinine affinities. *Folia Primatol.* 20:351–390.

Zucker, E.L., Clarke, M.R. 1998. Agonistic and affiliative relationships of adult female howlers (*Alouatta palliata*) in Costa Rica of a 4-year period. *Int. J. Primatol.* 19:433–449

CHAPTER 5

Summary Chapter: Patterns of Adaptation Among New World Monkeys with Some Notes on Conservation

INTRODUCTION

Although prosimians occur in the Eocene in North America, New World monkeys first appear in South America in the latest Oligocene. The paleontological record of the ceboids is relatively limited, with a scattering of isolated specimens from Argentina to Jamaica. However, because many of these are generally similar to modern lineages, it appears that many extant taxa have been distinct since at least the Miocene (Fleagle 1999). At present, how and from where the first primates reached South America are still unanswered questions. Although they most likely came to the then island continent by rafting, it is not yet known whether they arrived from Africa or North America.

Currently, 16 genera and approximately 57 species of New World monkeys are recognized (and there may be as many as 98 species; Rylands et al. 1996/97). They are found in the tropical and subtropical wooded areas of the Americas from the coastal forests of southern Mexico to southern Brazil and northern Argentina. These primates range from the smallest of all monkeys, the pygmy marmoset (weighing 110 gm), to spider, woolly, and woolly spider monkeys weighing around 10 kg. The New World monkeys differ from the Old World monkeys in that they are relatively small, there are fewer folivores, some have prehensile tails, and there are no terrestrial or savannah-living forms. Also, unlike African and Asian monkeys, congeneric species are rarely found living together. Most New World monkey species within the same genus displace one another geographically. This indicates that there may be important differences in the patterns and factors influencing the evolutionary history of New and Old World monkeys.

A great deal of research has been conducted on the South American monkeys over the past 40 years, and they were the subject of some of the earliest research by Carpenter in the 1930's. Perhaps one of the most important recent trends is the number of scientists from Latin America who have begun to conduct research in their own and neighboring countries (see Kinzey 1997). This has increased local interest in these animals and is (and will continue to be) the most important factor leading to success in their conservation. By this time, all genera of Neotropical monkeys have been the subject of at least brief study in their natural habitat. However, few studies have been done focusing on identified individuals over many generations and few species have been studied in more than one habitat.

Because of the relationships between the higher taxonomic groups of New World monkeys, there is still controversy as to how to classify these primates, especially at the family level. However, five subfamilies, Callitrichinae, Cebinae, Aotinae, Atelinae, and Pitheciinae are generally recognized. Each of these represents a major adaptive radiation within the Ceboidea. Furthermore, each of these subfamilies reflects a distinct adaptive package in which the member taxa share major ecological, behavioral, and morphological features. In Volume 1, I was struck by the diversity and variation that exists among the living species of prosimians. Certainly, there is a great deal of variation in behavior and ecology among the species of New World monkeys. However, it is these adaptive modalities and the shared character complexes within each of these five adaptive groups that best characterizes the New World monkeys (see Rosenberger and Strier 1989).

HABITAT AND LOCOMOTION

New World primates have a wide geographical distribution and live in a diversity of ecosystems. They range from the humid and subhumid forests on the east coast of Mexico through the humid and dry forests of Central America. In South America, they are found in the montane and cloud forests west of the Andes to the east of the Andes, including seasonally dry forests in the Venezuelan llanos to the Guianas and vast expanse of rain forests and savannahs of Amazonia and the eastern coastal forests of Brazil. Finally, there are the gallery, semideciduous, and deciduous forests and dry Chaco plant formations in the southern portions of the ranges of Neotropical monkeys. However, two-thirds of the species and 60 percent of all Neotropical taxa occur in Amazonia and, here, with the diversity of vegetation types, vertical stratification, and the variety of available habitats and microhabitats, as many as 14 sympatric monkeys can coexist in some localities (Rylands et al. 1996/1997).

Callitrichids are found throughout most of the range of Neotropical monkeys and are quite adaptable, living in a wide variety of habitat types. A major feature of most species, however, is the ability to exploit edge habitats. The ability to live in areas with a mix of forest types and ample edge in secondary forest appears to be a hallmark of most tamarin and marmoset species. Habitat diversity appears to be an essential requirement of many species. Of course, having sources of exudates is a necessity for these animals. *Saguinus fuscicollis* appears to be able to exploit a wider array of habitats than other species and is one of the few South American primates that can coexist with conspecifics. *Leontopithecus* may be more restricted than other species in that it needs tree holes for sleeping sites and is found in more primary rainforest habitats than other callitrichines.

Because of their claw-like nails, callitrichines are able to exploit large branches and trunks. However, this does not restrict their locomotion on the small, terminal branches of trees and bushes. In fact, most tamarins and marmosets exploit small terminal branches while feeding on fruits and flowers, searching for insects in the dense underbrush, and during normal progression. They are, in fact, mainly quadrupedal walkers and leapers. The claw-like nails primarily are used to exploit exudates which are located on larger branches or trunks and, thus, are mainly a postural and not locomotor adaptation. However, a few species such as *S. fuscicollis*, *C. pygmaeus* and many marmosets also use vertical trunks in vertical clinging and leaping (VCL) locomotion. *Callimico* also is a VCL but does not exploit gums.

The Cebinae occupy a greater variety of habitats than any other Neotropical primate subfamily. Capuchins inhabit every type of forest in the Neotropics. *Cebus apella* appears to be the most adaptable and is found to overlap with other species of *Cebus*. *Saimiri* is generally found in primary forest and prefers secondary and successional stages of forest growth. In fact, besides tamarins, *Saimari* and *C. apella* may use edge forests more frequently than any other South American monkey. Cebinae mainly use mid to under canopy. Squirrel monkeys are found lower than capuchins in more densely foliated areas. These species are quick, arboreal quadrupeds that use walking, running and leaping. Capuchins have a prehensile tail (squirrel monkeys do not), which evolved independently from that of the atelines. It is used mainly in postural activities while animals are foraging and feeding, but also during locomotion. Capuchins rarely suspend themselves solely by the tail.

Aotinae is found in a wide range of habitats, including primary and secondary forests. *Callicebus* is found in Amazonia and Atlantic Brazil. *Aotus* has a very wide geographic distribution including both Central and South America. *C. moloch* lives mainly in dense vegetation and has been referred to as the nearest thing to a swamp monkey in South America. *Callicebus* is mainly a quadrupedal walker. *Aotus* also is mainly an above branch quadruped. Aotines do not have a prehensile tails.

Atelines are large monkeys with prehensile tails. Spider and howler monkeys live in a wide variety of habitats. In fact, howler monkeys have the widest distribution, geographically and in habitat type, of any Neotropical genus, and they are often found in remnant forests and forest patches. Geographically, the two genera, *Ateles* and *Alouatta* are found from Mexico through Central America, and throughout South America. *Lagothrix* is much more restricted in geographical distribution and is only present in primary forest types. Woolly monkeys also are very sensitive to forest disturbance. *Brachyteles* occurs in both primary and secondary forests, and it seems to live in higher densities where both habitat types are available. It is mainly found in the mid to upper canopy.

Alouatta is a slow and deliberate quadruped; it usually moves very cautiously when on smaller branches. The prehensile tail is used mainly in suspensory feeding and little in locomotion. The howler monkey uses an energy minimizing strategy in locomotion. *Ateles,* on the other hand, is a fast and agile quadruped and uses its tail while locomoting on small branches where it moves with great speed and agility. Its arms and hands also are adapted to this quick, agile suspensory locomotion. The tail is used in both locomotion and in suspensory feeding. In fact, in foraging and feeding, spider monkeys use their tails 91% of the time. *Lagothrix* in many ways is intermediate between *Ateles* and *Alouatta* in its locomotion. It uses suspensory locomotion but is not as quick and agile as *Ateles*. However, over all, it should be considered an energy maximizer much like the spider monkey. Although *Brachyteles* is one of the largest and heaviest species, its locomotion also resembles that of the spider monkey. It uses rapid suspensory locomotion and climbing and can move through the canopy very quickly. The prehensile tail is used in many locomotor and postural contexts.

In *Ateles, Brachyteles,* and *Lagothrix,* rapid suspensory locomotion may be critical for moving between widely dispersed patches of high quality foods (Strier 1987, Rosenberger and Strier 1989). It generally has been assumed that the use of the prehensile tail in suspensory postures functions mainly for feeding in the periphery of trees. However, recent research indicates that inverted bipedal suspensory postures, both in spider monkeys and in howlers, are used more frequently close to the trunk. Furthermore, the tail is used more commonly when feeding on leaves than on fruit in both of these monkeys (Bergeson 1996, 1998).

The pithecines are restricted to Amazonia. *Chiropotes* and *Pithecia* are often found together in much of their range. *Chiropotes* is rarely found outside of high canopy forest, whereas *Pithecia* is less restricted and can be found in secondary forests and disturbed habitats. *Cacajao* is restricted in geographical range and in habitat. It is found only in a narrow range of the Amazon near the equator and mainly occurs in flooded and riverine forests. *Chiropotes* usually is found in the upper canopy where it is a quadrupedal walker and runner, but also an adept leaper. *Pithecia* is found mainly in the lower canopy. It moves quickly through the understory by jumping and leaping, and often remains in a vertical orientation while rapidly moving through the trees. It has a number of local names that relate to this very rapid and unusual locomotion. *Cacajao* has been described as a quadrupedal, pronograde clamberer. Pithecines do not have prehensile tails, and in fact, *Cacajao* is the only New World monkey that lacks a long tail. The functional significance of this short tail is unknown but may be related to the fact that the uakaris spend a great deal of time on the ground in some areas.

DIET

The five subfamilies of New World monkeys can be characterized by their major dietary propensities and each of these taxa is quite different from one another. The callitrichines can best be understood as making up a guild of exudate-feeders, with living species displaying trends toward greater and greater specialization for feeding on this resource. Cebines are mainly insectivorous omnivores. Aotines are small, highly frugivorous animals. Three atelines are large frugivores, whereas *Alouatta* is the only Neotropical monkey highly adapted for folivory. Finally, the pithecines are seed predators. Much of the behavior and morphology of these taxa is related to these dietary preferences.

The callitrichines feed on three major types of foods: insects, plant reproductive parts (fruits and flowers), and exudates. The insects eaten by tamarins and marmosets are larger than those normally fed upon by other Neotropical monkeys, and the fruits are usually found in small trees and vines, which produce small quantities—quantities not normally sufficient to satisfy large groups of the larger monkeys. Tamarins and marmosets use their claws to cling to large branches when feeding on exudates, and marmosets have dental adaptations to gouge bark and stimulate gum flow.

These three major components of tamarin and marmoset diet can be interrelated to many other aspects of the morphology, individual behavior, and social behavior. For example, in exploiting each of these food types, a different substrate is utilized, and this necessitates flexible locomotion. Using each of these food resources also requires different mechanisms for predator protection. In examining the adaptive patterns of the callitrichids (excluding *Callimico*), as stated above, these monkeys should be considered members of an exudate-feeding guild, and this adaptive path has molded all aspects of their ecology, behavior, and morphology. Within the taxon, there is an evolutionary trend from tamarins to marmosets (with differences among species related to more or less tree-gouging) to the pygmy marmosets who are the most specialized among the group.

The members of Cebinae are small frugivore/omnivores. The smaller *Saimiri* eats more insects, spending 75-85 percent of its time foraging for these creatures. In fact, in months when fruit is scarce, insects can comprise the entire diet. The fruit portion of the diet is mainly soft, berry-like fruit and some other plant reproductive parts. Where figs are available, they make up a major portion of the plant foods eaten. *Cebus* relies on ripe fruit for most of its calories and animal prey (mainly insects) for protein. *Cebus* also eats a small amount of vegetative matter and will hunt small vertebrates on occasion. Capuchins are very adaptable animals, and there is a great amount of variation between groups, populations, seasons, and species in dietary intake. At certain localities where certain resources are scarce, they are able to become quite specialized. Where available, capuchins spend a great deal of time eating palm fruits. They are slow, meticulous foragers and often spend a long time at one locality manipulating the substrate or using tools to extract foods. In hunting vertebrates and in tool use, these small monkeys are more similar to chimpanzees than any other nonhuman primate.

The Aotinae are mainly frugivores. The different forms of *Callicebus* supplement fruit with either leaves (*C. moloch* and *C. personatus*) or insects (*C. torquatus*). Wright (1989) believes that titi monkeys are often chased out of fruit trees by larger monkeys and must move into the understory to feed or use unripe fruit. *Aotus* is also mainly a frugivore, but it is able to utilize many of the same fruit species as the larger monkeys because of its nocturnal activity cycle. In some seasons, floral nectar can become an important component of the diet much like it does for the cathemeral mongoose lemur in Madagascar. *Aotus* also eats some insects.

Atelines eat mainly plant material and little or no animal foods. Rosenberger and Strier (1989) see an increasing specialization on fruit and the ability to utilize leaf material when necessary as being the factor leading to the morphological, behavioral, and ecological characteristics of these animals. They hypothesize that large body size permitted this increasing reliance on leaves (including immature ones) by atelines in comparison with other New World monkeys, even in the predominantly frugivorous forms. In fact, there is a continuum in this taxonomic group ranging from the extremely frugivorous *Ateles* to *Lagothrix*, which has the ability to utilize high quantities of seeds and young leaves when fruit is scarce, to *Brachyteles* in which over half of the annual diet is leaves, though fruit is preferred when available. *Alouatta* is behaviorally and morphologically adapted for a highly folivorous diet.

In fact, even though *Brachyteles* eats a high proportion of leaves, it shares a "frugivorous" foraging strategy with *Lagothrix* and *Ateles,* moving quickly and over great distances to obtain widely scattered foods. On the other hand, *Alouatta* uses a typical energy-minimizing foraging strategy of a folivore. In sympatric populations, *Brachyteles* is more frugivorous than *Alouatta*. Rosenberger and Strier (1989) believe that *Alouatta* possesses a number of elaborate folivorous adaptations derived since the ateline-alouattine last common ancestor, and thus, the higher degree of folivory observed in *Alouatta* should be considered an intrinsic adaptive specialization of the

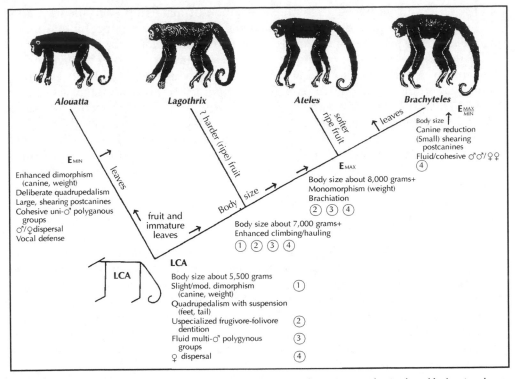

Figure 5-1 Adaptive radiation of the ateline primates, emphasizing ecological and behavioral patterns of the hypothetical last common ancestor (LCA) and their evolution. Circled numbers are keyed to four characteristics of the LCA; arrows indicate increase in labelled characteristic. Energetic paradigms (E min; E max; E $\frac{max}{min}$) are indicated. Specializations of the *Alouatta* and *Brachyteles* lineages are emphasized to show their convergence. [From Rosenberger & Strier 1989]

howler monkey lineage. Many other aspects of the behavior and morphology derive from these dietary foraging propensities (Rosenberger and Strier 1989, Fig. 5-1).

Pithecines fill a unique role among New World monkeys in that they are seed predators much like some species of *Propithecus* in Madagascar and *Colobus* in Africa. *Chiropotes* and *Cacajao* are able to bite into fruits with hard covers whereas *Pithecia* consumes hard and/or highly toxic seeds (Norconk et al. 1998). Because most animals are unable to utilize these hard and or toxic resources they are usually fairly abundant and may be available during the dry season when other resources are scarce (Norconk 1996). In order to exploit seeds, pithecines need morphological adaptations to obtain and digest these often hard and toxic foods.

CYCLES OF ACTIVITY

Some of the factors that affect activity cycles among primates are body size, diet, locomotor abilities, predator pressure, and social and reproductive behavior. As we have seen, these factors are usually interrelated, but in some species and taxa, certain factors seem to influence daily cycles more than others.

Most callitrichids are unusual in that they wake late in the morning and retire relatively early in the evening. It has been hypothesized that late-rising may be related to a greater opportunity of catching late-rising large insects. Settling early may be related to predator avoidance. These small animals sleep hidden in very dense foliage or, in some species, in tree holes.

Patterns of activity throughout the day are quite variable among callitrichid species, populations, and between seasons. For example, travel and activity are reduced soon after births, when infants are being carried. Activity increases when resources like nectar are a major source of food. One trait that appears to characterize callitrichids is an activity cycle that limits energy costs. Many populations rest in dense vegetation during the hottest portion of the day and alternate activity with rest throughout the day, sometimes spending approximately half of the already shortened day resting.

The relatively small and highly insectivorous cebines spend most of their time travelling and feeding (70–80% of the day) and little time resting and socializing (20–25%). As we would expect from insectivorous primates, they alternate short periods of foraging and feeding with short rest periods. Fruit, which is easier to locate than insects, is eaten immediately upon awakening, and then the animals shift mainly to insect foraging until late in the afternoon. Depending upon temperature and food availability, there is a tendency to rest in the hottest portion of midday. Of course, these general patterns are complicated by a number of cyclical factors that occur throughout the year, such as seasonal changes in availability and quantity of resources, seasonality of births, cycles of day length, and seasonal patterns of rainfall and temperature.

The activity cycles of aotines are difficult to characterize. Species of *Callicebus* appear to have activity cycles related to their main dietary supplements. *C. torquatus,* as we have seen, supplements its mainly fruit diet with insects and feeds continuously with short periods of rest, much like the highly insectivorous cebines. *C. moloch* and *C. personatus* have activity cycles more similar to folivorous primates, with two major feeding peaks in the morning and evening separated by a long rest period. *Aotus* is the only anthropoid active at night; it sleeps during the day in tree holes or in dense vegetation. The reasons for nocturnality in the night monkey are still a mystery. However, Wright (1996) believes that competition with larger frugivores and predator avoidance may be the most important factors.

Atelines, like other primates depending mainly on plant materials for food, can eat large quantities at one sitting but must have long periods of rest for digestion. During the day, *Ateles, Lagothrix,* and *Brachyteles* rest between 45–65 percent of the time, whereas the leaf eating *Alouatta* rests about 65–80 percent of the time. Generally, there is a continuum among the three more frugivorous forms, with those eating more leaves resting for longer periods. Where they have been studied sympatrically, *Brachyteles* rests less than *Alouatta* (49% vs. 72%) and travels more (29% vs. 11%). *Ateles, Lagothrix,* and *Brachyteles* have been characterized as energy maximizers because they use energy consuming modes of travel (fast, suspensory locomotion, long-distance travel, etc.). *Alouatta,* on the other hand, can be seen as an energy minimizer: moving slowly, having small home and day ranges, resting most of the day, and avoiding intergroup contact by exchanging loud vocalizations. Aspects of these species' social organizations also reflect these patterns of energy expenditure (see below).

Pithecia and *Chiropotes* are active from dawn to dusk but have shorter days (10 to 12 hours) than do Cebinae or other Atelinae. This may be due to their ability to utilize seeds which typically are high quality foods.

PREDATION

Size is a major factor in any discussion of predation. In general, primates can avoid many arboreal predators, but few terrestrial predators, by being larger than the predator. Since most New World monkeys spend little time on the ground, this limits but does not eliminate their vulnerability to terrestrial carnivores. Eagles and hawks are the major and most competent predators of primates in the Neotropics and worldwide (Hart 2000). The smaller Neotropical primates are preyed upon by both small and large predators, especially birds of prey, whereas the larger monkeys can only be preyed upon by larger predators.

Thus, the smaller monkeys are vulnerable to many predators, including many small and large carnivores, snakes, caiman, and especially birds of prey. Being the smallest anthropoids, callitrichids must have numerous means of countering predation. Terrestrial carnivores and snakes are mobbed and these monkeys have different alarm calls for arboreal and terrestrial pedators. Callitrichids are fast moving and quite cryptic; however, when groups feed on fruit they are quite visible. At these times, groups are cohesive, and members employ vigilant and sentinel behavior. Alarm calling and mobbing are common cooperative behaviors within both single species and mixed-species groups. While insect foraging, group members are spread out, cryptic, and in dense vegetation. While clinging to large tree trunks and feeding on exudates, the animals are solitary, and their coloration often makes them extremely difficult to see. Caine (1993) believes that predation is one of the major selective pressures leading to many aspects of the unique social system of the callitrichids.

Among the Cebinae, squirrel monkeys appear to be vulnerable to much the same predators as the callitrichids. They give alarm calls to most medium to large flying predatory birds but are relatively frequent prey items to these species. Squirrel monkeys mob and vocalize to terrestrial predators. Living in large groups and often moving in mixed-species groups, especially with capuchins, are important predator avoidance mechanisms. Capuchins have a well developed predator alarm system, and alpha males spend a great deal of time scanning the environment. However, even given this, capuchins were found to be the most common monkeys in the diet of the harpy eagle in a study of this bird in Guyana.

Aotines also are vulnerable to similar predators as the callitrichids. *Callicebus* is generally cryptic in coloration and while moving and resting. Night sleeping sites are chosen for predator protection. Wright (1996) hypothesizes that one of the major advantages of the nocturnal activity pattern of *Aotus* is predator avoidance. The only potential nocturnal predators of the night monkey where she did her study were owls who were probably too small to prey upon the monkeys.

Pithecines are similar in size to capuchins. They are potential prey to large raptors, large and medium sized carnivores, and to large snakes. *Pithecia* will mob terrestrial predators and flee quickly from large ones. Large birds elicit the most frequent alarm response, with one loud call that is echoed by all group members. The monkeys react to this call by descending from the canopy and hiding for long periods. Little has been reported on predator avoidance behavior of *Chiropotes* or *Cacajao*.

Due to their large size, atelines have fewer potential predators than do other Neotropical monkeys, but they are vulnerable to predation none the less. Large eagles, jaguars, ocelots, puma, and large snakes have been seen to prey on them. Young animals also are vulnerable to smaller predators. The slow moving howler monkey appears to be quite prone to predation. However, even the faster-moving woolly monkeys are frequent prey items, and two species of eagle in Colombia are locally referred to as "Aguilas Churuqueres" (woolly monkey hawks). The larger Neotropical monkeys also are hunted by humans for food, bait, medicinal and other purposes. The pithecines' long, bushy tails are used as "feather" dusters.

SOCIAL STRUCTURE AND ORGANIZATION

The social structure and organization of the Neotropical monkeys, as with other adaptations, are characterized by phylogenetic constraints, with each subfamily tending towards a particular pattern. There is a great amount of difference between subfamilies, and the New World monkeys display some patterns of social behavior that are not found in other primates.

Most callitrichids live in what has been termed a cooperative polyandrous social organization in which one female mates with more than one male during a breeding season. Both males and females migrate. Typically only one female gives birth to twins, and all group members raise the young cooperatively. These groups often contain more than one adult of each sex, though statistically groups with one adult female and two adult males are more common. Because of the energy constraints of carrying relatively large twins, it appears that more than one adult male increases the chances of infant survival. This social system is not found in any other primate taxa, although communal breeding is found in avian and other mammal species, and in the variegated lemur (see Volume 1).

This breeding system is paradoxical in some ways. Individual breeding females have the potential for rapid reproductive turnover: they normally bear twins and can potentially breed twice a year. However, only one female per group usually reproduces, even in groups with more than one adult female. Thus, extra adults seem to be necessary for infant care, and the energy to raise one set of twins at a time is as much as any one group appears to be able to muster. Extra adults are also likely to be valuable in spotting potential predators. In fact, mixed-species groups and merged groups often form during the day, adding more eyes and ears for protection.

Saimiri and *Cebus* live in multi-male, multi-female groups. Squirrel monkeys are found in the largest groups of any Neotropical monkey (20–70 individuals). The groups are cohesive, with members usually in close proximity. Given this basic structure, Boinski (1999) argues that other aspects of the social organization vary in different populations. In Central America, adult females have egalitarian social interactions and are not spatially aggregated, and females transfer between groups. Males stay in their natal group and maintain close associations with their birth cohort but not with females and infants. There is little agonism within groups. In Peruvian squirrel monkeys, females remain in their natal group and form stable alliances, probably based on kinship. Males migrate, are agonistic toward one another, and form hierarchies. However, in these groups, females are dominant to males and keep them at the periphery of the group. In Surinam squirrel monkeys, Boinski (1999) found that both sexes form a single linear hierarchy, with most males dominant to most females. Males are more affiliative than are females. Boinski (1999) believes that these differences are directly related to the general distribution of resources in the three areas where the different squirrel monkey populations are found; however, this hypothesis remains to be tested.

Capuchins live in smaller groups than squirrel monkeys (6–35 individuals). Groups are cohesive, though often scattered, but in vocal communication, when feeding on insects. Males disperse from their natal group and females are usually philopatric; however, female transfer may be more common than generally thought. Females form affiliations with other females, and these appear to be based on matrilineal kinship. Groups have a relatively stable dominance hierarchy that also may be dependent on matrilineal kin. Although matrilineal based hierarchies are common among Old World monkeys, they are not common among Neotropical primates. Males are vigilant for potential predators, other groups, and for migrating males, whereas females rarely take part in intergroup interactions or defense. In fact, females appear to be more preoccupied with factors internal and males toward factors external to the group.

Male-male interactions vary among different populations and species. Alliances and coalitions are common, especially among females, and can influence an individual's status in the group. Generally, social interactions are peaceful and mostly involve grooming. However, occasionally aggression can be very serious, resulting in injury or death. This can occur when dominant males attempt to evict subadult males from the group or during male takeovers. Adult males sometimes invade groups and fight with resident males, often injuring (even fatally) these males and also injuring females and infants in the process. In some capuchin populations, mating is promiscuous, whereas in others the alpha male does most of the mating.

Squirrel monkeys and capuchins often are found in mixed-species associations. It once was thought that the capuchins took an active role in maintaining these associations. However, it appears that squirrel monkeys are the main instigators. Terborgh (1983) provides evidence that squirrel monkeys benefit from the associations by taking advantage of both the capuchins' knowledge of the fruit sources available within their smaller home ranges and their well-developed predator alarm system.

All of the forms of aotines live in pair-bonded or monogamous groups. *Callicebus* displays what might be called classical monogamy in which the adult pair is territorial and uses either calling or calling and ritual displays to maintain essentially exclusive use of their home range (see Volume 1 for a discussion of territoriality). Why do these species maintain exclusive use of space? Easley (1982) believes that the necessity to protect relatively constant and predictable (but limited) resources requires this type of spacing between groups.

Aotus also lives in monogamous family groups but these are not territorial. Much like the nocturnal/ cathemeral mongoose lemur of Madagascar, group home ranges overlap. Intergoup encounters appear to function to maintain group integrity rather than to maintain exclusive boundaries and to allow overlapping groups to share resources on a time-sharing basis. Within the group, activity and movement is cohesive.

The social structure of the atelines is characterized by multi-male/multi-female groups, which are relatively large. All three genera, *Ateles, Lagothrix,* and *Brachyteles* exhibit female-biased dispersal, male philopatry, and extended patrilineal groups. Furthermore, they have the ability to break into small subgroups given different environmental and demographic conditions. The amount of cohesion within the groups and the nature of relationships between males, however, are quite different between these closely related genera (Strier 1994a).

Ateles groups are characterized by the existence of closed social groups (of 15–40+ individuals), which fragment into smaller, widely dispersed, foraging subgroups. This is a typical "fission fusion" social structure, and it most closely resembles that of the common chimpanzee. The size of subgroups is related to distribution and abundance of fruit resources throughout the year. Related to male philopatry, males are more affiliative with one another. However, male relationships are hierarchical and dominant males may mate more frequently. Males are dominant to females; but estrous females actively choose their mating partners and mate with a number of different males on the same day. Male affiliative associations are active in intergroup agonistic encounters.

In some populations of *Lagothrix,* group structure is very much like that of *Ateles,* whereas in other populations groups are more cohesive. Male associations are weaker in woolly monkeys than in spider monkeys. However, there are associations between males, and even though there is a dominance hierarchy and males are dominant to females, all males are successful in mating. There appears to be less male agonism between groups in male woolly monkeys than in spider monkeys.

Brachyteles group structure, like that of *Lagothrix,* is more or less cohesive depending on population and demography, with some groups having a fluid structure similar to *Ateles* and others being quite cohesive. In the muriqui, males spend more time in close association with each other than do any other male primates studied to date. There is extremely little agonism and there are no dominance hierarchies in muriqui groups. Mating is promiscuous with all adult and subadult males copulating with females and no apparent competition or attempt to monopolize estrous females. However, female mate choice leads to variable mating success among males.

The variations on this theme of fission fusion and cohesion, male philopatry and female dispersal, and the subtle differences in social organization among the atelines are all intriguing patterns that lend themselves to problem-oriented studies. It would be interesting to try to tease out the environmental and phylogenetic factors that relate to these differences.

Howler monkeys live in cohesive multi-male/multi-female groups. Generally, home ranges overlap extensively, and loud calls are used to maintain distance between groups without having to expend too much energy. Both males and females migrate, and thus, groups basically are made up of unrelated individuals. Overt social interaction is rare but subtle, and important dominance hierarchies exist both among the males and females. It appears that individuals of each sex must attain alpha status before being able to remain in a group. Agonism is rare, quick, and silent but can be quite dangerous, and males have died of injuries during fights. Males also invade and takeover groups, sometimes forming temporary coalitions, and this is sometimes associated with infant deaths or disappearances. In some groups and possibly species, dominant males have exclusive mating access to females, whereas in other groups mating is promiscuous and even extra-group males have a relatively high mating success. It is interesting to keep in mind that members of howler monkey groups cooperate just as do members of other primate groups. Since these individuals are not related, kinship is not an essential component for group living and intragroup cooperation.

The social structure and organization of the pithecines is not well known. All species live in multimale/multi-female groups. In *Pithecia* these groups are small (2–9 individuals with 2–5 adults). *Chiropotes* lives in larger groups (8–30 animals) which are usually cohesive. *Cacajao* lives in larger groups still (15–50 or even larger), though these groups sometimes split into smaller subgroups. All three species contain approximately 1:1 adult sex ratios. It is not known whether males or females or both sexes disperse from their natal group.

Until recently, most primatologists and biologists believed that male-dispersal and female philopatry was the "typical" primate pattern. However, this was mainly because cercopithecines, especially baboons and macaques, were the species whose social organizations were best known. It is also a typical pattern in many other mammals. However, now that New World monkeys have been studied in better detail, we realize that basing general assumptions on few taxa leads to faulty conclusions. In most New World monkeys for which data exist, either the female or both sexes disperse. We now know this is also true of many other primate taxa. In fact, as Strier (1994b:240) notes:

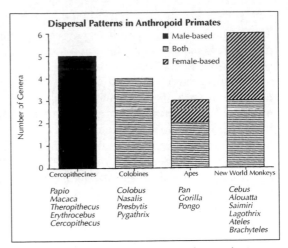

Figure 5-2 Dispersal patterns in anthropoid primates [From Strier 1994b]

> *Even when comparisons are restricted to just the polygynous or polygamous genera, fully 50% exhibit dispersal by both sexes (Fig. 5-2). This widespread phenomena severely challenges the assumption that kinship is an ubiquitous organizing principle in all primate societies.*

CONSERVATION

Currently, approximately one-third of all Neotropical primate taxa are listed by the Species Survival Commission (SSC) of the World Conservation Union (IUCN) as either "critically endangered", "endangered", or "vulnerable". This includes three genera, *Leontopithecus, Callimico,* and *Brachyteles,* and possibly a fourth, *Lagothrix.* The most critical regions are Middle America (Mexico and Central America), northern and Pacific Colombia and Equador, and the Atlantic forests of Brazil. However, Amazonia also is beginning to accumulate threatened species due to widespread destruction of its forests since the 1960's (Rylands et al. 1996/97). Furthermore, poor countries such as Guyana and Surinam, which are currently relatively undisturbed, are being "tempted" with quick riches for their valuable timber or other raw materials. If timbering and mining concessions are granted, forest destruction could proceed at a tremendous pace as has happened in South East Asia.

Although there are many causes for forest destruction and for primate extinctions, there are two major threats to the nonhuman primates in the Neotropics: habitat disturbance and hunting. Marsh et al. (1987) list six major categories of forest disturbance: 1) removal of selected products by traditional means, 2) clearance or damage of the forest understory, 3) changes in the water regime, 4) shifting cultivation, 5) commercial selective logging, and 6) large scale clearance usually for agriculture, mining, or ranching. Furthermore, any of these types of forest disturbance can lead to other pressures. For example, clear-felling is often preceded by shifting cultivation, and road construction can open forests to hunters or loggers.

Depending upon the region, one or another of these categories of destruction has been an important cause of habitat loss in Latin America. For example, the Tucurui hydroelectric dam flooded approximately 2,400 km^2, which included a large portion of the habitat of the black saki monkey. It is estimated that shifting cultivation accounts for the loss of 200,000 km^2 of tropical forest each year worldwide. Even more worrisome, however, is the potential for intensive logging to supply the international trade in logs and plywood. As the forests of South East Asia are becoming exhausted, the logging industry appears to be heading to the Neotropics. Colchester (1994) documents concessions in Guyana for one 25 year license (automatically renewable for another 25 years) to exploit 1.69 million hectares of forest in the North West, and negotiations for another 600,000 ha in the center of the country are underway. In the mid-1990's, similar concessions were being negotiated in Surinam for six million hectares of logging concessions. Thus, much of the relatively untouched tropical forests of the interior Amazon and Guianas could rapidly disappear.

However, even in areas where forests are protected from logging and other destructive forces, the effects of hunting have often been underestimated. Hunting may occur for several reasons: for local consumption, for export, and for the pet trade. Hunting for subsistence causes the largest decrease in primate densities (Mittermeier 1987). Increasingly, this includes not only meat for local consumption, but bush meat being transported to large population centers. Redford (1992:417–418) found that in hunted areas, large primate biomass drops 93.5 percent when compared with similar unhunted areas, and large primate density drops 80.7 percent. In many regions of the Neotropics, monkeys are a preferred food source. Although many indigenous people still use traditional means to hunt (e.g., bow and arrows and blowguns), shotguns are now commonly used. It has been estimated that the use of the shotgun increases the amount of game taken by one third (Yost and Kelly 1983). Although all Neotropical monkeys are potential food items, the larger species are preferred, especially *Lagothrix, Ateles, Alouatta,* and some *Cebus* species. Furthermore, atelines have slow reproductive turnover and this exacerbates their vulnerability.

In a recent article, Carey (1999) a correspondent for *Business Week,* describes the effects of hunting:

> *Dawn breaks on a tropical forest. Conservationists have protected the trees from the bite of the chain saw, and under the dense canopy, all seems primordial and pristine. But something is missing. Dawn normally brings a symphony of sound. But here there is only silence. No raucous cries of monkeys. No trilling avian melodies. No rustling of the underbrush. The animals are largely gone.*
>
> *By 2020, this silent dawn could be occurring almost anywhere in the world. Indeed, such "empty" forests already have begun to appear, in countries from Laos to Zaire. The cause is simple: Humans are*

killing the animals. Whether by snare or spear, trap or gun, people are taking a staggering toll on anything that can be eaten or sold for food or medicine. Wildlife biologists are only starting to tally the cost, but estimates range from up to 24 million animals killed each year in the Brazilian Amazon to 600,000 pounds of wild meat taken annually from the Korup National Park in West Africa alone. Hunting is thought to be responsible for more than one-quarter of all known extinctions where a cause can be attributed.

Thus, massive habitat destruction for immediate economic gain and hunting, often for commercial purposes, are the factors that must be dealt with in the near future if many of the nonhuman primates are to be protected from ultimate extinction. However, neither the causes nor the problems are simple. As stated in Volume 1, hunger, population increase, health problems, and the distribution of resources are not simple problems, and they must be studied, understood, and dealt with given the input of many biological and social sciences. There is one organization focusing mainly on the Neotropics that serves as a model for research and education in the tropics. The Organization of Tropical Studies (OTS) is a consortium of over 50 Universities and Research Institutions from the United States and Latin American. It was created in 1963 to acquire and disseminate a broad understanding of tropical environments. OTS conducts training and research programs from a logistic support base and field stations in Costa Rica. The most important aspect of this organization is that it is a brain bank and can tap the resources of faculty and researchers from all the different departments within the many member institutions. Recently, there has been increasing input from the social sciences, in addition to the traditional biological sciences, within this organization. This wide base of research, teaching, and understanding is necessary in order to wisely use the natural resources in the tropics in a sustainable manner. Cooperation among many disciplines, institutions, government agencies, and local peoples will be necessary to save the vital resources of the tropical forests for future generations of nonhuman and human primates.

BIBLIOGRAPHY

Bergeson, D.J. 1996. *The Positional Behavior and Prehensile Tail use of* Alouatta palliata, Ateles geoffroyi, *and* Cebus capucinus. Ph.D. Thesis. Washington University, St. Louis.

Bergeson, D.J. 1998. Patterns of suspensory feeding in *Alouatta palliata, Ateles geoffroyi,* and *Cebus capucinus* Pp. 45-60. In Primate Locomotion: Recent Advances. E. Strasser, J. Fleagle, A. Rosenberger, H. McHenry, Eds., New York, Plenum.

Boinski, S. 1999. The social organization of the squirrel monkeys: implications for ecological models of social evolution. *Evol. Anthropol.* 8:101–112.

Caine, N.G. 1993. Flexibility and co-operation as unifying themes in *Saguinus* social organization: the role of predation pressures. Pp. 200–219. In *Marmosets and Tamarins: Systematics, Behavior, and Ecology.* A.B. Rylands, Ed., Oxford, Oxford University Press.

Carey, J. 1999. What if the forests were silent? *Business Week.* August 30:102–103.

Colchester, M. 1994. The new sultans of the west: Asian loggers move in on Guyana's forests. Unpublished manuscript.

Easley, S.P. 1982. *Ecology and Behavior of Callicebus torquatus.* Ph.D. Thesis. Washington University, St. Louis.

Fleagle, J.G. 1999. *Primate Adaptation and Evolution.* New York, Academic Press.

Hart, D. 2000. *Primates as Prey: Ecological, Morphological and Behavioral Relationships Between Primates and Their Prey.* Ph.D. Thesis. Washington University, St. Louis.

Kinzey, W.G. 1997. New World primate studies. Pp. 743–748. In *History of Physical Anthropology: An Encyclopedia.* F. Spencer, Ed., New York, Garland.

Marsh, C.W., Johns, A.D., Ayres, J.M. 1987. Effects of habitat disturbance on rain forest primates. Pp. 83–107. In *Primate Conservation in the Tropical Rain Forest.* C.W. Marsh, R.A. Mittermeier, Eds., New York, Alan R. Liss.

Mittermeier, R.A. 1987. Effects of hunting on rain forest primates. Pp. 109–146. In *Primate Conservation in the Tropical Rain Forest.* C.W. Marsh, R.A. Mittermeier, Eds., New York, Alan R. Liss.

Norconk, M.A., Grafton, B.W., Conklin-Brittain, N.L. 1998. Seed dispersal by neotropical seed predators. *Am. J. Primatol.* 45:103–126.

Norconk, M.A. 1996. Seasonal variation in the diets of white-faced and bearded sakis (*Pithecia pithecia* and *Chiropotes satanus*) in Guri Lake, Venezuela. Pp. 403–423. In *Adaptive Radiations of Neotropical Primates.* M.A. Norconk, A.L. Rosenberger, P.A. Garber, Eds., New York, Plenum.

Redford, K. 1992. The empty forest. *Bioscience* 42:412–422.

Rosenberger, A.L., Strier, K.B. 1989. Adaptive radiation of the ateline primates. *J. Hum. Evol.* 18:717–750.

Rylands, A.B., Rodiguez-Luna, E., Cortés-Ortiz, L. 1996/97. Neotropical primate conservation—The species and the IUCN/SSC Primate Specialist Group Network. *Prim. Conserv.* 17:46–69.

Strier, K.B. 1987. Activity budgets of woolly spider monkeys, or muriquis (*Brachyteles arachnoides*). *Am. J. Primatol.* 13:385–396.

Strier, K.B. 1994a. Brotherhoods among atelins: kinship, affiliation, and competition. *Behaviour* 130:151–167.

Strier, K.B. 1994b. Myth of the typical primate. *Yrbk. Phys. Anthropol.* 37:233–271.

Terborgh, J. 1983. *Five New World Primates: A Study in Comparative Ecology.* Princeton, Princeton University Press.

Wright, P.C. 1989. The nocturnal primate niche in the New World. *J. Hum. Evol.* 18:635–658.

Wright, P.C. 1996. The neotropical primate adaptation to nocturnality. Pp. 369–382. In *Adaptive Radiations of Neotropical Primates.* M.A. Norconk, A.L. Rosenberger, P.A. Garber, Eds., New York, Plenum.

Yost, J.A., Kelley, P.M. 1983. Shotguns, blowguns, and spears: The analysis of technological efficiency. Pp. 189–224. In *Adaptive Responses of Native Amazonians.* R.B. Hames, W.T. Vickers, Eds., New York, Academic.

INDEX